ADVENTURE!

THRILLING TALES OF DISCOVERY

THIS BOOK IS DEDICATED TO

Marty Goeller

John Richard Stephens wishes to express his appreciation to Elaine Molina; Martha and Jim Goodwin; Scott Stephens; Marty Goeller; Terity, Natasha, and Debbie Burbach; Brandon, Alisha, and Kathy Hill; Jeff and Carol Whiteaker; Christopher, Doug, and Michelle Whiteaker; Pat Egner; Gabriel, Aurelia, Elijah, Nina Abeyta and Justin Weinberger; Jayla, Sin, and Bobby Gamboa; Eric, Tim, and Debbie Cissna; Norene Hilden; Doug and Shirley Strong; Barbara and Stan Main; Joanne and Monte Goeller; Irma and Joe Rodriguez; Danny and Mary Schutt; Les Benedict; Krystyne Gohnert; Dr. Rich Sutton; and to his agent, Charlotte Cecil Raymond.

Compilation © 2008 by John Richard Stephens

Acknowledgements and photo credits appear on p. 330.

Metro Books
122 Fifth Avenue
New York, NY 10011

ISBN-13: 978-1-4351-0503-4
ISBN-10: 1-4351-0503-6

Interior design by Jo Obarowski
Cover illustration by Tim Foley

Printed and bound in the United States of America

10 9 8 7 6 5 4 3 2 1

ADVENTURE!

THRILLING TALES OF DISCOVERY

EDITED BY

JOHN RICHARD STEPHENS

METRO BOOKS

NEW YORK

CONTENTS

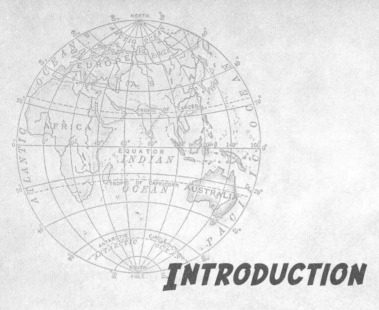

INTRODUCTION

JOHN RICHARD STEPHENS

*T*he Indiana Jones movies are among the most popular motion pictures of all time. Although his adventures were of course rooted in the finest traditions of pulp fiction, a number of story elements were also influenced by real people and events. The book you're holding in your hand right now is a collection of adventurous tales—many of them true—that are reminiscent of, and sometimes even the direct inspiration for, those wonderful movies.

The idea for this book first came to me when I was working on *Into the Mummy's Tomb*, an anthology of fiction and nonfiction stories about mummies and ancient Egypt. The fact that a couple of the selections read as though they had come straight out of *The Raiders of the Lost Ark* made me realize that I had in my files other stories and accounts that reminded me of Indiana Jones's adventures. I have always enjoyed such tales and, with this inspiration, I launched into compiling the book you are now reading.

These stories are set in exotic, faraway locations ranging from the jungles of the Amazon to the deserts of China. Many feature daring escapades of exploration and discovery, while others are tales of survival, with danger and suspense always being key features. These fascinating stories are overflowing with ancient tombs, gigantic spiders, shrunken heads, witch doctors, desert caravans, mysterious ruins with long dark tunnels full of bats, deadly quicksand, valuable treasures, devious bandits, dangerous booby traps, hungry crocodiles, hungrier piranha, vampire bats, huge stone idols, cannibals armed with poison blowguns, and, of course, lots of very large snakes.

As there are no adventurer-professors quite like Indiana Jones to be found in real life, his exploits were primarily modeled after matinee serials and pulp magazines of the 1940s and 1950s, with a touch of James Bond thrown in. Jones's creator George Lucas said, "In my version he was an international playboy like James Bond. A guy who went to casinos and nightclubs and had a lot of girlfriends. Steven [Spielberg] and Harrison [Ford] didn't like it." Those two men were, in fact, the ones who turned Jones into the fallible, uncertain, reluctant, yet highly resourceful, adventurer that became so popular. Although this pulp fiction archetype served as the primary inspiration in Indy's creation, a number of the movies' story and character elements were influenced by real people. Here are a few of the most commonly cited inspirations:

ROY CHAPMAN ANDREWS
(1884–1960)
Roy Chapman Andrews was a very enthusiastic explorer. "I wanted to go everywhere," he wrote. "I would have started on a day's notice for the North Pole or the South, to the jungle or the desert. It made not the slightest difference to me." He was also an adventurer, naturalist, and dinosaur hunter. And it was he who first used "Outer Mongolia" as a shorthand reference for any extremely remote, exotic location.

After graduating from college in Wisconsin, Andrews moved to New York and took a job mopping floors at the American Museum of Natural History. On getting his masters degree at Columbia University, he began traveling the world collecting zoological specimens for the museum. Andrews's travels took him to remote places, gathering lizards and snakes in the East Indies and dinosaur bones in Mongolia (in fact, his team found the first fossilized dinosaur eggs in 1923). He would be made director of the museum in 1934; not bad for a former janitor.

As an adventurer Andrews had dangerous encounters with just about everything, from sharks to sandstorms. He wrote, "In the [first] fifteen years [of field work] I can remember just ten times when I had really narrow escapes from death. Two were from drowning in typhoons, one was when our boat was charged by a wounded whale; once my wife and I were nearly eaten by wild dogs, once we were in great danger from fanatical lama priests; two were close calls when I fell over cliffs, once I was nearly caught by a huge python, and twice I might have been killed by bandits."

One night Andrews and his men killed 47 vipers in their tents. On another occasion he accidentally shot himself in the leg, explaining, "I felt almost happy" on discovering the bullet had missed his knee and he would not have a "stiff leg for the rest of my life."

HIRAM BINGHAM III
(1875–1956)

Hiram Bingham III is usually credited with the 1911 rediscovery of Machu Picchu— "the Lost City of the Incas"—high in the mountains of Peru, though he actually just brought the site to the world's attention. Much like Columbus's "discovery" of the Americas, there were already people living at Machu Picchu when he arrived. Still, it is remarkable that the site remained hidden for centuries from the Spanish invaders, colonists, and even the 19th-century explorers and later treasure hunters scouring the continent for ancient sites full of unplundered artifacts.

Bingham was a historian by training who had only just recently turned explorer at the time he became world famous for his discovery. He held degrees from Yale, U.C. Berkeley and Harvard; had taught history and politics at Harvard and Yale; and had served as preceptor under Woodrow Wilson at Princeton. While tracing ancient trade routes the previous year, he became fascinated with Incan ruins, so he organized a return expedition in 1911.

Bingham's group was camped out along Peru's Urubamba River, 44 miles northwest of Cuzco, when they were approached by a local farmer named Melchor Arteaga, who casually mentioned the old ruins high up in the mountains. Bingham described the following morning, saying, "The morning of July 24th dawned in a cold drizzle. Arteaga shivered and seemed inclined to stay in his hut. I offered to pay him well if he showed me the ruins. He demurred and said it was too hard a climb for such a wet day. But when he found I was willing to pay him a sol, three or four times the ordinary daily wage, he finally agreed to go. When asked just where the ruins were, he pointed straight up to the top of the mountain. No one supposed that they would be particularly interesting, and no one cared to go with me."

Arteaga, Bingham, and a policeman who was serving as Bingham's guide and interpreter set out at about ten in the morning. They soon had to cross a bridge so dilapidated that the explorer had to crawl across it on his hands and knees. After a treacherous climb, they eventually reached the ridge. Here he met two families who had been living and farming at Machu Picchu for about four years. Other farmers had lived there before that and locals had known of the site since at least 1894. While everyone rested in a small hut, 10-year-old Pablito Alvarez took Bingham out to show him around the extensive system of recently cleared terraces and the forest-covered temple, palace, and tomb ruins beyond.

"In the variety of its charms the power of its spell," Bingham wrote, "I know of no place in the world which can compare with it. Not only had it great snow peaks looming above the clouds more than two miles overhead; gigantic precipices of many-coloured granite rising sheer for thousands of feet above the foaming, glistening, roaring rapids, it has also, in striking contrast, orchids and tree ferns, the delectable beauty of luxurious vegetation and the mysterious witchery of the jungle. One is drawn irresistibly onwards by ever-recurring surprises through a deep, winding gorge, turning and twisting past overhanging cliffs of incredible height." Described by *National Geographic* as "arguably the greatest archaeological site in the Americas," Machu Picchu was built from 1460 to 1470, then abandoned a hundred years later—around the time the Conquistadors destroyed the Incan empire. Initially it was thought to be a place of refuge, though most scholars now believe it was a summer estate and the religious retreat of the Incan emperor Pachacuti.

After leading several other expeditions, Bingham went on to become an aviator and served as a lieutenant colonel in the Army Signal Corps during World War I, commanding a flying school in Issoudun, France. After the war, he was elected as the lieutenant governor of Connecticut and then went on to the U.S. Senate, where he became known as "The Flying Senator." In 1948 his book, *Lost City of the Incas*, became a bestseller.

SIR WILLIAM MATTHEW FLINDERS PETRIE
(1853–1942)

From a very early age, Flinders Petrie was interested in archeology. When he was eight, his parents considered him to be too frail to attend school, so they home-schooled him themselves. He taught himself geometry and trigonometry and learned surveying from his father. Not quite happy with his surveying equipment, he refined it, making it more accurate. After surveying a number of Britain's prehistoric monuments as a teenager—particularly Stonehenge—Petrie went to Egypt, where he was the first to accurately measure the Great Pyramids of Giza, disproving one popular theory on their construction. From 1880 to 1883, he conducted meticulous excavations at the Pyramids, examining every shovelful of dirt. While establishing himself as an archeologist at the Pyramids, he lived at the site, sleeping in a hammock in one of the empty tombs at the Giza necropolis.

Flinders Petrie went on to excavate some of Egypt's most important archeo-logical sites and was the one who identified Queen Nefertiti's palace complex. In spite of the fact that he had almost no formal schooling, he went on to become Professor of Egyptology at University College London, ultimately writing more than a hundred books and nearly 900 articles and reviews. But when he first went to Egypt, he was distressed at how quickly the sites were being plundered for artifacts and the monuments destroyed. He felt he had to do as much work as he could, as quickly as he could, before it was lost forever.

One of Petrie's early excavations was of the great temple at Tanis, where he directly supervised 170 workers himself by not having a foreman—a practice he continued on his later excavations. This pitted him against some Egyptologists, but he was popular with his men and it enabled him to make sure they were very careful with their work, leading to some discoveries that would have otherwise been lost. He also developed a number of archeological techniques that are still used today and was largely responsible for converting archeology from digging up artifacts into a methodical science, carefully removing and documenting each layer. All this earned Petrie the title of "The Father of Modern Archaeology." His methods of statistical analysis were so sophisticated, they were not used by oth-ers until they could be done on computers in the 1970s; he did them by writing on cards.

In addition to his intelligence and meticulous techniques, Petrie was a professor who didn't shy away from disagreeable tasks in the name of science. On one occasion, after squeezing through a tiny opening, he was lowered into a pitch-black burial chamber with only a candle to light his way and found himself waist-deep in water. Sifting through the debris in the partially submerged sarcophagi with his hands, all he found of the bodies were burnt bone fragments and charcoal from the charred coffins. He also spent many difficult hours climbing rope ladders on a cliff face at Sehel Island—which sits in the Nile in Southern Egypt—in order to photograph and sketch thousands of early Egyptian inscriptions.

Later Petrie focused his attention on Palestine for a number of years, becoming one of the first archeologists to conduct scientific excavations in the Holy Land. After he died in Jerusalem, his head was actually removed and preserved, as he insisted it should be given to the Royal College of Surgeons of London so they could study his brain for its high level of intelligence.

GIOVANNI BATTISTA BELZONI
(1778–1823)

Giovanni Belzoni—also known as The Great Belzoni—was a circus strongman turned archeologist and explorer. Born in Italy, he joined a monastic order at 16, but, when threatened with jail after becoming involved in some political entanglements, he fled to England. Being 6′7″ tall and bulky, Belzoni joined the circus and toured Europe as a "Patagonian Samson". In his mid-twenties, he married an Englishwoman and settled down in England for a few years, but left for Egypt in order to sell a hydraulic device he invented to increase the availability of the Nile's water. Even though the device worked, Mohammed Ali Pasha was not impressed and threw Belzoni out of his palace.

Belzoni's career as collector of Egyptian antiquities was launched when the British consul to Egypt asked him to gather artifacts for the British Museum. Belzoni carefully extracted and shipped back to England a 7.25-ton granite bust of Ramses II that is still on display at the museum. At this point in history, archeology was still a primitive science just a few steps above treasure-seeking, focused primarily on the bounty hunter-like gathering of artifacts for museums. Belzoni excelled at this, and even though today his techniques seem destructive and heavy-handed, they were nevertheless innovative and relatively advanced for his time. Howard Carter—the discoverer of Tutankhamen's tomb—described him as "one of the most remarkable men in the entire history of Archaeology."

Belzoni went on to investigate sites throughout the Middle East and Africa. Most notable were his excavations at Karnak, clearing sand from the great temple at Abu Simbel, and the opening up of the sepulcher of Seti I, some eighteen feet underground. In the Valley of Kings, he discovered the tombs of Amenhotep III, Ramses I, Merneptah, and Ay. He was also the first person since ancient times to enter the inner chambers of the pyramid of Khafre at Giza.

Belzoni died in Benin, while traveling to Timbuktu. It's generally said he died of dysentery, but famed 19th-century traveler and *1001 Arabian Nights* translator Richard Burton claimed Belzoni was in fact robbed and murdered.

COLONEL PERCY HARRISON FAWCETT (1867–1925?)

"In the forests were various beasts still unfamiliar to zoologists," Colonel Percy Fawcett wrote in *Lost Trails, Lost Cities,* "such as the *milta,* which I have seen twice, a black doglike cat about the size of a foxhound. There were snakes and insects yet unknown to scientists; and in the forests of the Madidi some mysterious and enormous beast has frequently been disturbed in the swamps—possibly a primeval monster like those reported in other parts of the continent. Certainly tracks have been found belonging to no known animal—huge tracks, far greater than could have been made by any species we know."

Fawcett was a British archeologist and explorer who made eight expeditions into the rain forests of Bolivia, Brazil, and Peru between 1906 and 1925. On one of these trips in the Beni Swamps of Madre de Dios, he saw a huge creature he thought might be a diplodocus—a 25-ton, 80-foot-long dinosaur that looks a lot like a brontosaurus. Similar sightings were made by various tribes east of the Ucayali.

It was accounts such as these that inspired Sir Arthur Conan Doyle to write *The Lost World,* his 1912 novel about a South American plateau where dinosaurs and other long-disappeared creatures have somehow survived since prehistoric times. Fawcett met with Conan Doyle while he was writing *The Lost World,* describing to the writer the almost inaccessible, flat-topped Ricardo Franco Hills which the colonel and his party had attempted to climb, and the jungle-covered Huanchaca plateau on top, which Conan Doyle ultimately used as the location for his novel. *The Lost World* was followed by many similar stories, such as Edgar Rice Burroughs's *The Land That Time Forgot*, the *King Kong* movies, and Michael Crichton's *Jurassic Park*.

While it is hardly likely Fawcett actually saw a dinosaur, he did find tracks of a snake that he estimated was 80 feet long. On another occasion he shot and killed an enormous anaconda. He didn't have anything to measure it with, but estimated it was 62 feet long and 12 inches in diameter.

Traveling through the Amazon jungles could be extremely dangerous and difficult. It could take up six hours to trek only two miles through the dense foliage, so Fawcett and his party would travel by water whenever possible; several times they were almost killed coursing through rapids. On one occasion Fawcett's party had just rounded a steep bluff when they suddenly heard the crash of a huge waterfall just ahead. One raft reached the shore, but it was too late for Fawcett's. He later wrote, "the raft seemed to poise there for an instant before it fell from under us. Turning over two or three times as it shot through the air, the balsa crashed down into the black depths.... Looking back we saw what we had come through. The fall was about twenty feet high, and where river dropped the canyon narrowed to a mere ten feet across; through this bottleneck the huge volume of water gushed with terrific force, thundering down into the a welter of brown foam and black-topped rocks. It seemed incredible that we could have survived that maelstrom!"

The water contained other dangers. The colonel had to swim many rivers carrying a rope to the other side so the supplies could be transported across. But he had to make sure he had no sores or cuts, or he could quickly fall victim to piranha. At one point, one of his men tried washing blood from his hands in the river and had two of his fingers bitten off.

And this was only the beginning of the jungle's dangers. There were ants and other biting insects, sometimes carrying exotic diseases. Upon his arrival at Cobija, Fawcett was told that the town's death rate was almost fifty percent a year.

There were also jaguars, vampire bats, wild bulls, and a variety of deadly snakes. Once the party came across a seven-foot bushmaster—the largest pit viper in the world. As many of the men jumped back, one of them killed it with two bullets.

The gunman soon discovered he had barely escaped death himself, as his skin had two dents from the viper's fangs. His tobacco pouch had prevented them from penetrating him. These deadly snakes have been known to grow to 14 feet in length.

Jungles, forests, and swamps are generally loaded with spiders, and—as you would expect with the Amazon—some are gigantic and extremely poisonous, such as the apazauca spider. One night as Fawcett was getting into his sleeping bag, he felt one of these scurry up his arm, onto his neck. He described the spider as "hairy and revolting." When he tried to brush it off, it clung to his hand and wouldn't let go. He was finally able to shake it off without being bitten.

Other dangers Fawcett and his men faced were sunstroke, sprains or broken bones, and starvation. They were once forced to go twenty days without food. Fawcett finally spotted a deer and shot it. They ate it all, including its fur. And then there were the natives, who were wary of strangers and often didn't like anyone passing through their territory without paying something for permission. On one occasion, while floating down the Chocolatal River, the boat's pilot went to check out a road by himself. When Fawcett later found him, there were 42 arrows in his corpse.

In 1925, Fawcett, his son, and a young friend named Rimell all mysteriously disappeared. They had set off in the Mato Grosso region of Brazil in search of a lost city they'd heard tales about. Even though he'd left a note saying that if they didn't return, no search parties should be sent in after them (as it was too dangerous and the rescuers probably wouldn't make it out alive), still many have tried find him, or discover what became of him. Fawcett was right. More than thirteen expeditions were launched, one as recently as 1996, with more than a hundred people having died over the decades trying to discover what happened to Fawcett and his companions.

There were various rumors and reports, of course. Some said the three were killed by wild animals, or by any number of tribes like the Arumás, the Iaruna, the Kalapalos, the Suyás, or the Xavantes. Some claimed to have found their bones, while others said Fawcett had become a cannibal chief. Some even claimed to have seen their shrunken heads. But none of these claims were ever verified.

Making things even more intriguing was Fawcett's interest in the occult. Just a few months before his disappearance, Fawcett commented in a letter about the use of extrasensory information in archeology. "Psychics," he wrote, "may give very genuine information, but it has to be carefully sifted as there are so many cross currents, particularly when not in trance."

Because of this, there have been some stranger theories regarding Fawcett's disappearance and what he was really searching for. There are those who claim it wasn't really the ruins of the Lost City that he intended to find, it was a thriving subterranean city or immense underground network of cites populated by the highly intelligent descendants of the survivors of Atlantis and/or the several-thousand-year-old Atlanteans themselves. Some say the colonel and his son found the hidden entrance and walked the several miles down through the caverns to the mystic city, starting a new life there, and that all this is connected with appearances of UFOs in the area.

More recently, someone claiming to have access to secret papers of Fawcett's says that they reveal he intended to establish his own enlightened colony that would eventually lead the world in an ecologically and spiritually advanced direction.

Interestingly, fact meets fiction in Rob MacGregor's *Indiana Jones and the Seven Veils*. In this novel, Indy ventures into Brazil's tropical forests in search of the missing Colonel Percy Fawcett, who (in the book's version of events) had been seeking a fabled city populated by red-headed descendants of the Druids. These transplanted Celts use magical powers and human blood to keep their city hidden. Fawcett escapes with Indy, only to die when their plane crashes.

*   *   *

These are just a few of interesting and unique personalities who populate the fields of anthropology, archeology, and exploration, whose lives bear more than a few resemblances to that of Indiana Jones. There are many more, and most had fascinating experiences or dangerous encounters that are worth reading about. These intrepid explorers were often thrust into life-threatening situations because of their curiosity, their desire for knowledge, their aspiration for discovery, or even their craving for ancient treasures.

While some of this anthology's tales were chosen specifically because they contain elements found in the movies—such as Belzoni getting trapped in a room full of collapsing mummies, much as happened to Jones in the first film—

I was primarily interested in seeking out exciting accounts of archeologists, naturalists, explorers, and adventurers from the golden age of discovery—the 19th and early 20th century—when so many parts of the world map had yet to be filled in. Although a number of the stories that fulfilled that criteria are fictional, like Rudyard Kipling's thrilling classic *The Man Who Would Be King*, most are authentic accounts of events that really happened when intrepid explorers like American diplomat and archeologist John Lloyd Stephens or Scottish missionary Dr. David Livingstone took their lives in their own hands and ventured bravely into the dark unknown...

RAIDING MUMMIES' TOMBS

AMELIA B. EDWARDS

(British novelist and Egyptologist)

It is a long and shelterless ride from the palms to the desert; but we come to the end of it at last, mounting just such another sand-slope as that which leads up from the Gizeh road to the foot of the Great Pyramid. The edge of the plateau here rises abruptly from the plain in one long range of low perpendicular cliffs pierced with dark mouths of rock-cut sepulchres, while the sand-slope by which we are climbing pours down through a breach in the rock, as an Alpine snowdrift flows through a mountain gap from the ice-level above.

And now, having dismounted through compassion for our unfortunate little donkeys, the first thing we observe is the curious mixture of debris underfoot. At Gizeh one treads only sand and pebbles; but here at Sakkara the whole plateau is thickly strewn with scraps of broken pottery, limestone, marble, and alabaster; flakes of green and blue glaze; bleached bones; shreds of yellow linen; and lumps of some odd-looking dark brown substance, like dried-up sponge. Presently some one picks up a little noseless head of one of the common blue-ware funereal statuettes, and immediately we all fall to work, grubbing for treasure—a pure waste of precious time; for though the sand is full of debris, it has been sifted so often and so carefully by the Arabs that it no longer contains anything worth looking for.

1

Meanwhile, one finds a fragment of iridescent glass—another, a morsel of shattered vase—a third, an opaque bead of some kind of yellow paste. And then, with a shock which the present writer, at all events, will not soon forget, we suddenly discover that these scattered bones are human—that those linen shreds are shreds of cerement cloths—that yonder odd-looking brown lumps are rent fragments of what once was living flesh! And now for the first time we realise that every inch of this ground on which we are standing, and all these hillocks and hollows and pits in the sand, are violated graves.

"Ce n'est que le premier pas que coûte." We soon became quite hardened to such sights, and learned to rummage among dusty sepulchres with no more compunction than would have befitted a gang of professional body-snatchers. These are experiences upon which one looks back afterwards with wonder, and something like remorse; but so infectious is the universal callousness, and so overmastering is the passion for relic-hunting, that I do not doubt we should again do the same things under the same circumstances. Most Egyptian travellers, if questioned, would have to make a similar confession. Shocked at first, they denounce with horror the whole system of sepulchral excavation, legal as well as predatory; acquiring, however, a taste for scarabs and funerary statuettes, they soon begin to buy with eagerness the spoils of the dead; finally they forget all their former scruples, and ask no better fortune, than to discover and confiscate a tomb for themselves.

> **"**Dead men are not useless; and the excavator must not cheat the world of any part of its great perquisite. The dead are the property of the living and the archaeologist is the world's agent for the estate of the grave.**"**
> —*Egyptologist* ARTHUR WEIGALL

*   *   *

The thing that now caught the painter's eye, however, was a long crack running transversely down the face of the rock. It was such a crack as might have been caused, one would say, by blasting.

He stooped—cleared the sand away a little with his hand—observed that the crack widened—poked in the point of his stick; and found that it penetrated to a depth of two or three feet. Even then, it seemed to him to stop, not because it encountered any obstacle, but because the crack was not wide enough to admit the thick end of the stick.

This surprised him. No mere fault in the natural rock, he thought, would go so deep. He scooped away a little more sand; and still the cleft widened. He introduced the stick a second time. It was a long palm-stick like an alpenstock, and it measured about five feet in length. When he probed the cleft with it this second time, it went in freely up to where he held it in his hand—that is to say, to a depth of quite four feet.

Convinced now that there was some hidden cavity in the rock, he carefully examined the surface. There were yet visible a few hieroglyphic characters and part of two cartouches, as well as some battered outlines of what had once been figures. The heads of these figures were gone (the face of the rock, with whatever may have been sculptured upon it, having come away bodily at this point), while from the waist downwards they were hidden under the sand. Only some hands and arms, in short, could be made out.

They were the hands and arms, apparently, of four figures; two in the centre of the composition, and two at the extremities. The two centre ones, which seemed to be back to back, probably represented gods; the outer ones, worshippers.

All at once, it flashed upon the painter that he had seen this kind of group many a time before—*and generally over a doorway.*

Feeling sure now that he was on the brink of a discovery, he came back; fetched away Salame and Mehemet Ali; and, without saying a syllable to any one, set to work with these two to scrape away the sand at the spot where the crack widened.

Meanwhile, the luncheon bell having rung thrice, we concluded that the painter had rambled off somewhere into the desert; and so sat down without him. Towards the close of the meal, however, came a pencilled note, the contents of which ran as follows:—

"Pray come immediately—I have found the entrance to a tomb. Please send some sandwiches—A. M'C."

To follow the messenger at once to the scene of action was the general impulse. In less than ten minutes we were there, asking breathless questions, peeping in through the fast-widening aperture, and helping to clear away the sand.

All that Sunday afternoon, heedless of possible sunstroke, unconscious of fatigue, we toiled upon our hands and knees, as for bare life, under the burning sun. We had all the crew up, working like tigers. Every one helped; even the dragoman and the two maids. More than once, when we paused for a moment's breathing space, we said to each other: "If those at home could see us, what would they say!"

And now, more than ever, we felt the need of implements. With a spade or two and a wheelbarrow, we could have done wonders; but with only one small fire-shovel, a birch broom, a couple of charcoal baskets, and about twenty pairs of hands, we were poor indeed. What was wanted in means, however, was made up in method. Some scraped away the sand; some gathered it into baskets; some carried the baskets to the edge of the cliff, and emptied them into the river. The Idle Man distinguished himself by scooping out a channel where the slope was steepest; which greatly facilitated the work. Emptied down this shoot and kept continually going, the sand poured off in a steady stream like water.

> "I was looking intently, though almost unconsciously, at a pigeon on the head of Isis, the capital of one of the front columns of the temple. It was a beautiful shot; it could not have been finer if the temple had been built expressly to shoot pigeons from. I fired: the shot went smack into the beautifully sculptured face of the goddess, and put out one of her eyes; the pigeon fell at the foot of the column, and while the goddess seemed to weep over her fallen state, and to reproach for this renewed insult to herself and to the arts, I picked up the bird and returned to my boat."
>
> —*explorer* JOHN LLOYD STEPHENS

Meanwhile the opening grew rapidly larger. When we first came up—that is, when the painter and the two sailors had been working on it for about an hour— we found a hole scarcely as large as one's hand, through which it was just possible to catch a dim glimpse of painted walls within. By sunset, the top of the doorway was laid bare, and where the crack ended in a large triangular fracture, there was an aperture about a foot and a half square, into which Mehemet Ali was the first to squeeze his way. We passed him in a candle and a box of matches; but he came out again directly, saying that it was a most beautiful Birbeh, and quite light within.

The writer wriggled in next. She found herself looking down from the top of a sandslope into a small square chamber. This sand-drift, which here rose to within a foot and a half of the top of the doorway, was heaped to the ceiling in the corner behind the door, and thence sloped steeply down, completely covering the floor. There was light enough to see every detail distinctly—the painted frieze running round just under the ceiling; the bas-relief sculptures on the walls, gorgeous with unfaded colour; the smooth sand, pitted near the top, where Mehemet Ali had trodden, but undisturbed elsewhere by human foot; the great gap in the middle of the ceiling, where the rock had given way; the fallen fragments on the floor, now almost buried in sand.

Satisfied that the place was absolutely fresh and untouched, the writer crawled out, and the others, one by one, crawled in. When each had seen it in turn, the opening was barricaded for the night; the sailors being forbidden to enter it, lest they should injure the decorations.

THEODORE DAVIS
(American Egyptologist)

The chamber was as dark as dark could be and extremely hot. Our first quest was the name of the owner of the tomb, as to which we had not the slightest knowledge or suspicion. We held up our candles, but they gave so little light and so dazzled our eyes that we could see nothing except the glitter of gold. In a moment or two, however, I made out a very large wooden coffin, known as a funeral sled, which was used to contain all the coffins of the dead person and his mummy and to convey them to his tomb. It was about six feet high and eight feet long, made of wood covered with bitumen, which was as bright as the day it was put on. Around the upper part of the coffin was a stripe of gold-foil, about six inches wide, covered with hieroglyphs. On calling Monsieur [Sir Gaston] Maspero's attention to it, he immediately handed me his candle, which, together with my own, I held before my eyes, close to the inscriptions so that he could read them. In an instant he said, "Iouiya." Naturally excited by the announcement, and blinded by the glare of the candles, I involuntarily advanced them very near the coffin; whereupon Monsieur Maspero cried out, "Be careful!" and pulled my hands back. In a moment we realized that, had my candles touched the bitumen, which I came dangerously near doing, the coffin would have been in a blaze. As the entire contents of the tomb were inflammable, and directly opposite the coffin was a corridor leading to the open air and making a draught, we undoubtedly should have lost our lives, as the only escape was by the corridor, which would have necessitated climbing over the stone wall barring the doorway. This would have retarded our exit for at least ten minutes.

As soon as we realized the danger we had escaped, we made our way out of the chamber and, seating ourselves in the corridor, sent for workmen, who took down the door blocking the doorway. Then the electricians brought down the wires with bulbs attached, and we made our second entry into the chamber, each of us furnished with electric lights which we held over our heads, and we saw that every foot of the chamber was filled with objects brilliant with gold. In a corner stood a chariot, the pole of which had been broken by the weight of a coffin lid that the robber had evidently deposited upon it. Within a foot or two of the chariot stood two alabaster vases of great beauty and in perfect condition.

From the neck of one of the vases hung shreds of mummy-cloth which had originally covered the mouth of the vase. Evidently the robber, expecting the contents to be valuable, tore off the cloth. Three thousand years thereafter I looked into the vase with like expectation; both of us were disappointed, for it contained only a liquid which was first thought to be honey, but which subsequently proved to be natron.

The mummies of Iouiya and Touiyou were lying in their coffins. Originally each mummy was enclosed in three coffins; the inner one holding the body. Evidently the robber had taken the inner coffins out and then had taken off their lids, though he did not take the bodies out of their coffins, but contented himself with stripping off the mummy-cloth in which they were wrapped. The stripping was done by scratching off the cloth with his nails, seeking only the gold ornaments or jewels. At least that seems to have been the manner of robbing the bodies, as we found in both coffins, on either side of the bodies, great quantities of mummy-cloth torn into small bits. Among the shreds were found numerous valuable religious symbols, several scarabs, and various objects of interest and beauty. In lifting the body of Iouiya from his coffin, we found a necklace of large beads made of gold and of lapis lazuli, strung on a strong thread, which the robber had evidently broken when scratching off the mummy-cloth, causing the beads to fall behind the mummy's neck.

The robber had also overlooked a gold plate about the size of the palm of a man's hand, which had been inserted by the embalmer to conceal the incision he had made in extracting the dead man's heart for special mummification.

> "We broke through[...] and we found the god lying at the rear of the tomb, and we found the burial place of his queen next to him. We opened their sarcophagi and the coffins in which they were and found the noble mummy of the king with a collar upon it and a large number of amulets. A collar of gold was around his neck, and a crown of gold. The noble mummy of the king was completely covered in gold and his coffins were decorated with gold and silver inside and outside, and were inlaid with every sort of precious stone. We collected the gold that we found on the mummy of the god, and we took all that was on the queen in the same way, and we set fire to their coffins. We took all the possessions of gold, silver and bronze and divided it between us."
>
> —the confession of tomb robber AMUNPANEFER *at his trial in c. 1120* B.C.

When I first saw the mummy of Touiyou she was lying in her coffin, covered from her chin to her feet with very fine mummy-cloth arranged with care. Why this was done no one can positively state, but I am disposed to think that the robber was impressed by the dignity of the dead woman whose body he had desecrated. I had occasion to sit by her in the tomb for nearly an hour, and having nothing else to do or see, I studied her face and indulged in speculations germane to the situation, until her dignity and character so impressed me that I almost found it necessary to apologize for my presence.

From all the evidence furnished by the acts of the robber, it seems reasonable to conclude that the entry into the tomb was made within the lifetime of some person who had exact knowledge of its location. Evidently the robber had tunneled through the overlying *débris* which concealed the door of the tomb; otherwise he would have been compelled to remove a mass of rock and soil which would have required many days, and would also have exposed the robbery to the first passer-by. When the robber found the outer doorway barred by a wall, he took off enough of it to enable him to crawl through; and when he reached the second and last doorway, he found a corresponding wall, which he treated in the same manner. He seems to have had either a very dim light or none at all, for when he was in the burial chamber he selected a large stone scarab, the neck-yoke of the chariot, and a wooden staff of office, all of which were covered with thick gold foil, which evidently he thought to be solid gold: he carried them up the corridor until he came to a gleam of daylight, when he discovered his error and left them on the floor of the corridor, where I found them.

When the robber got out of the tomb, he carefully concealed the doorway and his tunnel with stones and *débris*, and did it so effectively, that it was not disturbed until its discovery three thousand years later.

GIOVANNI BELZONI

(Italian collector of antiquities for the British government)

Taking Mrs. Belzoni with me, I visited Portugal, Spain and Malta, from which latter place we embarked for Egypt[...]. Here I had the good fortune to be the discoverer of many remains of antiquity of that primitive nation. I succeeded in opening one of the two famous Pyramids of Ghizeh, as well as several of the Tombs of the Kings at Thebes. Among the latter, that which has been pronounced by one of the most distinguished scholars of the age to be the tomb of Psammuthis, is at this moment the principal, the most perfect and splendid monument in that country. The celebrated bust of young Memnon, which I brought from Thebes, is now in the British Museum; and the alabaster sarcophagus, found in the Tombs of the Kings, is on its way to England.

Near the second cataract of the Nile, I opened the temple of Ybsambul; then made a journey to the coast of the Red Sea, to the city of Berenice, and afterwards an excursion in the western Elloah, or Oasis. I now embarked for Europe, and after an absence of twenty years, returned to my native land, and to the bosom of my family; from whence I proceeded to England.

On my arrival in Europe I found so erroneous accounts had been given to the public of my operations and discoveries in Egypt, that it appeared to be my duty to publish a plain statement of facts; and should anyone call its correctness in question, I hope they will do it openly, that I may be able to prove the truth of my assertions.

[…]Gournow is a tract of rocks, about two miles in length, at the foot of the Libyan mountains, on the west of Thebes, and was the burial place of the great city of a hundred gates. Every part of these rocks is cut out by art, in the form of large and small chambers, each of which has its separate entrance; and though they are very close to each other, it is seldom that there is any interior communication from one to the other. I can truly say, it is impossible to give any description sufficient to convey the smallest idea of those subterranean abodes, and their inhabitants. There are no sepulchres in any part of the world like them; there are no excavations or mines, that can be compared to these truly astonishing places; and no exact description can be given of their interior, owing to the difficulty of visiting these places. The inconvenience of entering into them is such, that it is not everyone who can support the exertion.

A traveller is generally satisfied when he has seen the large hall, the gallery, the staircase, and as far as he can conveniently go: besides, he is taken up with the strange works he observes cut in various places, and painted on each side of the walls: so that when he comes to a narrow and difficult passage, or to have to descend to the bottom of a well or cavity, he declines taking such trouble, naturally supposing that he cannot see in these abysses anything so magnificent as what he sees above, and consequently deeming it useless to proceed any farther. Of some of these tombs many persons could not stand the suffocating air, which often causes fainting. A vast quantity of dust rises, so fine that it enters into the throat and nostrils, and chokes the nose and mouth to such a degree, that it requires great power of lungs to resist it and the strong effluvia of the mummies.

This is not all: the entry or passage where the bodies are is roughly cut in the rocks, and the falling of the sand from the upper part or ceiling of the passage causes it to be nearly filled up. In some places there is not more than the vacancy of a foot left, which you must contrive to pass through in a creeping posture like a snail, on pointed and keen stones, that cut like glass. After getting through these passages, some of them two or three hundred yards long, you generally find a more commodious place, perhaps high enough to sit. But what a place of rest! surrounded by bodies, by heaps of mummies in all directions; which, previous to my being accustomed to the sight, impressed me with horror. The blackness of the wall, the faint light given by the candles or torches for want of air, the different objects that surrounded me, seeming to converse with each other, and the Arabs with the candles or torches in their hands, naked and covered with dust, themselves resembling living mummies, absolutely formed a scene that cannot be described. In such a situation I found myself several times, and often returned exhausted and fainting, till at last I became inured to it, and indifferent to what I suffered, except from the dust, which never failed to choke my throat and nose; and though fortunately I am destitute of the sense of smelling, I could taste that the mummies were rather unpleasant to swallow. After the exertion of entering into such a place, through a passage of fifty, a hundred, three hundred, or perhaps six hundred yards, nearly overcome, I sought a resting place, found one, and contrived to sit; but when my weight bore on the body of an Egyptian, it crushed it like a bandbox. I naturally had recourse to my hands to sustain my weight, but they found no better support; so that I sunk altogether among the broken mummies, with a crash of bones, rags, and wooden cases, which raised such a dust as kept me motionless for a quarter of an hour, waiting till it subsided again. I could not remove from the place, however, without increasing it, and every step I took I crushed a mummy in some part or other. Once I was conducted from such a place to another resembling it, through a passage of about twenty feet in length, and no wider than that a body could be forced through. It was choked with mummies, and I could not pass without putting my face in contact with that of some decayed Egyptian; but as the passage inclined downwards, my own weight helped me on; however, I could not avoid being covered with bones, legs, arms and heads rolling from above. Thus I proceeded from one cave to another, all full of mummies piled up in various ways, some standing, some lying, and some on their heads. The purpose of my researches was to rob the Egyptians of their papyri; of which I found a few hidden in their breasts, under their arms, in the space above the knees, or on the legs, and covered by the numerous folds of cloth, that envelop the mummy. The people of Gournow, who made a trade of antiquities of this sort, are very jealous of strangers, and keep them as secret as possible, deceiving the travellers by pretending, that they have arrived at the end of the pits, when they are scarcely at the entrance. I could never prevail on them to conduct me into these places till my second voyage, when I succeeded in obtaining admission into any cave where mummies were to be seen.

My permanent residence in Thebes was the cause of my success. The Arabs saw that I paid particular attention to the situation of the entrance into the tombs, and that they could not avoid being seen by me when they were at work digging in search of a new tomb, though they are very cautious when any stranger is in Gournow not to let it be known where they go to open the earth; and as travellers generally remain in that place a few days only, they used to leave off digging during that time. If any traveller be curious enough to ask to examine the interior of a tomb, they are ready to show him one immediately, and conduct him to some of the old tombs, where he sees nothing but the grottoes in which mummies formerly had been deposited, or where there are but few, and these already plundered; so that he can form but a poor idea of the real tombs, where the remains were originally placed.

M. Mathey, a witness to the unwrapping of an unusual mummy in 1886, wrote, "It is difficult to give an adequate description of the face thus laid bare. I can only say that no countenance has ever more faithfully recreated a picture of such affecting and hideous agony. His features, horribly distorted, surely showed that the wretched man must have been deliberately asphyxiated, most probably by being buried alive."

The people of Gournow live in the entrance of such caves as have already been opened, and by making partitions with earthen walls, they form habitations for themselves, as well as for their cows, camels, buffaloes, sheep, goats, dogs, etc. I do not know whether it is because they are so few in number, that the Government takes so little notice of what they do; but it is certain that they are the most unruly people in Egypt. At various times many of them have been destroyed, so that they are reduced from three thousand, the number they formerly reckoned, to three hundred, which form the population of the present day. They have no mosque, nor do they care for one; for though they have at their disposal a great quantity of all sorts of bricks, which abound in every part of Gournow, from the surrounding tombs, they have never built a single house. They are forced to cultivate a small tract of land, extending from the rocks to the Nile, about a mile in breadth, and two and a half in length; and even this is in part neglected; for if left to their own will, they would never take a spade in their hands, except when they go to dig for mummies; which they find to be more profitable employment than agriculture. This is the fault of travellers, who are so pleased the moment they are presented with any piece of antiquity, that, without thinking of the injury resulting from the example to their successors, they give a great deal more than the people really expect. Hence it has arisen, that they now set such an enormous price on antiquities, and in particular on papyri. Some of them have accumulated a considerable sum of money, and are become so indifferent, that they remain idle, unless whatever price they demand to be given them; and it is to be observed, that it is a fixed point in their minds, that the Franks would not be so liberal, unless the articles were worth ten times as much as they pay for them.[...]

After having described the tombs, the mummies, the rocks and the rogues of Gournow, it is time to cross the Nile and return to Carnak.[...] My daily employment kept me in continual motion. In the morning I used to give my directions for the works at Carnak. The Arabs generally come to work at the rising of the sun, and leave off from noon till two or three o'clock. When I had many employed, I divided them into parties, and set an overseer over each, to see that they worked at the proper hours, and on the allotted spots of ground, which I had previously marked out; but generally some of our people were obliged to be there, for no trust is to be reposed in the Arabs, if they should find any small pieces of antiquity. Before noon I used to cross the river and inspect the works at Gournow. Having been there the year before, and had dealings with these people, I was at home in every part of Thebes, knew every Arab there, and they knew me as well. Mr. Beechy had taken possession of the temple at Luxor, without requesting permission from the gods, and we made a dwelling place of one of the chambers: I believe it must have been the *sekos* [i.e., sanctuary]. By the help of some mats we procured a very tolerable accommodation, but could not prevent the dust from coming on our beds, and clothes to which for my part I had long before become indifferent. We could not sleep any longer in the boat; for in consequence of the provision we had on board, such quantities of large rats accompanied us all the way to Luxor, that we had no peace day or night, and at last they succeeded in fairly dislodging us. We thought to have been a match for them, however, for we caused all the provision to be taken out, and the boat to be sunk at Luxor, but as they were good swimmers, they saved their lives, and hid themselves in the holes of the pier; and when the provision had been put on board again, they all returned cheerfully, a few excepted, and were no doubt grateful to us for having given them a fresh appetite and a good bathing.

In Gournow our researches continued among the mummies. The Arabs had become quite unconcerned about the secret of the tombs; for they saw it was their interest to search, as they were rewarded for what they found, and those who were duly paid were indifferent whether we or their brethren found a tomb. The men were divided into two classes. The most knowing were making researches on their own account, employing eight or ten to assist them. They indicated the ground where they hoped to find a tomb, and sometimes were fortunate enough to hit on the entrance of a mummy pit in the first attempt. At other times after spending two or three days, they often found only a pit filled with mummies of the inferior class, which had nothing among them worthy of notice: so that, even to the most skilful explorer, it was a mere chance what he should find. On the other hand, in some of the tombs of the better class they found very good specimens of antiquity, of all sorts. I met with some difficulty at first in persuading these people to work in search of tombs,

> " At Tanis the mice were simply unbearable. Being field-mice, they would not walk into traps like civilized mice, so the explorer's only resource was to burn a night-light and shoot them. Now to lie in bed and shoot mice with a revolver is surely a form of sport exclusively reserved for the explorer in Egypt. "
> —*Egyptologist* AMELIA B. EDWARDS

and receive a regular daily payment; for they conceived it to be against their interest, supposing I might obtain the antiquities at too cheap a rate: but when they saw, that sometimes they received their pay regularly, and I had nothing for it, they found it was rather in their favour, to secure twenty paras (three pence) a day, than run the risk of having nothing for their labour, which often happened with those who worked at adventure.

It was from these works that I became better acquainted with the manner in which the Egyptians regulated their burial places; and I plainly saw the various degrees and customs of the divers classes, from the peasant to the king. The Egyptians had three different methods of embalming their dead bodies, which, Herodotus informs us, were according to the expense the persons who presented the dead bodies to the mummy-makers chose to incur. This father of history thus expresses himself on the subject:

> Certain persons were appointed by the laws to the exercise of this profession. When a dead boy was brought to them, they exhibited to the friends of the deceased different models, highly finished in wood. The most perfect of these, they said, resembles one, whom I do not think it religious to name on such an occasion; the second was of less price, and inferior in point of execution; the other was still more mean. They then inquired after which model the deceased should be represented. When the price was determined, the relations retired, and the embalmers proceeded in their work. In the most perfect specimens of their art, they extracted the brain through the nostrils, partly with a piece of iron, and partly by the infusion of drugs. They then, with an Ethiopian stone, made an incision in the side, through which drew out the intestines. These they cleaned thoroughly, washing them in palm-wine, and afterwards covering them with pounded aromatics. They then filled the body with powder of pure myrrh, cassia, and other spices, without frankincense. Having sewn up the body, it was covered with nitre for the space of seventy days, which time they were not allowed to exceed. At the end of this period, being first washed, it was closely wrapped in bandages of cotton, dipped in gum, which the Egyptians use as a glue. It was then returned to the relations,

who enclosed the body in a case of wood, made to resemble a human figure, and placed it against the wall in the repository of their dead. This was the most costly mode of embalming.

For those who wished to be at less expense, the following method was adopted. They neither drew out the intestines, nor made any incision in the dead body, but injected a liniment made from the cedar. After taking proper means to secure the injected oil within the body, it was covered with nitre for the time above specified. On the last day they withdrew the liquid before introduced, which brought with it all the intestines. The nitre dried up and hardened the flesh, so that the corpse appeared little but skin and bone. In this state the body was returned, and no further care taken concerning it.

There was a third mode of embalming, appropriated to the poor. A particular kind of lotion was made to pass through the body, which was afterwards merely left in nitre for the above space of seventy days and then returned.

Such is the account given us by Herodotus.

Nothing can more plainly distinguish the various classes of people, than the manner of their preservation: but there are many other remarks that may be made to the same effect. I shall describe how I found the mummies of the principal class untouched, and hence we may judge how they were prepared and deposited in their respective places. I am sorry that I am obliged to contradict my old guide, Herodotus; for in this point, and many others, he was not well informed by the Egyptians. In the first place, speaking of the mummies in their cases, he mentions them as erect: but it is somewhat singular, that in so many pits as I have opened, I never saw a single mummy standing. On the contrary, I found them lying regularly, in horizontal rows, and some were sunk into a cement, which must have been nearly fluid when the cases were placed on it. The lower classes were not buried in cases: they were dried up, as it appears, after the regular preparation of the seventy days. Mummies of this sort were in the proportion of about ten to one of the better class, as near as I could calculate by the quantity I have seen of both; and it appeared to me, that, after the operation of the nitre, adopted by the mummy-makers, these bodies may have been dried in the sun. Indeed for my own part, I am persuaded it was so; as there is not the smallest quantity of gum or anything else to be found on them. The linen in which they are folded is of a coarser sort, and less in quantity; they have no ornaments about them of any consequence, and they are piled up in layers so as to crowd several caves excavated for the purpose in a rude manner. In general these tombs are to be found in the lower grounds, at the foot of the mountains of Gournow; and some extend as far as the border to which the inundation reaches. They are to be entered by a small aperture, arched over, or by a shaft four or five feet square, at the bottom of which are entrances into various chambers, all choked up with mummies: and though there is scarcely anything to be found on them, many of these tombs have been rummaged, and left in the most confused state.

I must not omit that among these tombs we saw some which contained the mummies of animals intermixed with human bodies. There were bulls, cows, sheep, monkeys, foxes, bats, crocodiles, fishes, and birds in them; idols often occur; and one tomb was filled with nothing but cats, carefully folded in red and white linen, the head covered by a mask representing the cat, and made of the same linen. I have opened all these sorts of animals. Of the bull, the calf, and the sheep there is no part but the head which is covered with linen, and the horns projecting out of the cloth; the rest of the body being represented by two pieces of wood, eighteen inches wide and three feet long, in an horizontal direction, at the end of which was another, placed perpendicularly, two feet high, to form the breast of the animal. The calves and sheep are of the same structure, and large in proportion to the bulls. The monkey is in its full form, in a sitting posture. The fox is squeezed up by the bandages, but in some measure the shape of the head is kept perfect. The crocodile is left in its own shape, and after being well bound round with linen, the eyes and mouth are painted on this covering. The birds are squeezed together, and lose their shape, except the ibis, which is found like a fowl ready to be cooked, and bound round with linen like all the rest.

It is somewhat singular that such animals are not to be met within the tombs of the higher sort of people; while few or no papyri are to be found among the lower order, and if any occur they are only small pieces stuck upon the breast with a little gum or asphaltum, being probably all that the poor individual could afford to himself. In those of the better classes other objects are found. I think they ought to be divided into several classes, as I cannot confine myself to three. I do not mean to impute error to Herodotus when he speaks of the three modes of embalming; but I will venture to assert that the high, middling and poorer classes, all admit of farther distinction. In the same pit where I found mummies in cases, I found others without; and in these, papyri are most likely to be met with. I remarked, that the mummies in the cases have no papyri; at least I never observed any: on the contrary, in those without cases they are often obtained. It appears to me that such people as could afford it would have a case to be buried in, on which the history of their lives was painted; and those who could not afford a case, were contented to have their lives written on papyri, rolled up and placed above their knees. Even in the appearance of the cases there is a great difference: some are exceedingly plain, others more ornamented, and some very richly adorned with figures well painted. The cases are generally made of Egyptian sycamore: apparently this was the most plentiful wood in the country, as it is usually employed for the different utensils. All the cases have a human face, male or female. Some of the large cases contain others within them, either of wood or of plaster, painted. The inner cases are sometimes fitted to the body of the mummy: others are only covers to the body, in form of a man or woman, easily distinguishable by the beard and the breast, like that on the outside. Some of the mummies have garlands of flowers, and leaves of the acacia, or stunt tree, over their heads and breasts. This tree is often seen on the banks of the Nile, above Thebes, and particularly in Nubia. The flower when fresh is yellow, and of a very hard substance, appearing as if artificial. The leaves also are very strong, and though dried and turned brown, they still retain their firmness. In the inside of these mummies are found lumps of asphaltum, sometimes so large as to weigh two pounds. The entrails of these mummies are often found bound up in linen and asphaltum. What does not incorporate with the fleshy part, remains of the natural colour of the pitch; but that which does incorporate becomes brown, and evidently mixed with the grease of the body, forming a mass, which on pressure crumbles into dust. The wooden case is first covered with a layer or two of cement, not unlike plaster of Paris; and on this are sometimes cast figures in *basso rilievo*, for which they make niches cut in stone. The whole case is painted; the ground generally yellow, the figures and hieroglyphics blue, green, red and black.

The last is very seldom used. The whole of the painting is covered with a varnish, which preserves it very effectually. Some of the colours, in my humble opinion, were vegetable, for they are evidently transparent; besides, I conceive it was easier for the Egyptians to produce vegetable colours than mineral, from the great difficulty of grinding the latter to such perfection.

The next sort of mummy that drew my attention, I believe I may with reason conclude to have been appropriate to the priests. They are folded in a manner totally different from the others, and so carefully executed as to show the great respect paid to those personages. The bandages are strips of red and white linen intermixed, covering the whole body and forming a curious effect from the two colours. The arms and legs are not enclosed in the same envelope with the body, as in the common mode, but are bandaged separately, even the fingers and toes being preserved distinct. They have sandals of painted leather on their feet, and bracelets on their arms and wrists. They are always found with their arms across the breast, but not pressing it; and though the body is bound with such a quantity of linen, the shape of the person is carefully preserved in every limb. The cases in which mummies of this sort are found are somewhat better executed, and I have seen one, that had the eyes and eyebrows of enamel, beautifully executed in imitation of nature.[...]

The tombs containing the better classes of people are of course superior to the others. There are some more extensive than the rest, having various apartments, adorned with figures representing different actions of life. Funeral processions are generally predominant. Agricultural processes, religious ceremonies, and more ordinary occurrences such as feasting, etc. are to be seen everywhere.[...] It would be impossible to describe the numerous little articles found in them, which are well adapted to show the domestic habits of the ancient Egyptians. It is here the smaller idols are occasionally found, either lying on the ground, or in the cases of the mummies. Vases are sometimes found containing the embalmed entrails

> "[...] secure your head to your bones [...] collect your bones, gather together your limbs, throw sand from off your flesh."
>
> —*spells 13 and 373 from the* PYRAMID TEXTS, OLD KINGDOM

of the mummies. These are generally made of baked clay, and painted over; their sizes differ from eight inches to eighteen; their covers represent the head of some divinity, bearing either the human form, or that of a monkey, fox, cat, or some other animal. I met with a few of these vases of alabaster in the Tombs of the Kings, but unfortunately they were broken. A great quantity of pottery is found, and also wooden vessels in some of the tombs as if the deceased had resolved to have all he possessed deposited along with him. The most singular among these things are the ornaments, in particular the small works in clay and other composition. I have been fortunate to find many specimens of their manufactures, among which is leaf gold, beaten nearly as thin as ours. The gold appears to me extremely pure and of a finer colour than is generally seen in our own.

OPENING KING TUTANKHAMEN'S TOMB

HOWARD CARTER *with* A. C. MACE
(British archeologists)

*T*his was to be our final season in The Valley. Six full seasons we had excavated there, and season after season had drawn a blank; we had worked for months at a stretch and found nothing, and only an excavator knows how desperately depressing that can be; we had almost made up our minds that we were beaten, and were preparing to leave The Valley and try our luck elsewhere; and then—hardly had we set hoe to ground in our last despairing effort than we made a discovery that far exceeded our wildest dreams. Surely, never before in the whole history of excavation has a full digging season been compressed within the space of five days.

Let me try and tell the story of it all. It will not be easy, for the dramatic suddenness of the initial discovery left me in a dazed condition, and the months that have followed have been so crowded with incident that I have hardly had time to think. Setting it down on paper will perhaps give me a chance to realize what has happened and all that it means.

I [had] arrived in Luxor on October 28th [of 1922], and by November 1st I had enrolled my workmen and was ready to begin. Our former excavations had stopped short at the north-east corner of the tomb of Rameses VI, and from this

21

point I started trenching southwards. It will be remembered that in this area there were a number of roughly constructed workmen's huts, used probably by the labourers in the tomb of Rameses. These huts, built about three feet above bed-rock, covered the whole area in front of the Ramesside tomb, and continued in a southerly direction to join up with a similar group of huts on the opposite side of The Valley, discovered by [Theodore] Davis in connexion with his work on the Akhenaten cache. By the evening of November 3rd we had laid bare a sufficient number of these huts for experimental purposes, so, after we had planned and noted them, they were removed, and we were ready to clear away the three feet of soil that lay beneath them.

Hardly had I arrived on the work site next morning (November 4th) than the unusual silence, due to the stoppage of the work, made me realize that something out of the ordinary had happened, and I was greeted by the announcement that a step cut in the rock had been discovered underneath the very first hut to be attacked. This seemed too good to be true, but a short amount of extra clearing revealed the fact that we were actually in the entrance of a steep cut in the rock, some thirteen feet below the entrance to the tomb of Rameses VI, and a similar depth from the present bed level of The Valley. The manner of cutting was that of the sunken stairway entrance so common in The Valley, and I almost dared to hope that we had found our tomb at last. Work continued feverishly throughout the whole of that day and the morning of the next, but it was not until the afternoon of November 5th that we succeeded in clearing away the masses of rubbish that overlay the cut, and were able to demarcate the upper edges of the stairway on all its four sides.

It was clear by now beyond any question that we actually had before us the entrance to a tomb, but doubts, born of previous disappointments, persisted in creeping in. There was always the horrible possibility, suggested by our experience in the Thothmes III Valley, that the tomb was an unfinished one, never completed and never used: if it had been finished there was the depressing probability that it had been completely plundered in ancient times. On the other hand, there was just the chance of an untouched or only partially plundered tomb, and it was with ill-suppressed excitement that I watched the descending steps of the staircase, as one by one they came to light. The cutting was excavated in the side of a small hillock, and, as the work progressed, its western edge receded under the slope of the rock until it was, first partially, and then completely, roofed in, and became a passage, 10 feet high by 6 feet wide. Work progressed more rapidly now; step succeeded step, and at the level of the twelfth, towards sunset, there was disclosed the upper part of a doorway, blocked, plastered, and sealed.

A sealed doorway—it was actually true, then! Our years of patient labour were to be rewarded after all, and I think my first feeling was one of congratulation that my faith in The Valley had not been unjustified. With excitement growing to fever heat I searched the seal impressions on the door for evidence of the identity of the owner, but could find no name: the only decipherable ones were those of the well-known royal necropolis seal, the jackal and nine captives. Two facts, however, were clear: first, the employment of this royal seal was certain evidence that the tomb had been constructed for a person of very high standing; and second, that the sealed door was entirely screened from above by workmen's huts of the Twentieth Dynasty was sufficiently clear proof that at least from that date it had never been entered. With that for the moment I had to be content.

While examining the seals I noticed, at the top of the doorway, where some of the plaster had fallen away, a heavy wooden lintel. Under this, to assure myself of the method by which the doorway had been blocked, I made a small peephole, just large enough to insert an electric torch, and discovered that the passage beyond the door was filled completely from floor to ceiling with stones and rubble—additional proof this of the care with which the tomb had been protected.

It was a thrilling moment for an excavator. Alone, save for my native workmen, I found myself, after years of comparatively unproductive labour, on the threshold of what might prove to be a magnificent discovery. Anything, literally anything, might lie beyond that passage, and it needed all my self-control to keep from breaking down the doorway, and investigating then and there.

One thing puzzled me, and that was the smallness of the opening in comparison with the ordinary Valley tombs. The design was certainly of the Eighteenth Dynasty. Could it be the tomb of a noble buried here by royal consent? Was it a royal cache, a hiding-place to which a mummy and its equipment had been removed for safety? Or was it actually the tomb of the king for whom I had spent so many years in search?

Once more I examined the seal impressions for a clue, but on the part of the door so far laid bare only those of the royal necropolis seal already mentioned were clear enough to read. Had I but known that a few inches lower down there was a perfectly clear and distinct impression of the seal of Tutankhamen, the king I most desired to find, I would have cleared on, had a much better night's rest in consequence, and saved myself nearly three weeks of uncertainty. It was late, however, and darkness was already upon us. With some reluctance I re-closed the small hole that I had made, filled in our excavation for protection during the night, selected the most trustworthy of my workmen—themselves almost as excited as I was—to watch all night above the tomb, and so home by moonlight, riding down The Valley.

Naturally my wish was to go straight ahead with our clearing to find out the full extent of the discovery, but Lord Carnarvon was in England, and in fairness to him I had to delay matters until he could come. Accordingly, on the morning of November 6th I sent him the following cable:—"At last have made wonderful discovery in Valley; a magnificent tomb with seals intact; re-covered same for your arrival; congratulations."

My next task was to secure the doorway against interference until such time as it could finally be re-opened. This we did by filling our excavation up again to surface level, and rolling on top of it the large flint boulders of which the workmen's huts had been composed. By the evening of the same day, exactly forty-eight hours after we had discovered the first step of the staircase, this was accomplished. The tomb had vanished. So far as the appearance of the ground was concerned there never had been any tomb, and I found it hard to persuade myself at times that the whole episode had not been a dream.

I was soon to be reassured on this point. News travels fast in Egypt, and within two days of the discovery congratulations, inquiries, and offers of help descended upon me in a steady stream from all directions. It became clear, even at this early stage, that I was in for a job that could not be tackled single-handed, so I wired to [A. R.] Callender, who had helped me on various previous occasions, asking him if possible to join me without delay, and to my relief he arrived on the very next day. On the 8th I had received two messages from Lord Carnarvon in answer to my cable, the first of which read, "Possibly come soon," and the second, received a little later, "Propose arrive Alexandria 20th."

❝The whole mountainside on the western bank of the river is one vast Necropolis. The open doors of tombs are seen in long ranges, and at different elevations, and on the plain large pits have been opened, in which have been found a thousand mummies at a time. For many years, and until a late order of the pasha preventing it, the Arabs have been in the habit of rifling the tombs to sell the mummies to travelers. Thousands have been torn from the places where pious hands had laid them, and the bones meet the traveler at every step. The Arabs use the mummy-cases for firewood, the bituminous matters used in the embalmment being well adapted to ignition; and the epicurean traveler may cook his breakfast with the coffin of a king. Notwithstanding the depredations that have been committed, the mummies that have been taken away and scattered all over the world, those that have been burnt, and others that now remain in fragments around the tombs, the numbers yet undisturbed are no doubt infinitely greater; for the practice of embalming is known to have existed from the earliest periods recorded in the history of Egypt; and, by a rough computation, founded upon the age, the population of the city, and the average duration of human life, it is supposed that there are from eight to ten millions of mummied bodies in the vast Necropolis of Thebes.❞

—*explorer JOHN LLOYD STEPHENS*

We had thus nearly a fortnight's grace, and we devoted it to making preparations of various kinds, so that when the time of re-opening came, we should be able, with the least possible delay, to handle any situation that might arise. On the night of the 18th I went to Cairo for three days, to meet Lord Carnarvon and make a number of necessary purchases, returning to Luxor on the 21st. On the 23rd Lord Carnarvon arrived in Luxor with his daughter, Lady Evelyn Herbert, his devoted companion in all his Egyptian work, and everything was in hand for the beginning of the second chapter of the discovery of the tomb. Callender had been busy all day clearing away the upper layer of rubbish, so that by morning we should be able to get into the staircase without any delay.

By the afternoon of the 24th the whole staircase was clear, sixteen steps in all, and we were able to make a proper examination of the sealed doorway. On the lower part the seal impressions were much clearer, and we were able without any difficulty to make out on several of them the name of Tutankhamen. This added enormously to the interest of the discovery. If we had found, as seemed almost certain, the tomb of that shadowy monarch, whose tenure of the throne coincided with one of the most interesting periods in the whole of Egyptian history, we should indeed have reason to congratulate ourselves.

With heightened interest, if that were possible, we renewed our investigation of the doorway. Here for the first time a disquieting element made its appearance. Now that the whole door was exposed to light it was possible to discern a fact that had hitherto escaped notice—that there had been two successive openings and re-closings of a part of its surface: furthermore, that the sealing originally discovered, the jackal and nine captives, had been applied to the re-closed portions, whereas the scalings of Tutankhamen covered the untouched part of the doorway, and were therefore those with which the tomb had been originally secured. The tomb then was not absolutely intact, as we had hoped. Plunderers had entered it, and entered it more than once—from the evidence of the huts above, plunderers of a date not later than the reign of Rameses VI—but that they had not rifled it completely was evident from the fact that it had been re-sealed.[1]

Then came another puzzle. In the lower strata of rubbish that filled the staircase we found masses of broken potsherds and boxes, the latter bearing the names of Akhenaten, Smenkhkare and Tutankhamen, and, what was much more upsetting, a scarab of Thothmes III and a fragment with the name of Amenhetep III. Why this mixture of names? The balance of evidence so far would seem to indicate a cache rather than a tomb, and at this stage in the proceedings we inclined more and more to the opinion that we were about to find a miscellaneous collection of objects of the Eighteenth Dynasty kings, brought from Tell el Amarna by Tutankhamen and deposited here for safety.

So matters stood on the evening of the 24th. On the following day the sealed doorway was to be removed, so Callender set carpenters to work making a heavy wooden grille to be set up in its place. Mr. Engelbach, Chief Inspector of the Antiquities Department, paid us a visit during the afternoon, and witnessed part of the final clearing of rubbish from the doorway.

---

[1] From later evidence we found that this re-sealing could not have taken place later than the reign of Horemheb, i.e. from ten to fifteen years after the burial.

On the morning of the 25th the seal impressions on the doorway were carefully noted and photographed, and then we removed the actual blocking of the door, consisting of rough stones carefully built from floor to lintel, and heavily plastered on their outer faces to take the seal impressions.

This disclosed the beginning of a descending passage (not a staircase), the same width as the entrance stairway, and nearly seven feet high. As I had already discovered from my hole in the doorway, it was filled completely with stone and rubble, probably the chip from its own excavation. This filling, like the doorway, showed distinct signs of more than one opening and re-closing of the tomb, the untouched part consisting of clean white chip, mingled with dust, whereas the disturbed part was composed mainly of dark flint. It was clear that an irregular tunnel had been cut through the original filling at the upper corner on the left side, a tunnel corresponding in position with that of the hole in the doorway.

As we cleared the passage we found, mixed with the rubble of the lower levels, broken potsherds, jar scalings, alabaster jars, whole and broken, vases of painted pottery, numerous fragments of smaller articles, and water skins, these last having obviously been used to bring up the water needed for the plastering of the doorways. These were clear evidence of plundering, and we eyed them askance. By night we had cleared a considerable distance down the passage, but as yet saw no sign of second doorway or of chamber.

The day following (November 26th) was the day of days, the most wonderful that I have ever lived through, and certainly one whose like I can never hope to see again. Throughout the morning the work of clearing continued, slowly perforce, on account of the delicate objects that were mixed with the filling. Then, in the middle of the afternoon, thirty feet down from the outer door, we came upon a second sealed doorway, almost an exact replica of the first. The seal impressions in this case were less distinct, but still recognizable as those of Tutankhamen and of the royal necropolis. Here again the signs of opening and re-closing were clearly marked upon the plaster. We were firmly convinced by this time that it was a cache that we were about to open, and not a tomb. The arrangement of stairway, entrance passage and doors reminded us very forcibly of the cache of Akhenaten and Tyi material found in the very near vicinity of the present excavation by Davis, and the fact that Tutankhamen's seals occurred there likewise seemed almost certain proof that we were right in our conjecture. We were soon to know. There lay the sealed doorway, and behind it was the answer to the question.

Slowly, desperately slowly it seemed to us as we watched, the remains of passage debris that encumbered the lower part of the doorway were removed, until at last we had the whole door clear before us. The decisive moment had arrived. With trembling hands I made a tiny breach in the upper left hand corner. Darkness and blank space, as far as an iron testing-rod could reach, showed that whatever lay beyond was empty, and not filled like the passage we had just cleared. Candle tests were applied as a precaution against possible foul gases, and then, widening the hole a little, I inserted the candle and peered in, Lord Carnarvon, Lady Evelyn and Callender standing anxiously beside me to hear the verdict. At first I could see nothing, the hot air escaping from the chamber causing the candle flame to flicker, but presently, as my eyes grew accustomed to the light, details of the room within emerged slowly from the mist, strange animals, statues, and gold—everywhere the glint of gold. For the moment—an eternity it must have seemed to the others standing by—I was struck dumb with amazement, and when Lord Carnarvon, unable to stand the suspense any longer, inquired anxiously, "Can you see anything?" it was all I could do to get out the words, "Yes, wonderful things." Then widening the hole a little further, so that we both could see, we inserted an electric torch.

I suppose most excavators would confess to a feeling of awe—embarrassment almost—when they break into a chamber closed and sealed by pious hands so many centuries ago. For the moment, time as a factor in human life has lost its meaning. Three thousand, four thousand years maybe, have passed and gone since human feet last trod the floor on which you stand, and yet, as you note the signs of recent life around you—the half-filled bowl of mortar for the door, the blackened lamp, the finger-mark upon the freshly painted surface, the farewell garland dropped upon the threshold—you feel it might have been but yesterday. The very air you breathe, unchanged throughout the centuries, you share with those who laid the mummy to its rest. Time is annihilated by little intimate details such as these, and you feel an intruder.

That is perhaps the first and dominant sensation, but others follow thick and fast—the exhilaration of discovery, the fever of suspense, the almost overmastering impulse, born of curiosity, to break down seals and lift the lids of boxes, the thought—pure joy to the investigator—that you are about to add a page to history, or solve some problem of research, the strained expectancy—why not confess it? of the treasure-seeker. Did these thoughts actually pass through our minds at the time, or have I imagined them since? I cannot tell. It was the discovery that my memory was blank, and not the mere desire for dramatic chapter-ending, that occasioned this digression.

Surely never before in the whole history of excavation had such an amazing sight been seen as the light of our torch revealed to us.[...] imagine how[...it] appeared to us as we looked down[...] from our spy-hole in the blocked doorway, casting the beam of light from our torch—the first light that had pierced the darkness of the chamber for three thousand years—from one group of objects to another, in a vain attempt to interpret the treasure that lay before us. The effect was bewildering, overwhelming. I suppose we had never formulated exactly in our minds just what we had expected or hoped to see, but certainly we had never dreamed of anything like this, a roomful—a whole museumful it seemed—of objects, some familiar, but some the like of which we had never seen, piled one upon another in seemingly endless profusion.

Gradually the scene grew clearer, and we could pick out individual objects. First, right opposite to us—we had been conscious of them all the while but refused to believe in them—were three great gilt couches, their sides carved in the form of monstrous animals, curiously attenuated in body, as they had to be to serve their purpose, but with heads of startling realism. Uncanny beasts enough to look upon at any time: seen as we saw them, their brilliant gilded surfaces picked out of the darkness by our electric torch, as though by limelight, their heads throwing grotesque distorted shadows on the wall behind them, they were almost terrifying. Next, on the right, two statues caught and held our attention; two life-sized figures of a king in black, facing each other like sentinels, gold kilted, gold sandalled, armed with mace and staff, the protective sacred cobra upon their foreheads.

*   *   *

By the middle of February our work in the Antechamber was finished. With the exception of the two sentinel statues, left for a special reason, all its contents had been removed to the laboratory, every inch of its floor had been swept and sifted for the last bead or fallen piece of inlay, and it now stood bare and empty. We were ready at last to penetrate the mystery of the sealed door.

Friday, the 17th, was the day appointed, and at two o'clock those who were to be privileged to witness the ceremony met by appointment above the tomb. [...] By a quarter past two the whole company had assembled, so we removed our coats and filed down the sloping passage into the tomb.

In the Antechamber everything was prepared and ready, and to those who had not visited it since the original opening of the tomb it must have presented a strange sight. We had screened the statues with boarding to protect them from possible damage, and between them we had erected a small platform, just high enough to enable us to reach the upper part of the doorway, having determined, as the safest plan, to work from the top downwards. A short distance back from the platform there was a barrier, and beyond, knowing that there might be hours of work ahead of us, we had provided chairs for the visitors. On either side standards had been set up for our lamps, their light shining full upon the doorway. Looking back, we realize what a strange, incongruous picture the chamber must have presented, but at the time I question whether such an idea even crossed our minds. One thought and one only was possible. There before us lay the sealed door, and with its opening we were to blot out the centuries and stand in the presence of a king who reigned three thousand years ago. My own feelings as I mounted the platform were a strange mixture, and it was with a trembling hand that I struck the first blow.

My first care was to locate the wooden lintel above the door: then very carefully I chipped away the plaster and picked out the small stones which formed the uppermost layer of the filling. The temptation to stop and peer inside at every moment was irresistible, and when, after about ten minutes' work, I had made a hole large enough to enable me to do so, I inserted an electric torch. An astonishing sight its light revealed, for there, within a yard of the doorway, stretching as far as one could see and blocking the entrance to the chamber, stood what to all appearance was a solid wall of gold. For the moment there was no clue as to its meaning, so as quickly as I dared I set to work to widen the hole. This had now become an operation of considerable difficulty, for the stones of the masonry were not accurately squared blocks built regularly upon one another, but rough slabs of varying size, some so heavy that it took all one's strength to lift them: many of them, too, as the weight above was removed, were left so precariously balanced that the least false movement would have sent them sliding inwards to crash upon the contents of the chamber below. We were also endeavouring to preserve the seal-impressions upon the thick mortar of the outer face, and this added considerably to the difficulty of handling the stones. [Arthur C.] Mace and [A. R.] Callender were helping me by this time, and each stone was cleared on a regular system. With a crowbar I gently eased it up, Mace holding it to prevent it falling forwards; then he and I lifted it out and passed it back to Callender, who transferred it on to one of the foremen, and so, by a chain of workmen, up the passage and out of the tomb altogether.

With the removal of a very few stones the mystery of the golden wall was solved. We were at the entrance of the actual burial-chamber of the king, and that which barred our way was the side of an immense gilt shrine built to cover and protect the sarcophagus. It was visible now from the Antechamber by the light of the standard lamps, and as stone after stone was removed, and its gilded surface came gradually into view, we could, as though by electric current, feel the tingle of excitement which thrilled the spectators behind the barrier.[…] We who were doing the work were probably less excited, for our whole energies were taken up with the task in hand—that of removing the blocking without an accident. The fall of a single stone might have done irreparable damage to the delicate surface of the shrine, so, directly the hole was large enough, we made an additional protection for it by inserting a mattress on the inner side of the door-blocking, suspending it from the wooden lintel of the doorway. Two hours of hard work it took us to clear away the blocking, or at least as much of it as was necessary for the moment; and at one point, when near the bottom, we had to delay operations for a space while we collected the scattered beads from a necklace brought by the plunderers from the chamber within and dropped upon the threshold. This last was a terrible trial to our patience, for it was a slow business, and we were all of us excited to see what might be within; but finally it was done, the last stones were removed, and the way to the innermost chamber lay open before us.

In clearing away the blocking of the doorway we had discovered that the level of the inner chamber was about four feet lower than that of the Antechamber, and this, combined with the fact that there was but a narrow space between door and shrine, made an entrance by no means easy to effect. Fortunately, there were no smaller antiquities at this end of the chamber, so I lowered myself down, and then, taking one of the portable lights, I edged cautiously to the corner of the shrine and looked beyond it. At the corner two beautiful alabaster vases blocked the way, but I could see that if these were removed we should have a clear path to the other end of the chamber; so, carefully marking the spot on which they stood, I picked them up—with the exception of the king's wishing-cup they were of finer quality and more graceful shape than any we had yet found—and passed them back to the Antechamber. Lord Carnarvon and M. Lacau now joined me, and, picking our way along the narrow passage between shrine and wall, paying out the wire of our light behind us, we investigated further.

It was, beyond any question, the sepulchral chamber in which we stood, for there, towering above us, was one of the great gilt shrines beneath which kings were laid. So enormous was this structure (17 feet by 11 feet, and 9 feet high, we found afterwards) that it filled within a little the entire area of the chamber, a space of some two feet only separating it from the walls on all four sides, while its roof, with cornice top and torus moulding, reached almost to the ceiling. From top to bottom it was overlaid with gold, and upon its sides there were inlaid panels of brilliant blue faience, in which were represented, repeated over and over, the magic symbols which would ensure its strength and safety. Around the shrine, resting upon the ground, there were a number of funerary emblems, and, at the north end, the seven magic oars the king would need to ferry himself across the waters of the underworld. The walls of the chamber, unlike those of the Antechamber, were decorated with brightly painted scenes and inscriptions, brilliant in their colours, but evidently somewhat hastily executed.

These last details we must have noticed subsequently, for at the time our one thought was of the shrine and of its safety. Had the thieves penetrated within it and disturbed the royal burial? Here, on the eastern end, were the great folding doors, closed and bolted, but not sealed, that would answer the question for us. Eagerly we drew the bolts, swung back the doors, and there within was a second shrine with similar bolted doors, and upon the bolts a seal, intact. This seal we determined not to break, for our doubts were resolved, and we could not penetrate further without risk of serious damage to the monument. I think at the moment we did not even want to break the seal, for a feeling of intrusion had descended heavily upon us with the opening of the doors, heightened, probably, by the almost painful impressiveness of a linen pall, decorated with golden rosettes, which drooped above the inner shrine. We felt that we were in the presence of the dead King and must do him reverence, and in imagination could see the doors of the successive shrines open one after the other till the innermost disclosed the King himself. Carefully, and as silently as possible, we re-closed the great swing doors, and passed on to the farther end of the chamber.

Here a surprise awaited us, for a low door, eastwards from the sepulchral chamber, gave entrance to yet another chamber, smaller than the outer ones and not so lofty. This doorway, unlike the others, had not been closed and sealed. We were able, from where we stood, to get a clear view of the whole of the contents, and a single glance sufficed to tell us that here, within this little chamber, lay the greatest treasures of the tomb. Facing the doorway, on the farther side, stood the most beautiful monument that I have ever seen—so lovely that it made one gasp with wonder and admiration. The central portion of it consisted of a large shrine-shaped chest, completely overlaid with gold, and surmounted by a cornice of sacred cobras. Surrounding this, freestanding, were statues of the four tutelary goddesses of the dead—gracious figures with outstretched protective arms, so natural and lifelike in their pose, so pitiful and compassionate the expression upon their faces, that one felt it almost sacrilege to look at them. One guarded the shrine on each of its four sides, but whereas the figures at front and back kept their gaze firmly fixed upon their charge, an additional note of touching realism was imparted by the other two, for their heads were turned sideways, looking over their shoulders towards the entrance, as though to watch against surprise. There is a simple grandeur about this monument that made an irresistible appeal to the imagination, and I am not ashamed to confess that it brought a lump to my throat. It is undoubtedly the Canopic chest and contains the jars which play such an important part in the ritual of mummification.

There were a number of other wonderful things in the chamber, but we found it hard to take them in at the time, so inevitably were one's eyes drawn back again and again to the lovely little goddess figures. Immediately in front of the entrance lay the figure of the jackal god Anubis, upon his shrine, swathed in linen cloth, and resting upon a portable sled, and behind this the head of a bull upon a stand—emblems, these, of the underworld. In the south side of the chamber lay an endless number of black shrines and chests, all closed and sealed save one, whose open doors revealed statues of Tutankhamen standing upon black leopards. On the farther wall were more shrine-shaped boxes and miniature coffins of gilded wood, these last undoubtedly containing funerary statuettes of the king. In the centre of the room, left of the Anubis and the bull, there was a row of magnificent caskets of ivory and wood, decorated and inlaid with gold and blue faience, one, whose lid we raised, containing a gorgeous ostrich-feather fan with ivory handle, fresh and strong to all appearance as when it left the maker's hand. There were also, distributed in different quarters of the chamber, a number of model boats with sails and rigging all complete, and, at the north side, yet another chariot.

Such, from a hurried survey, were the contents of this innermost chamber. We looked anxiously for evidence of plundering, but on the surface there was none. Unquestionably the thieves must have entered, but they cannot have done more than open two or three of the caskets. Most of the boxes, as has been said, have still their seals intact, and the whole contents of the chamber, in fortunate contrast to those of the Antechamber and the Annexe, still remain in position exactly as they were placed at the time of burial.

How much time we occupied in this first survey of the wonders of the tomb I cannot say, but it must have seemed endless to those anxiously waiting in the Antechamber. Not more than three at a time could be admitted with safety, so, when Lord Carnarvon and M. Lacau came out, the others came in pairs: first Lady Evelyn Herbert, the only woman present, with Sir William Garstin, and then the rest in turn. It was curious, as we stood in the Antechamber, to watch their faces as, one by one, they emerged from the door. Each had a dazed, bewildered look in his eyes, and each in turn, as he came out, threw up his hands before him, an unconscious gesture of impotence to describe in words the wonders that he had seen. They were indeed indescribable, and the emotions they had aroused in our minds were of too intimate a nature to communicate, even though we had the words at our command. It was an experience which, I am sure, none of us who were present is ever likely to forget, for in imagination—and not wholly in imagination either—we had been present at the funeral ceremonies of a king long dead and almost forgotten.

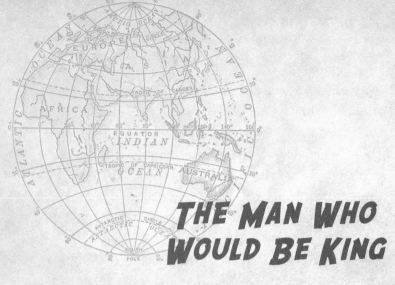

THE MAN WHO WOULD BE KING

RUDYARD KIPLING

(novelist)

"Brother to a prince and fellow to a beggar
if he be found worthy."

The law, as quoted, lays down a fair conduct of life, and one not easy to follow. I have been fellow to a beggar again and again under circumstances which prevented either of us finding out whether the other was worthy. I have still to be brother to a prince, though I once came to kinship with what might have been a veritable and was promised the reversion of a kingdom—army, law-courts, revenue, and policy all complete. But I greatly fear that my king is dead and if I want a crown I must go hunt it for myself.

The beginning of everything was in a railway train upon the road to Mhow from Ajmer. There had been a deficit in the budget, which necessitated travelling, not second-class, which is only half as dear as first-class, but by intermediate, which is very awful indeed. There are no cushions in the intermediate class, and the population are either intermediate, which is Eurasian, or native, which for a long night journey is nasty, or loafer, which is amusing though intoxicated. Intermediates do not buy from refreshment-rooms. They carry their food in bundles and pots, and buy sweets from the native sweetmeat-sellers, and drink the roadside water. That is why in hot weather intermediates are taken out of the carriages dead, and in all weathers are most properly looked down upon.

My particular intermediate happened to be empty till I reached Nasirabad, when a big black-browed gentleman in shirt-sleeves entered, and, following the custom of intermediates, passed the time of day. He was a wanderer and a vagabond like myself, but with an educated taste for whisky. He told tales of things he had seen and done, of out-of-the-way corners of the empire into which he had penetrated, and of adventures in which he risked his life for a few days' food.

"If India was filled with men like you and me, not knowing more than the crows where they'd get their next day's rations, it isn't seventy millions of revenue the land would be paying—it's seven hundred millions," said he; and as I looked at his mouth and chin I was disposed to agree with him.

We talked politics—the politics of loaferdom, that sees things from the underside where the lath and plaster are not smoothed off; and we talked postal arrangements because my friend wanted to send a telegram back from the next station to Ajmer, the turning-off place from the Bombay to the Mhow line as you travel westward. My friend had no money beyond eight annas, which he wanted for dinner, and I had no money at all owing to the hitch in the budget before mentioned. Further, I was going into a wilderness where, though I should resume touch with the treasury, there were no telegraph offices. I was, therefore, unable to help him in any way.

"We might threaten a station-master and make him send a wire on tick," said my friend, "but that'd mean inquiries for you and for me, and *I've* got my hands full these days. Did you say you were travelling back along this line within any days?"

"Within ten," I said.

"Can't you make it eight?" said he. "Mine is rather urgent business."

"I can send your telegram within ten days if that will serve you," I said.

"I couldn't trust the wire to fetch him now I think of it. It's this way. He leaves Delhi on the twenty-third for Bombay. That means he'll be running through Ajmer about the night of the twenty-third."

"But I'm going into the Indian desert," I explained.

"Well *and* good," said he. "You'll be changing at Marwar Junction to get into Jodhpur territory—you must do that—and he'll be coming through Marwar

Junction in the early morning of the twenty-fourth by the Bombay mail. Can you be at Marwar Junction on that time? 'Twon't be inconveniencing you, because I know that there's precious few pickings to be got out of these Central India States—even though you pretend to be correspondent of the *Backwoodsman*."

"Have you ever tried that trick?" I asked.

"Again and again, but the residents find you out, and then you get escorted to the border before you've time to get your knife into them. But about my friend here. I *must* give him a word o' mouth to tell him what's come to me, or else he won't know where to go. I would take it more than kind of you if you was to come out of Central India in time to catch him at Marwar Junction and say to him: 'He has gone south for the week.' He'll know what that means. He's a big man with a red beard, and a great swell he is. You'll find him sleeping like a gentleman with all his luggage round him in a second-class apartment. But don't you be afraid. Slip down the window and say: 'He has gone South for the week,' and he'll tumble. It's only cutting your time of stay in those parts by two days. I ask you as a stranger—going to the West," he said with emphasis.

"Where have *you* come from?" said I.

"From the East," said he, "and I am hoping that you will give him the message on the Square—for the sake of my mother as well as your own."

Englishmen are not usually softened by appeals to the memory of their mothers, but for certain reasons, which will be fully apparent, I saw fit to agree.

"It's more than a little matter," said he, "and that's why I asked you to do it; and now I know that I can depend on you doing it. A second-class carriage at Marwar Junction, and a red-haired man asleep in it. You'll be sure to remember. I get out at the next station, and I must hold on there till he comes or sends me what I want."

"I'll give the message if I catch him," I said, "and for the sake of your mother as well as mine I'll give you a word of advice. Don't try to run the Central India States just now as the correspondent of the *Backwoodsman*. There's a real one knocking about here, and it might lead to trouble."

"Thank you," said he simply, "and when will the swine be gone? I can't starve because he's ruining my work. I wanted to get hold of the Degumber Rajah down here about his father's widow, and give him a jump."

"What did he do to his father's widow, then?"

"Filled her up with red pepper and slippered her to death as she hung from a beam. I found that out myself, and I'm the only man that would dare going into the state to get hush-money for it. They'll try to poison me, same as they did in Chortumna when I went on the loot there. But you'll give the man at Marwar Junction my message?"

He got out at a little roadside station, and I reflected. I had heard more than once of men personating correspondents of newspapers and bleeding small native states with threats of exposure, but I had never met any of the caste before. They lead a hard life, and generally die with great suddenness. The native states have a wholesome horror of English newspapers, which may throw light on their peculiar methods of government, and do their best to choke correspondents with champagne, or drive them out of their mind with four-in-hand barouches. They do not understand that nobody cares a straw for the internal administration of native states so long as oppression and crime are kept within decent limits and the ruler is not drugged, drunk, or diseased from one end of the year to the other. They are the dark places of the earth, full of unimaginable cruelty, touching the railway and the telegraph on one side, and on the other the days of Harunal-Raschid. When I left the train I did business with divers kings, and in eight days passed through many changes of life. Sometimes I wore dress-clothes and consorted with princes and politicals, drinking from crystal and eating from silver. Sometimes I lay out upon the ground and devoured what I could get from a plate made of leaves, and drank the running water, and slept under the same rug as my servant. It was all in the day's work.

Then I headed for the great Indian desert upon the proper date, as I had promised, and the night mail set me down at Marwar Junction, where a funny little happy-go-lucky native-managed railway runs to Jodhpur. The Bombay mail from Delhi makes a short halt at Marwar. She arrived as I got in, and I had just time to hurry to her platform and go down the carriages. There was only one second-class on the train. I slipped the window and looked down upon a flaming red beard, half covered by a railway rug. That was my man, fast asleep, and I dug him gently in the ribs. He woke with a grunt, and I saw his face in the light of the lamps. It was a great and shining face.

"Tickets again?" said he.

"No," said I. "I am to tell you that he is gone south for the week. He has gone south for the week!"

The train had begun to move out. The red man rubbed his eyes. "He has gone south for the week," he repeated. "Now that's just like his impidence. Did he say that I was to give you anything? 'Cause I won't."

"He didn't," I said, and dropped away, and watched the red lights die out in the dark. It was horribly cold because the wind was blowing off the sands. I climbed into my own train—not an intermediate carriage this time—and went to sleep.

If the man with the beard had given me a rupee I should have kept it as a memento of a rather curious affair. But the consciousness of having done my duty was my only reward.

Later on I reflected that two gentlemen like my friends could not do any good if they foregathered and personated correspondents of newspapers, and might, if they blackmailed one of the little rat-trap states of Central India or southern Rajputana, get themselves into serious difficulties. I therefore took some trouble to describe them as accurately as I could remember to people who would be interested in deporting them, and succeeded, so I was later informed, in having them headed back from the Degumber borders.

Then I became respectable, and returned to an office where there were no kings and no incidents outside the daily manufacture of a newspaper. A newspaper office seems to attract every conceivable sort of person, to the prejudice of discipline. Zenana-mission ladies arrive and beg that an editor will instantly abandon all his duties to describe a Christian prize-giving in a back slum of a perfectly inaccessible village; colonels who had been over-passed for command sit down and sketch the outline of a series of ten, twelve, or twenty-four leading articles on "Seniority versus Selection"; missionaries wish to know why they have not been permitted to escape from their regular vehicles of abuse and swear at a brother-missionary under special patronage of the editorial "we"; stranded theatrical companies troop up to explain that they cannot pay for their advertisements, but on their return from New Zealand or Tahiti will do so with interest; inventors of patent punkah-pulling machines, carriage couplings, and unbreakable swords and axle-trees call with specifications in their pockets and hours at their disposal; tea-companies enter and elaborate their prospectuses with the office pens; secretaries of ball-committees clamour to have the glories of their last dance more fully described; strange ladies rustle in and say, "I want a hundred lady's cards printed *at once*, please," which is manifestly part of an editor's duty; and every dissolute ruffian that ever tramped the Grand Trunk Road makes it his business to ask for employment as a proof-reader. And, all the time, the telephone-bell is ringing madly, and kings are being killed on the Continent, and empires are saying, "You're another," and Mr. Gladstone is calling down brimstone upon the British dominions and the little black copyboys are whining, "*kaa-pi chay-ha-yeh*" (copy wanted) like tired bees, and most of the paper is as blank as Modred's shield.

But that is the amusing part of the year. There are six other months when none ever come to call, and the thermometer walks inch by inch up to the top of the glass, and the office is darkened to just above reading-light, and the press-machines are red-hot of touch, and nobody writes anything but accounts of amusements in the hill-stations or obituary notices. Then the telephone becomes a tinkling terror, because it tells you of the sudden deaths of men and women that you knew intimately, and the prickly-beat covers you with a garment, and you sit down and write: "A slight increase of sickness is reported from the Khuda Janta Khan district. The outbreak is purely sporadic in its nature, and, thanks to the energetic efforts of the district authorities, is now almost at an end. It is, however, with deep regret we record the death, etc."

Then the sickness really breaks out, and the less recording and reporting the better for the peace of the subscribers. But the empires and the kings continue to divert themselves as selfishly as before, and the foreman thinks that a daily paper really ought to come out once in twenty-four hours, and all the people at the hill-stations in the middle of their amusements say: "Good gracious! Why can't the paper be sparkling? I'm sure there's plenty going on up here."

That is the dark half of the moon, and as the advertisements say, "must be experienced to be appreciated."

It was in that season, and a remarkably evil season, that the paper began running the last issue of the week on Saturday night, which is to say Sunday morning, after the custom of a London paper. This was a great convenience, for immediately after the paper was put to bed, the dawn would lower the thermometer from ninety-six degrees to almost eighty-four degrees for half an hour, and in that chill—you have no idea how cold is eighty-four degrees on the grass until you begin to pray for it—a very tired man could get off to sleep ere the heat roused him.

One Saturday night it was my pleasant duty to put the paper to bed alone. A king or courtier or a courtesan or a community was going to die or get a new constitution or do something that was important on the other side of the world, and the paper was to be held open till the latest possible minute in order to catch the telegram.

It was a pitchy-black night, as stifling as a June night can be, and the *loo*, the red-hot wind from the westward, was booming among the tinder-dry trees and pretending that the rain was on its heels. Now and again a spot of almost boiling water would fall on the dust with the flop of a frog, but all our weary world knew that was only pretence. It was a shade cooler in the press-room than the office, so I sat there while the type ticked and clicked, and the night-jars hooted at the windows, and the all but naked compositors wiped the sweat from their foreheads and called for water. The thing that was keeping us back, whatever it was, would not come off, though the *loo* dropped, and the last type was set, and the whole round earth stood still in the choking heat, with its finger on its lip, to wait the event. I drowsed and wondered whether the telegraph was a blessing and whether this dying man or struggling people might be aware of the inconvenience the delay was causing. There was no special reason beyond the heat and worry to make tension, but as the clock-hands crept up to three o'clock and the machines spun their fly-wheels two and three times to see that all was in order before I said the word that would set them off, I could have shrieked aloud.

Then the roar and rattle of the wheels shivered the quiet into little bits. I rose to go away, but two men in white clothes stood in front of me. The first one said, "It's him!" The second said, "So it is!" And they both laughed almost as loudly as the machinery roared, and mopped their foreheads. "We seed there was a light burning across the road, and we were sleeping in that ditch there for coolness, and I said to my friend here, 'The office is open. Let's come along and speak to him as turned us back from the Degumber State,'" said the smaller of the two. He was the man I had met in the Mhow train, and his fellow was the red-bearded man of Marwar Junction. There, was no mistaking the eyebrows of the one or the beard of the other.

I was not pleased, because I wished to go to sleep, not to squabble with loafers. "What do you want?" I asked.

"Half an hour's talk with you, cool and comfortable, in the office," said the red-bearded man. "We'd *like* some drink—the contrack doesn't begin yet, Peachey, so you needn't look—but what we really want is advice. We don't want money. We ask you as a favour, because we found out you did us a bad turn about Degumber State."

I led from the press-room to the stifling office with the maps on the walls, and the red-haired man rubbed his hands. "That's something like," said he. "This was the proper shop to come to. Now, sir, let me introduce to you Brother Peachey Carnehan, that's him, and Brother Daniel Dravot, that is *me*, and the less said about our professions the better, for we have been most things in our time. Soldier, sailor, compositor, photographer, proof-reader, street-preacher, and correspondents of the *Backwoodsman* when we thought the paper wanted one. Carnehan is sober, and so am I. Look at us first, and see that's sure. It will save you cutting into my talk. We'll take one of your cigars apiece, and you shall see us light up."

I watched the test. The men were absolutely sober, so I gave them each a tepid whisky and soda.

"Well *and* good," said Carnehan of the eyebrows, wiping the froth from his moustache. "Let me talk now, Dan. We have been all over India, mostly on foot. We have been boiler-fitters, engine-drivers, petty contractors, and all that, and we have decided that India isn't big enough for such as us."

They certainly were too big for the office. Dravot's beard seemed to fill half the room and Carnehan's shoulders the other half, as they sat on the big table. Carnehan continued: "The country isn't half worked out because they that governs it won't let you touch it. They spend all their blessed time in governing it, and you can't lift a spade, nor chip a rock, nor look for oil, nor anything like that without all the government saying, 'Leave it alone, and let us govern.' Therefore, such *as* it is, we will let it alone and go away to some other place where a man isn't crowded and can come to his own. We are not little men, and there is nothing that we are afraid of except drink, and we have signed a contrack on that. *Therefore*, we are going away to be kings."

"Kings in our own right," muttered Dravot.

"Yes, of course," I said. "You've been tramping in the sun, and it's a very warm night, and hadn't you better sleep over the notion? Come tomorrow."

"Neither drunk nor sunstruck," said Dravot. "We have slept over the notion half a year and require to see books and atlases, and we have decided that there is only one place now in the world that two strong men can Sar-a-*whack*. They call it Kafiristan. By my reckoning it's the top right-hand corner of Afghanistan, not more than three hundred miles from Peshawar. They have two and thirty heathen idols there, and we'll be the thirty-third and -fourth. It's a mountaineous country, and the women of those parts are very beautiful."

"But that is provided against in the contrack," said Carnehan. "Neither woman nor liquor, Daniel."

"And that's all we know, except that no one has gone there, and they fight, and in any place where they fight, a man who knows how to drill men can always be a king. We shall go to those parts and say to any king we find—'D'you want to vanquish your foes?' and we will show him how to drill men, for that we know better than anything else. Then we will subvert that king and seize his throne and establish a dynasty."

"You'll be cut to pieces before you're fifty miles across the border," I said. "You have to travel through Afghanistan to get to that country. It's one mass of mountains and peaks and glaciers, and no Englishman has been through it. The people are utter brutes, and even if you reached them you couldn't do anything."

"That's more like," said Carnehan. "If you could think us a little more mad we would be more pleased. We have come to you to know about this country, to read a book about it, and to be shown maps. We want you to tell us that we are fools and to show us your books." He turned to the bookcases.

"Are you at all in earnest?" I said.

"A little," said Dravot sweetly. "As big a map as you have got, even if it's all blank where Kafiristan is, and any books you've got. We can read, though we aren't very educated."

I uncased the big thirty-two-miles-to-the-inch map of India, and two smaller frontier maps, hauled down volume INF-KAN of the *Encyclopaedia Britannica,* and the men consulted them.

"See here!" said Dravot, his thumb on the map. "Up to Jagdallak, Peachey and me know the road. We was there with Roberts' army. We'll have to turn off to the right at Jagdallak through Laghmann territory. Then we get among the hills— fourteen thousand feet—fifteen thousand—it will be cold work there, but it don't look very far on the map."

I handed him Wood on the "Sources of the Oxus." Carnehan was deep in the Encyclopaedia.

"They're a mixed lot," said Dravot reflectively, "and it won't help us to know the names of their tribes. The more tribes, the more they'll fight, and the better for us. From Jagdallak to Ashang. H'mm!"

"But all the information about the country is as sketchy and inaccurate as can be," I protested. "No one knows anything about it really. Here's the file of the United Services' Institute. Read what Bellew says."

"Blow Bellew!' said Carnehan. "Dan, they're a stinkin' lot of heathens, but this book here says they think they're related to us English."

I smoked while the men pored over Raverty, Wood, the maps, and the encyclopaedia.

"There is no use your waiting," said Dravot politely.

"It's about four o'clock now. We'll go before six o'clock if you want to sleep, and we won't steal any of the papers. Don't you sit up. We're two harmless lunatics, and if you come tomorrow evening down to the Serai we'll say good-bye to you."

"You *are* two fools," I answered. "You'll be turned back at the frontier or cut up the minute you set foot in Afghanistan. Do you want any money or a recommendation down-country? I can help you to the chance of work next week."

"Next week we shall be hard at work ourselves, thank you," said Dravot. "It isn't so easy being a king as it looks. When we've got our kingdom in going order we'll let you know, and you can come up and help us to govern it."

"Would two lunatics make a contrack like that?" said Carnehan with subdued pride, showing me a greasy half-sheet of notepaper on which was written the following. I copied it, then and there, as a curiosity:

This Contract between me and you persuing witnesseth in the name of
God—Amen and so forth.

(ONE)   That me and you will settle this matter together, i. e., to be
                Kings of Kafiristan.

(TWO)   That you and me will not, while this matter is being settled,
                look at any Liquor, nor any Woman black, white, or brown, so
                as to get mixed up with one or the other harmful.

(THREE) That we conduct ourselves with Dignity and Discretion, and if
                one of us gets into trouble the other will stay by him.

Signed by you and me this day.

Peachey Taliaferro Carnehan

Daniel Dravot

Both Gentlemen at Large

"There was no need for the last article," said Carnehan, blushing modestly,
"but it looks regular. Now you know the sort of men that loafers are—we *are* loafers,
Dan, until we get out of India—and do you think that we would sign a contrack
like that unless we was in earnest? We have kept away from the two things that
make life worth having."

"You won't enjoy your lives much longer if you are going to try this idiotic
adventure. Don't set the office on fire," I said, "and go away before nine o'clock."

I left them still poring over the maps and making notes on the back of the
"contrack." "Be sure to come down to the Serai tomorrow," were their parting words.

The Kumharsen Serai is the great four-square sink of humanity where the
strings of camels and horses from the North load and unload. All the nationalities
of Central Asia may be found there, and most of the folk of India proper. Balkh
and Bokhara there meet Bengal and Bombay and try to draw eye-teeth. You can
buy ponies, turquoises, Persian pussy-cats, saddle-bags, fat-tailed sheep, and musk
in the Kumharsen Serai, and get many strange things for nothing. In the afternoon
I went down to see whether my friends intended to keep their word or were lying
there drunk.

A priest attired in fragments of ribbons and rags stalked up to me, gravely
twisting a child's paper whirligig. Behind him was his servant, bending under the

load of a crate of mud toys. The two were loading up two camels, and the inhabitants of the Serai watched them with shrieks of laughter.

"The priest is mad," said a horse-dealer to me. "He is going up to Kabul to sell toys to the amir. He will either be raised to honour or have his head cut off. He came in here this morning and has been behaving madly ever since."

"The witless are under the protection of God," stammered a flat-cheeked Usbeg in broken Hindi. "They foretell future events."

"Would they could have foretold that my caravan would have been cut up by the Shinwaris almost within shadow of the pass!" grunted the Eusufzai agent of a Rajputana trading-house whose goods had been diverted into the hands of other robbers just across the border, and whose misfortunes were the laughing-stock of the bazaar. "Ohé, priest, whence come you and whither do you go?"

"From Roum have I come," shouted the priest, waving his whirligig; "from Roum, blown by the breath of a hundred devils across the sea! O thieves, robbers, liars, the blessing of Pir Khan on pigs, dogs, and perjurers! Who will take the protected of God to the North to sell charms that are never still to the amir? The camels shall not gall, the sons shall not fall sick, and the wives shall remain faithful while they are away, of the men who give me place in their caravan. Who will assist me to slipper the king of the Roos with a golden slipper with a silver heel? The protection of Pir Khan be upon his labours!" He spread out the skirts of his gaberdine and pirouetted between the lines of tethered horses.

"There starts a caravan from Peshawar to Kabul in twenty days, *Huzrut*," said the Eusufzai trader. "My camels go therewith. Do thou also go and bring us good luck."

"I will go even now!" shouted the priest. "I will depart upon my winged camels and be at Peshawar in a day! Ho! Hazar Mir Khan," he yelled to his servant, "drive out the camels, but let me first mount my own."

He leapt on the back of his beast as it knelt, and, turning round to me, cried, "Come thou also, Sahib, a little along the road, and I will sell thee a charm—an amulet that shall make thee king of Kafiristan."

Then the light broke upon me, and I followed the two camels out of the Serai till we reached open road and the priest halted.

"What d'you think o' that?" said he in English. "Carnehan can't talk their patter, so I've made him my servant. He makes a handsome servant. 'Tisn't for nothing that I've been knocking about the country for fourteen years. Didn't I do that talk neat? We'll hitch on to a caravan at Peshawar till we get to Jagdallak, and then we'll see if we can get donkeys for our camels and strike into Kafiristan. Whirligigs for the amir, O Lor! Put your hand under the camel-bags and tell me what you feel."

I felt the butt of a Martini, and another and another.

"Twenty of 'em," said Dravot placidly. "Twenty of 'em, and ammunition to correspond, under the whirligigs and the mud dolls."

"Heaven help you if you are caught with those things!" I said. "A Martini is worth her weight in silver among the Pathans."

"Fifteen hundred rupees of capital—every rupee we could beg, borrow, or steal—are invested on these two camels," said Dravot. "We won't get caught. We're going through the Khyber with a regular caravan. Who'd touch a poor mad priest?"

"Have you got everything you want?" I asked, overcome with astonishment.

"Not yet, but we shall soon. Give us a memento of your kindness, *brother*. You did me a service yesterday, and that time in Marwar. Half my kingdom shall you have, as the saying is." I slipped a small charm compass from my watch-chain and handed it up to the priest.

"Good-bye," said Dravot, giving me his hand cautiously. "It's the last time we'll shake hands with an Englishman these many days. Shake hands with him, Carnehan," he cried as the second camel passed me.

Carnehan leaned down and shook hands. Then the camels passed away along the dusty road, and I was left alone to wonder. My eye could detect no failure in the disguises. The scene in the Serai proved that they were complete to the native mind. There was just the chance, therefore, that Carnehan and Dravot would be able to wander through Afghanistan without detection. But beyond, they would find death—certain and awful death.

Ten days later a native correspondent, giving me the news of the day from Peshawar, wound up his letter with: "There has been much laughing here on account of a certain mad priest who is going in his estimation to sell petty gauds and insignificant trinkets which he ascribes as great charms to H. H., the amir of Bokhara. He passed through Peshawar and associated himself to the Second

Summer caravan that goes to Kabul. The merchants are pleased because through superstition they imagine that such mad fellows bring good fortune."

The two, then, were beyond the border. I would have prayed for them, but that night a real king died in Europe and demanded an obituary notice.

The wheel of the world swings through the same phases again and again. Summer passed and winter thereafter, and came and passed again. The daily paper continued, and I with it, and upon the third summer there fell a hot night, a night issue, and a strained waiting for something to be telegraphed from the other side of the world, exactly as had happened before. A few great men had died in the past two years, the machines worked with more clatter, and some of the trees in the office garden were a few feet taller. But that was all the difference.

I passed over to the press-room, and went through just such a scene as I have already described. The nervous tension was stronger than it had been two years before, and I felt the heat more acutely. At three o'clock I cried, "Print off," and turned to go, when there crept to my chair what was left of a man. He was bent into a circle, his head was sunk between his shoulders, and he moved his feet one over the other like a bear. I could hardly see whether he walked or crawled—this rag-wrapped, whining cripple who addressed me by name, crying that he was come back. "Can you give me a drink?" he whimpered. "For the Lord's sake, give me a drink!"

I went back to the office, the man following with groans of pain, and I turned up the lamp.

"Don't you know me?" he gasped, dropping into a chair, and he turned his drawn face, surmounted by a shock of grey hair, to the light.

I looked at him intently. Once before had I seen eyebrows that met over the nose in an inch-broad black band, but for the life of me I could not tell where.

"I don't know you," I said, handing him the whisky. "What can I do for you?"

He took a gulp of the spirit raw and shivered in spite of the suffocating heat.

"I've come back," he repeated; "and I was the king of Kafiristan—me and Dravot—crowned kings we was! In this office we settled it—you setting there and giving us the books. I am Peachey—Peachey Taliaferro Carnehan, and you've been setting here ever since—O Lord!"

I was more than a little astonished, and expressed my feelings accordingly.

"It's true," said Carnehan with a dry cackle, nursing his feet, which were wrapped in rags. "True as gospel. Kings we were, with crowns upon our heads—me and Dravot—poor Dan—oh, poor, poor Dan, that would never take advice, not though I begged of him!"

"Take the whisky," I said, "and take your own time. Tell me all you can recollect of everything from beginning to end. You got across the border on your camels. Dravot dressed as a mad priest and you his servant. Do you remember that?"

"I ain't mad—yet, but I shall be that way soon. Of course I remember. Keep looking at me, or maybe my words will go all to pieces. Keep looking at me in my eyes, and don't say anything."

I leaned forward and looked into his face as steadily as I could. He dropped one hand upon the table and I grasped it by the wrist. It was twisted like a bird's claw, and upon the back was a ragged, red, diamond-shaped scar.

"No, don't look there. Look at *me*," said Carnehan. "That comes afterwards, but for the Lord's sake don't distrack me! We left with that caravan, me and Dravot playing all sorts of antics to amuse the people we were with. Dravot used to make us laugh in the evenings when all the people was cooking their dinners—cooking their dinners, and—What did they do then? They lit little fires with sparks that went into Dravot's beard, and we all laughed—fit to die. Little red fires they was, going into Dravot's big red beard—so funny." His eyes left mine, and he smiled foolishly.

"You went as far as Jagdallak with that caravan," I said at a venture, "after you had lit those fires. To Jagdaljak, where you turned off to try to get into Kafiristan."

"No, we didn't neither. What are you talking about? We turned off before Jagdallak, because we heard the roads was good. But they wasn't good enough for our two camels—mine and Dravot's. When we left the caravan, Dravot took off his clothes, and mine too, and said we would be heathen, because the Kafirs didn't allow Muhammadans to talk to them. So we dressed betwixt and between, and such a sight as Daniel Dravot I never saw yet nor expect to see again. He burned half his beard, and slung a sheepskin over his shoulder, and shaved his head into patterns. He shaved mine too, and made me wear outrageous things to look like a heathen. That was in a most mountaineous country, and our camels couldn't go along anymore because of the mountains. They were tall and black, and coming home I saw them fight like wild goats—there are lots of goats in Kafiristan. And these mountains, they never keep still, no more than the goats. Always fighting they are, and don't let you sleep at night."

"Take some more whisky," I said very slowly. "What did you and Daniel Dravot do when the camels could go no further because of the rough roads that led into Kafiristan?"

"What did which do? There was a party called Peachey Taliaferro Carnehan that was with Dravot. Shall I tell you about him? He died out there in the cold. Slap from the bridge fell old Peachey, turning and twisting in the air like a penny whirligig that you can sell to the amir. No; they was two for three ha'pence, those whirligigs, or I am much mistaken and woeful sore.... And then these camels were no use and Peachey said to Dravot, 'For the Lord's sake let's get out of this before our heads are chopped off,' and with that they killed the camels all among the mountains, not having anything in particular to eat, but first they took off the boxes with the guns and the ammunition, till two men came along driving four mules. Dravot up and dances in front of them, singing, 'Sell me four mules.' Says the first men, 'If you are rich enough to buy, you are rich enough to rob'; but before ever he could put his hand to his knife, Dravot breaks his neck over his knee, and the other party runs away. So Carnehan loaded the mules with the rifles that was taken off the camels, and together we starts forward into those bitter cold mountaineous parts, and never a road broader than the back of your hand."

He paused for a moment, while I asked him if he could remember the nature of the country through which he had journeyed.

"I am telling you as straight as I can, but my head isn't as good as it might be. They drove nails through it to make me hear better how Dravot died. The country was mountaineous and the mules were most contrary and the inhabitants was dispersed and solitary. They went up and up, and down and down, and that other party, Carnehan, was imploring of Dravot not to sing and whistle so loud, for fear of bringing down the tremenjus avalanches. But Dravot says that if a king couldn't sing it wasn't worth being king, and whacked the mules over the rump, and never took no heed for ten cold days. We came to a big level valley all among the mountains, and the mules were near dead, so we killed them, not having anything in special for them or us to eat. We sat upon the boxes and played odd and even with the cartridges that was jolted out.

"Then ten men with bows and arrows ran down that valley, chasing twenty men with bows and arrows, and the row was tremenjus. They was fair men—fairer than you or me—with yellow hair and remarkable well built. Says Dravot, unpacking the guns, 'This is the beginning of the business. We'll fight for the ten men,' and with that he fires two rifles at the twenty men, and drops one of them at two hundred yards from the rock where he was sitting. The other men began to run, but Carnehan and Dravot sits on the boxes picking them off at all ranges, up and down the valley. Then we goes up to the ten men that had run across the snow too, and they fires a footy little arrow at us. Dravot, he shoots above their heads, and they all falls down flat. Then he walks over them and kicks them, and then he lifts them up and shakes hands all round to make them friendly like. He calls them and gives them the boxes to carry, and waves his hand for all the world as though he was king already. They takes the boxes and him across the valley and up the hill into a pine wood on the top, where there was half a dozen big stone idols. Dravot, he goes to the biggest—a fellow they call Imbra—and lays a rifle and a cartridge at his feet, rubbing his nose respectful with his own nose, patting him on the head, and saluting in front of it. He turns round to the men and nods his head and says, 'That's all right. I'm in the know too, and all these old jim-jams are my friends.' Then he opens his mouth and points down it, and when the first man brings him food, he says, 'No'; and when the second man brings him food he says 'No'; but when one of the old priests and the boss of the village brings him food, he says, 'Yes,' very haughty, and eats it slow. That was how we came to our first village, without any trouble, just as though we had tumbled from the skies. But we tumbled from one of those damned ropebridges, you see, and you couldn't expect a man to laugh much after that?"

"Take some more whisky and go on," I said. "That was the first village you came into. How did you get to be king?"

"I wasn't king," said Carnehan. "Dravot, he was the king, and a handsome man he looked with the gold crown on his head, and all. Him and the other party stayed in that village, and every morning Dravot sat by the side of old Imbra, and the people came and worshipped. That was Dravot's order. Then a lot of men came into the valley, and Carnehan and Dravot picks them off with the rifles before they knew where they was, and runs down into the valley and up again the other side and finds another village, same as the first one, and the people all falls down flat on their faces, and Dravot says, 'Now what is the trouble between you two villages?' and the people points to a woman, as fair as you or me, that was carried off, and Dravot takes her back to the first village and counts up the dead—eight there was. For each dead man Dravot pours a little milk on the ground and waves his arms like a whirligig, and 'That's all right,' says he. Then he and Carnehan takes the big boss of each village by the arm and walks them down into the valley, and shows them how to scratch a line with a spear right down the valley, and gives each a sod of turf from both sides of the line. Then all the people comes down and shouts like the devil and all, and Dravot says, 'Go and dig the land, and be fruitful and multiply,' which they did, though they didn't understand. Then we asks the names of things in their lingo—bread and water and fire and idols and such—and Dravot leads the priest of each village up to the idol and says he must sit there and judge the people, and if anything goes wrong he is to be shot.

"Next week they was all turning up the land in the valley as quiet as bees and much prettier, and the priests heard all the complaints and told Dravot in dumb show what it was about. 'That's just the beginning,' says Dravot. 'They think we're gods.' He and Carnehan picks out twenty good men and shows them how to click off a rifle, and form fours, and advance in line, and they was very pleased to do so, and clever to see the hang of it. Then he takes out his pipe and his baccy-pouch and leaves one at one village, and one at the other, and off we two goes to see what was to be done in the next valley. That was all rock, and there was a little village there, and Carnehan says, 'Send 'em to the old valley to plant,' and takes 'em there and gives 'em some land that wasn't took before. They were a poor lot, and we blooded 'em with a kid before letting 'em into the new king-dom. That was to impress the people, and then they settled down quiet, and Carnehan went back to Dravot, who had got into another valley, all snow and ice and most mountaineous. There was no people there, and the army got afraid, so Dravot shoots one of them, and goes on till he finds some people in a village, and the army explains that unless the people wants to be killed they had better not shoot their little matchlocks; for they had matchlocks. We make friends with the priest, and I stays there alone with two of the army, teaching the men how to drill; and a thundering big chief comes across the snow with kettledrums and horns twanging, because he heard there was a new god kicking about. Carnehan sights for the brown of the men half a mile across the snow and wings one of them. Then he sends a message to the chief that unless he wished to be killed, he must come and shake hands with me and leave his arms behind. The chief comes alone first, and Carnehan shakes hands with him and whirls his arms about, same as Dravot used, and very much surprised that chief was, and strokes my eyebrows. Then Carnehan goes alone to the chief and asks him in dumb show if he had an enemy he hated. 'I have,' says the chief. So Carnehan weeds out the pick of his men and sets the two of the army to show them drill, and at the end of two weeks the men can manoeuvre about as well as volunteers. So he marches with the chief to a great big plain on the top of a mountain, and the chief's men rushes into a village and takes it, we three Martinis firing into the brown of the enemy. So we took that village too, and I gives the chief a rag from my coat and says, 'Occupy till I come,' which was scriptural. By way of a reminder, when me and the army was eighteen hundred yards away, I drops a bullet near him standing on the snow, and all the people falls flat on their faces. Then I sends a letter to Dravot wherever he be by land or by sea."

At the risk of throwing the creature out of train, I interrupted: "How could you write a letter up yonder?"

"The letter? Oh! The letter! Keep looking at me between the eyes, please. It was a string-talk letter, that we'd learned the way of it from a blind beggar in the Punjab."

I remember that there had once come to the office a blind man with a knotted twig and a piece of string which he wound round the twig according to some cipher of his own. He could, after the lapse of days or hours, repeat the sentence which he had reeled up. He had reduced the alphabet to eleven primitive sounds, and he tried to teach me his method, but I could not understand.

"I sent that letter to Dravot," said Carnehan, "and told him to come back because this kingdom was growing too big for me to handle, and then I struck for the first valley, to see how the priests were working. They called the village we took, along with the chief, Bashkai, and the first village we took Er-Heb. The priests at Er-Heb was doing all right, but they had a lot of pending cases about land to show me, and some men from another village had been firing arrows at night. I went out and looked for that village and fired four rounds at it from a thousand yards. That used all the cartridges I cared to spend, and I waited for Dravot, who had been away two or three months, and I kept my people quiet.

"One morning I heard the devil's own noise of drums and horns, and Dan Dravot marches down the hill with his army and a tail of hundreds of men, and, which was the most amazing, a great gold crown on his head. 'My Gord, Carnehan,' says Daniel, 'this is a tremenjus business, and we've got the whole country as far as it's worth having. I am the son of Alexander by Queen Semiramis, and you're my younger brother and a god too! It's the biggest thing we've ever seen. I've been marching and fighting for six weeks with the army, and every footy little village for fifty miles has come in rejoiceful; and more than that, I've got the key of the whole show, as you'll see, and I've got a crown for you! I told 'em to make two of 'em at a place called Shu, where the gold lies in the rock like suet in mutton. Gold I've seen, and turquoise I've kicked out of the cliffs, and there's garnets in the sands of the river, and here's a chunk of amber that a man brought me. Call up all the priests and, here, take your crown.'

"One of the men opens a black hair bag, and I slips the crown on. It was too small and too heavy, but I wore it for the glory. Hammered gold it was—five pound weight, like a hoop of a barrel.

"'Peachey,' says Dravot, 'we don't want to fight no more. The craft's the trick, so help me!' and he brings forward that same chief that I left at Bashkai—Billy Fish we called him afterwards, because he was so like Billy Fish that drove the big tank-engine at Mach on the Bolan in the old days. 'Shake hands with him,' says Davot, and I shook hands and nearly dropped, for Billy Fish gave me the grip. I said nothing, but tried him with the fellow craft grip. He answers, all right, and I tried the master's grip, but that was a slip. 'A fellow craft he is!' I says to Dan. 'Does he know the word?' 'He does,' says Dan, 'and all the priests know. It's a miracle! The chiefs and the priests can work a fellow craft lodge in a way that's very like ours, and they've cut the marks on the rocks, but they don't know the third degree, and they've come to find out. It's Gord's truth. I've known these long years that the Afghans knew up to the fellow craft degree, but this is a miracle.

A god and a grand-master of the craft am I, and a lodge in the third degree I will open, and we'll raise the head priests and the chiefs of the villages.'

"'It's against all the law,' I says, 'holding a lodge without warrant from anyone; and you know we never held office in any lodge.'

"'It's a master-stroke o' policy,' says Dravot. 'It means running the country as easy as a four-wheeled bogie on a down grade. We can't stop to inquire now, or they'll turn against us. I've forty chiefs at my heels, and passed and raised according to their merit they shall be. Billet these men on the villages, and see that we run up a lodge of some kind. The temple of Imbra will do for the lodge-room. The women must make aprons as you show them. I'll hold a levee of chiefs tonight and lodge tomorrow.'

"I was fair run off my legs, but I wasn't such a fool as not to see what a pull this craft business gave us. I showed the priests' families how to make aprons of the degrees, but for Dravot's apron the blue border and marks was made of turquoise lumps on white hide, not cloth. We took a great square stone in the temple for the master's chair, and little stones for the officers' chairs, and painted the black pavement with white squares, and did what we could to make things regular.

"At the levee which was held that night on the hillside with big bonfires, Dravot gives out that him and me were gods and sons of Alexander, and past grand-masters in the craft, and was come to make Kafiristan a country where every man should eat in peace and drink in quiet, and specially obey us. Then the chiefs come round to shake hands, and they were so hairy and white and fair it was just shaking hands with old friends. We gave them names according as they was like men we had known in India—Billy Fish, Holly Dilworth, Pikky Kergan, that was bazaar-master when I was at Mhow, and so on, and so on.

"*The* most amazing miracles was at lodge next night. One of the old priests was watching us continuous, and I felt uneasy, for I knew we'd have to fudge the ritual, and I didn't know what the men knew. The old priest was a stranger come in from beyond the village of Bashkai. The minute Dravot puts on the master's apron that the girls had made for him, the priest fetches a whoop and a howl and tries to overturn the stone that Dravot was sitting on. 'It's, all up now,' I says. 'That comes of meddling with the craft without warrant!' Dravot never winked an eye, not when ten priests took and tilted over the grand-master's chair—which was to say the stone of Imbra. The priest begins rubbing the bottom end of it to clear away the black dirt, and presently he shows all the other priests the master's mark, same as was on Dravot's apron, cut into the stone. Not even the priests of the temple of Imbra knew it was there. The old chap falls flat on his face at Dravot's feet and kisses 'em. 'Luck again,' says Dravot across the lodge to me; 'they say it's the missing mark that no one could understand the why of. We're more than safe now.' Then he bangs the butt of his gun for a gavel and says, 'By virtue of the authority vested in me by my own right hand and the help of Peachey, I declare myself grand-master of all free-masonry in Kafiristan in this the mother lodge o' the country, and king of Kafiristan equally with Peachey!' At that he puts on his crown and I puts on mine—I was doing senior warden—and we opens the lodge in most ample form. It was a amazing miracle! The priests moved in lodge through the first two degrees almost without telling, as if the memory was coming back to them. After that Peachey and Dravot raised such as was worthy—high priests and chiefs of far-off villages. Billy Fish was the first, and I can tell you we scared the soul out of him. It was not in any way according to ritual, but it served our turn. We didn't raise more than ten of the biggest men, because we didn't want to make the degree common. And they was clamouring to be raised.

"'In another six months,' says Dravot, 'we'll hold another communication and see how you are working.' Then he asks them about their villages, and learns that they was fighting one against the other, and were sick and tired of it. And when they wasn't doing that they was fighting with the Muhammadans. 'You can fight those when they come into our country,' says Dravot. 'Tell off every tenth man of your tribes for a frontier guard, and send two hundred at a time to this valley to be drilled. Nobody is going to be shot or speared anymore so long as he does well, and I know that you won't cheat me, because you're white people—sons of Alexander—and not like common black Muhammadans. You are *my* people, and by God,' says he, running off into English at the end, 'I'll make a damned fine nation of you, or I'll die in the making!'

"I can't tell all we did for the next six months, because Dravot did a lot I couldn't see the hang of, and he learned their lingo in a way I never could. My work was to help the people plough, and now and again go out with some of the army and see what the other villages were doing, and make 'em throw rope-bridges across the ravines which cut up the country horrid. Dravot was very kind to me, but when he walked up and down in the pine wood pulling that bloody red beard of his with both fists, I knew he was thinking plans I could not advise about, and I just waited for orders.

"But Dravot never showed me disrespect before the people. They were afraid of me and the army, but they loved Dan. He was the best of friends with the priests and the chiefs, but anyone could come across the hills with a complaint and Dravot would hear him out fair and call four priests together and say what was to be done. He used to call in Billy Fish from Bashkai, and Pikky Kergan from Shu, and an old chief we called Kafuzelum—it was like enough to his real name—and hold councils with 'em when there was any fighting to be done in small villages. That was his council of war, and the four priests of Bashkai, Shu, Khawak, and Madora was his privy council. Between the lot of 'em they sent me, with forty men and twenty rifles, and sixty men carrying turquoises, into the Ghorband country to buy those hand-made Martini rifles, that come out of the amir's workshops at Kabul, from one of the amir's Herati regiments that would have sold the very teeth out of their mouths for turquoises.

"I stayed in Ghorband a month, and gave the governor there the pick of my baskets for hush-money, and bribed the colonel of the regiment some more; and between the two and the tribespeople, we got more than a hundred hand-made Martinis, a hundred good Kohat Jezails that'll throw to six hundred yards, and forty man-loads of very bad ammunition for the rifles. I came back with what I had and distributed 'em among the men that the chiefs sent in to me to drill. Dravot was too busy to attend to those things, but the old army that we first made helped me, and we turned out five hundred men that could drill and two hundred that knew how to hold arms pretty straight. Even those corkscrewed, hand-made guns was a miracle to them. Dravot talked big about powder-shops and factories, walking up and down in the pine wood when the winter was coming on.

"'I won't make a nation,' says he; 'I'll make an empire! These men aren't Foreigners; they're English! Look at their eyes, look at their mouths. Look at the way they stand up. They sit on chairs in their own houses. They're the Lost Tribes, or something like it, and they've grown to be English. I'll take a census in the spring if the priests don't get frightened. There must be a fair two million of 'em in these hills. The villages are full o' little children. Two million people, two hundred and fifty thousand fighting men—and all English! They only want the rifles and a little drilling. Two hundred and fifty thousand men ready to cut in on Russia's right flank when she tries for India! Peachey, man,' he says, chewing his beard in great hunks, 'We shall be emperors—emperors of the earth! Rajah Brooke will be a suckling to us. I'll treat with the viceroy on equal terms. I'll ask him to send me twelve picked English—twelve that I know of—to help us govern a bit. There's Mackray, sergeant-pensioner at Segowli—many's the good dinner he's given me, and his wife a pair of trousers. There's Donkin, the warder of Tounghoo jail; there's hundreds that I could lay my hand on if I was in India. The viceroy shall do it for me; I'll send a man through in the spring for those men, and I'll write for a dispensation from the grand lodge for what I've done as grand-master. That—and all the Sniders, that'll be thrown out when the native troops in India take up the Martini. They'll be worn smooth, but they'll do for fighting in these hills. Twelve English, a hundred thousand Sniders ran through the amir's country in driblets—I'd be content with twenty thousand in one year—and we'd be an empire. When everything was shipshape, I'd hand over the crown—this crown I'm wearing now—to Queen Victoria, on my knees, and she'd say, "Rise up, Sir Danial Dravot." Oh, it's big! It's big, I tell you! But there's so much to be done in every place—Bashkai, Khawak, Shu, and everywhere else.'

"'What is it?' I says. 'There are no more men coming in to be drilled this autumn. Look at those fat black clouds. They're bringing the snow.'

"'It isn't that,' says Daniel, putting his hand very hard on my shoulder; 'and I don't wish to say anything that's against you, for no other living man would have followed me and made me what I am as you have done. You're a first-class commander-in-chief, and the people know you but—it's a big country, and some-how you can't help me, Peachey, in the way I want to be helped.'

"'Go to your blasted priests then!' I said, and I was sorry when I made that remark, but it did hurt me sore to find Daniel talking so superior when I'd drilled all the men and done all he told me.

"'Don't let's quarrel, Peachey,' says Daniel, without cursing. 'You're a king too, and the half of this kingdom is yours; but can't you see, Peachey, we want cleverer men than us now—three or four of 'em that we can scatter about for our deputies. It's a hugeous great state, and I can't always tell the right thing to do, and I haven't time for all I want to do, and here's the winter coming on, and all.' He put half his beard into his mouth, all red like the gold of his crown.

"'I'm sorry, Daniel,' says I. 'I've done all I could. I've drilled the men and shown the people how to stack their oats better; and I've brought in those tinware rifles from Ghorband—but I know what you're driving at. I take it kings always feel oppressed that way.'

"'There's another thing too,' says Dravot, walking up and down. 'The winter's coming, and these people won't be giving much trouble, and if they do we can't move about. I want a wife.'

"'For Gord's sake leave the women alone!' I says. 'We've both got all the work we can, though I *am* a fool. Remember the contrack, and keep clear o' women.'

"'The contrack only lasted till such time as we was kings; and kings we have been these months past,' says Dravot, weighing his crown in his hand. 'You go get a wife too, Peachey—a nice, strappin', plump girl that'll keep you warm in the winter. They're prettier than English girls, and we can take the pick of 'em. Boil 'em once or twice in hot water, and they'll come out like chicken and ham.'

"'Don't tempt me!' I says. 'I will not have any dealings with a woman, not till we are a damn side more settled than we are now. I've been doing the work o' two men, and you've been doing the work of three. Let's lie off a bit and see if we can get some better tobacco from Afghan country and run in some good liquor; but no women.'

"'Who's talking o' *women?*' says Dravot. 'I said *wife*—a queen to breed a king's son for the king. A queen out of the strongest tribe, that'll make them your blood-brothers and that'll lie by your side and tell you all the people thinks about you and their own affairs. That's what I want.'

"'Do you remember that Bengali woman I kept at Mogul Serai when I was a plate-layer?' says I. 'A fat lot o' good she was to me. She taught me the lingo and one or two other things; but what happened? She ran away with the station-master's servant and half my month's pay. Then she turned up at Dadur Junction in tow of a half-caste, and had the impidence to say I was her husband—all among the drivers in the running-shed, too!'

"'We've done with that,' says Dravot; 'these women are whiter than you or me, and a queen I will have for the winter months.'

" 'For the last time o' asking, Dan, do *not*,' I says. 'It'll only bring us harm. The Bible says that kings ain't to waste their strength on women, 'specially when they've got a new raw kingdom to work over.'

" 'For the last time of answering, I will,' said Dravot, and he went away through the pine-trees looking like a big red devil, the sun being on his crown and beard and all.

"But getting a wife was not as easy as Dan thought. He put it before the council, and there was no answer till Billy Fish said that he'd better ask the girls. Dravot damned them all round. 'What's wrong with me?' he shouts, standing by the idol Imbra. 'Am I a dog or am I not enough of a man for your wenches? Haven't I put the shadow of my hand over this country? Who stopped the last Afghan raid?' It was me really, but Dravot was too angry to remember. 'Who bought your guns? Who repaired the bridges? Who's the grand-master of the sign cut in the stone?' says he, and he thumped his hand on the block that he used to sit on in lodge and at council, which opened like lodge always. Billy Fish said nothing, and no more did the others. 'Keep your hair on, Dan,' said I; 'and ask the girls. That's how it's done at home, and these people are quite English.'

" 'The marriage of the king is a matter of state,' says Dan in a white-hot rage, for he could feel, I hope, that he was going against his better mind. He walked out of the council-room, and the others sat still, looking at the ground.

" 'Billy Fish,' says I to the chief of Bashkai, 'what's the difficulty here? A straight answer to a true friend.'

" 'You know,' says Billy Fish. 'How should a man tell you who knows everything? How can daughters of men marry gods or devils? It's not proper.'

"I remembered something like that in the Bible; but if, after seeing us as long as they had, they still believed we were gods, it wasn't for me to undeceive them.

" 'A God can do anything,' says I. 'If the king is fond of a girl, he'll not let her die.'

" 'She'll have to,' said Billy Fish. 'There are all sorts of gods and devils in these mountains, and now and again a girl marries one of them and isn't seen anymore. Besides, you two know the mark cut in the stone. Only the gods know that. We thought you were men till you showed the sign of the master.'

"I wished then that we had explained about the loss of the genuine secrets of a master-mason at the first go-off, but I said nothing. All that night there was a blowing of horns in a little dark temple halfway down the hill and I heard a girl crying fit to die. One of the priests told us that she was being prepared to marry the king.

"'I'll have no nonsense of that kind,' says Dan. 'I don't want to interfere with your customs, but I'll take my own wife.'

"'The girl's a little bit afraid,' says the priest. 'She thinks she's going to die, and they are a-heartening of her up down in the temple.'

"'Hearten her very tender then' says Dravot, 'or I'll hearten you with the butt of a gun so you'll never want to be heartened again.' He licked his lips, did Dan, and stayed up walking about more than half the night, thinking of the wife that he was going to get in the morning. I wasn't any means comfortable, for I knew that dealings with a woman in foreign parts, though you was a crowned king twenty times over, could not but be risky. I got up very early in the morning while Dravot was asleep, and I saw the priests talking together in whispers, and the chiefs talking together too, and they looked at me out of the corners of their eyes.

"'What is up, Fish?' I says to the Bashkai man, who was wrapped up in his furs and looked splendid to behold.

"'I can't rightly say,' says he; 'but if you can make the king drop all this non-sense about marriage, you'll be doing him and me and yourself a great service.'

"'That I do believe,' says I. 'But sure, you know, Billy, as well as me, having fought against and for us, that the king and me are nothing more than two of the finest men that God Almighty ever made. Nothing more, I do assure you.'

"'That may be,' says Billy Fish, 'and yet I should be sorry if it was.' He sinks his head upon his great fur cloak for a minute and thinks. 'King,' says he, 'be you man or god or devil, I'll stick by you today. I have twenty of my men with me, and they will follow me. Well go to Bashkai until the storm blows over.'

"A little snow had fallen in the night, and everything was white except the greasy fat clouds that blew down and down from the north. Dravot came out with his crown on his head, swinging his arms, and stamping his feet, and looking more pleased than Punch.

"'For the last time, drop it, Dan,' says I in a whisper; 'Billy Fish here says that there will be a row.'

"'A row among my people!' says Dravot. 'Not much. Peachey, you're a fool not to get a wife too. Where's the girl?' says he with a voice as loud as the braying of a jackass. 'Call up all the chiefs and priests, and let the emperor see if his wife suits him.'

"There was no need to call anyone. They were all there leaning on their guns and spears round the clearing in the centre of the pine wood. A lot of priests went down to the little temple to bring up the girl, and the horns blew fit to wake the dead. Billy Fish saunters round and gets as close to Daniel as he could, and behind him stood his twenty men with matchlocks. Not a man of them under six feet. I was next to Dravot, and behind me was twenty men of the regular army. Up comes the girl, and a strapping wench she was, covered with silver and turquoises, but white as death, and looking back every minute at the priests.

"'She'll do,' said Dan, looking her over. 'What's to be afraid of, lass? Come and kiss me.' He puts his arm round her. She shuts her eyes, gives a bit of a squeak, and down goes her face in the side of Dan's flaming red beard.

"'The slut's bitten me!' says he, clapping his hand to his neck, and, sure enough, his hand was red with blood. Billy Fish and two of his matchlock-men catches hold of Dan by the shoulders and drags him into the Bashkai lot, while the priests howls in their lingo, 'Neither god nor devil, but a man!' I was all taken aback, for a priest cut at me in front, and the army behind began firing into the Bashkai men.

"'God A'mighty!' says Dan. 'What is the meaning o' this?'

"'Come back! Come away!' says Billy Fish. 'Ruin and mutiny is the matter. We'll break for Bashkai if we can.'

"I tried to give some sort of orders to my men—the men o' the regular army—but it was no use, so I fired into the brown of 'em with an English Martini and drilled three beggars in a line. The valley was full of shouting, howling creatures, and every soul was shrieking, 'Not a god nor a devil, but only a man!' The Bashkai troops stuck to Billy Fish all they were worth, but their matchlocks wasn't half as good as the Kabul breech-loaders and four of them dropped. Dan was bellowing like a bull, for he was very wrathy; and Billy Fish had a hard job to prevent him running out of the crowd.

"'We can't stand,' says Billy Fish. 'Make a run for it down the valley! The whole place is against us.' The matchlock-men ran, and we went down the valley in spite of Dravot. He was swearing horrible and crying out he was a king. The priests rolled great stones on us, and the regular army fired hard, and there wasn't more than six men not counting Dan, Billy Fish, and me, that came down to the bottom of the valley alive.

"Then they stopped firing, and the horns in the temple blew again. 'Come away—for Gord's sake come away!' says Billy Fish. 'They'll send runners out to all the villagers before ever we get to Bashkai. I can protect you there, but I can't do anything now.'

"My own notion is that Dan began to go mad in his head from that hour. He stared up and down like a stuck pig. Then he was all for walking back alone and killing the priests with his bare hands, which he could have done. 'An emperor am I,' says Daniel, 'and next year I shall be a knight of the queen.'

"'All right, Dan,' says I, 'but come along now while there's time.'

"'It's your fault,' says he, 'for not looking after your army better. There was mutiny in the midst, and you didn't know—you damned engine-driving, plate-laying, missionary's pass-hunting hound!' He sat upon a rock and called me every foul name he could lay tongue to. I was too heart-sick to care, though it was all his foolishness that brought the smash.

"'I'm sorry, Dan,' says I, 'but there's no accounting for natives. This business is our fifty-seven. Maybe we'll make something out of it yet, when we've got to Bashkai.'

"'Let's get to Bashkai, then,' says Dan, 'and, by God, when I come back here again I'll sweep the valley so there isn't a bug in a blanket left!'

"We walked all that day, and all that night Dan was stumping up and down on the snow, chewing his beard, and muttering to himself.

"'There's no hope o' getting clear,' said Billy Fish. The priests will have sent runners to the villages to say that you are only men. Why didn't you stick on as gods till things was more settled? I'm a dead man,' says Billy Fish, and he throws himself down on the snow and begins to pray to his gods.

"Next morning we was in a cruel bad country—all up and down, no level ground at all, and no food either. The six Bashkai men looked at Billy Fish hungry-way as if they wanted to ask something, but they said never a word.

"At noon we came to the top of a flat mountain all covered with snow, and when we climbed up into it, behold, there was an army in position waiting in the middle!

"'The runners have been very quick,' says Billy Fish with a little bit of a laugh. 'They are waiting for us.'

""Three or four men began to fire from the enemy's side, and a chance shot took Daniel in the calf of the leg. That brought him to his senses. He looks across the snow at the army, and sees the rifles that we had brought into the country.

"'We're done for,' says he. 'They are Englishmen, these people, and it's my blasted nonsense that has brought you to this. Get back, Billy Fish, and take your men away; you've done what you could, and now cut for it. Carnehan,' says he, 'shake hands with me and go along with Billy. Maybe they won't kill you. I'll go and meet 'em alone. It's me that did it. Me, the king!'

"'Go!' says I. 'Go to hell, Dan. I'm with you here. Billy Fish, you clear out, and we two will meet those folk.'

"'I'm a chief,' says Billy Fish, quite quiet. 'I stay with you. My men can go.'

"The Bashkai fellows, didn't wait for a second word, but ran off; and Dan and me and Billy Fish walked across to where the drums were drumming and the horns were horning. It was cold—awful cold. I've got that cold in the back of my head now. There's a lump of it there."

The punkah-coolies had gone to sleep. Two kerosene lamps were blazing in the office, and the perspiration poured down my face and splashed on the blotter as I leaned forward. Carnehan was shivering, and I feared that his mind might go. I wiped my face, took a fresh grip of the piteously mangled hands, and said, "What happened after that?"

The momentary shift of my eyes had broken the clear current.

"What was you pleased to say?" whined Carnehan. "They took them without any sound. Not a little whisper all along the snow, not though the king knocked down the first man that set hand on him—not though old Peachey fired his last cartridge into the brown of 'em. Not a single solitary sound did those swines make. They just closed up tight, and I tell you their furs stunk. There was a man called Billy Fish, a good friend of us all, and they cut his throat, sir, then and there, like a pig; and the king kicks up the bloody snow and says, 'We've had a dashed fine run for our money. What's coming next?' But Peachey, Peachey Taliaferro, I tell you, sir, in confidence as betwixt two friends, he lost his head, sir. No, he didn't, neither. The king lost his head, so he did, all along o' one of those cunning rope-bridges. Kindly let me have the paper-cutter, sir. It tilted this way. They marched him a mile across that snow to a rope-bridge over a ravine with a river at the bottom. You may have seen such. They prodded him behind like an ox. 'Damn your eyes!' says the king. 'D'you suppose I can't die like a gentleman?' He turns to Peachey—Peachey that was crying, like a child. 'I've brought you to this, Peachey,' says he. 'Brought you out of your happy life to be killed in Kafiristan, where you was late commander-in-chief of the emperor's forces. Say you forgive me, Peachey.' 'I do,' says Peachey. 'Fully and freely do I forgive you, Dan.' 'Shake hands, Peachey,' says he. 'I'm going now.' Out he goes, looking neither right nor left, and when he was plumb in the middle of those dizzy dancing ropes. 'Cut, you beggars,' he shouts; and they cut, and old Dan fell, turning round and round and round, twenty thousand miles, for he took half an hour to fall till he struck the water, and I could see his body caught on a rock with the gold crown close beside.

"But do you now what they did to Peachey between two pine-trees? They crucified him, sir, as Peachey's hands will show. They used wooden pegs for his hands and his feet; and he didn't die. He hung there and screamed, and they took him down next day and said it was a miracle that he wasn't dead. They took him down—poor old Peachey that hadn't done them any harm—that hadn't done them any—"

He rocked to and fro and wept bitterly, wiping his eyes with the back of his scarred hands and moaning like a child for some ten minutes.

"They was cruel enough to feed him up in the temple, because they said he was more of a god than old Daniel that was a man. Then they turned him out on the snow and told him to go home, and Peachey came home in about a year, begging along the roads quite safe; for Daniel Dravot, he walked before and said: 'Come along, Peachey. It's a big thing we're doing.' The mountains, they danced at night, and the mountains, they tried to fall on Peachey's head, but Dan, he held up his hand, and Peachey came along bent double. He never let go of Dan's hand, and he never let go of Dan's head. They gave it to him as a present in the temple to remind him not to come again, and though the crown was pure gold, and Peachey was starving, never would Peachey sell the same. You knew Dravot, sir! You knew Right Worshipful Brother Dravot! Look at him now!"

He fumbled in the mass of rags round his bent waist, brought out a black horsehair bag embroidered with silver thread, and shook therefrom onto my table—the dried, withered head of Daniel Dravot! The morning sun that had long been paling the lamps struck the red beard and blind, sunken eyes; struck, too, a heavy circlet of gold studded with raw turquoises, that Carnehan placed tenderly on the battered temples.

"You be'old now," said Carnehan, "the emperor in his 'abit as he lived—the king of Kafiristan with his crown upon his head. Poor old Daniel that was a monarch once!"

I shuddered, for in spite of defacements manifold, I recognized the head of the man of Marwar Junction. Carnehan rose to go. I attempted to stop him. He was not fit to walk abroad. "Let me take away the whisky, and give me a little money," he gasped. "I was a king once. I'll go to the deputy commissioner and ask to set in the poorhouse till I get my health. No, thank you, I can't wait till you get a carriage for me. I've urgent private affairs—in the South—at Marwar."

He shambled out of the office and departed in the direction of the deputy commissioner's house. That day at noon I had occasion to go down the blinding hot mall, and I saw a crooked man crawling along the white dust of the roadside, his hat in his hand, quavering dolorously after the fashion of street-singers at home. There was not a soul in sight, and he was out of all possible earshot of the houses. And he sang through his nose, turning his head from right to left:

> The son of man goes forth to war,
>   A golden crown to gain;
> His blood-red banner streams afar—
>   Who follows in his train?

I waited to hear no more, but put the poor wretch into my carriage and drove him off to the nearest missionary for eventual transfer to the asylum. He repeated the hymn twice while he was with me, whom he did not in the least recognize, and I left him singing it to the missionary.

Two days later I inquired after his welfare of the superintendent of the asylum.

"He was admitted suffering from sun-stroke. He died early yesterday morning," said the superintendent. "Is it true that he was half an hour bare-headed in the sun at midday?"

"Yes," said I, "but do you happen to know if he had anything upon him by any chance when he died?"

"Not to my knowledge," said the superintendent.

And there the matter rests.

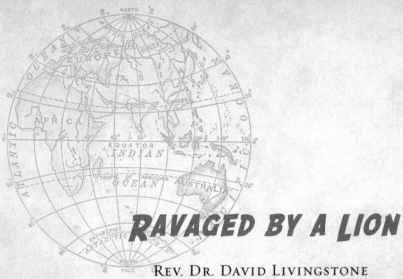

RAVAGED BY A LION

REV. DR. DAVID LIVINGSTONE

(Scottish missionary and explorer)

Returning towards Kuruman, I selected the beautiful valley of Mabotsa (lat. 25° 14′ south, long. 26° 30′?) as the site of a missionary station; and thither I removed in 1843. Here an occurrence took place concerning which I have frequently been questioned in England, and which, but for the importunities of friends, I meant to have kept in store to tell my children when in my dotage. The Bakatla of the village Mabotsa were much trolled by lions, which leaped into the cattle-pens by night, and destroyed their cows. They even attacked the herds in open day. This was so unusual an occurrence that the people believed that they were bewitched—"given," as they said, "into the power of the lions by a neighbouring tribe." They went once to attack the animals, but, being rather a cowardly people compared to Bechuanas in general on such occasions, they returned without killing any.

It is well known that if one in a troop of lions is killed the others take the hint and leave that part of the country. So the next time the herds were attacked, I went with the people, in order to encourage them to rid themselves of the annoyance by destroying one of the marauders. We found the lions on a small hill about a quarter of a mile in length, and covered with trees. A circle of men was formed round it, and they gradually closed up, ascending pretty near to each other. Being down below on the plain with a native schoolmaster, named Mebálwe, a most excellent man, I saw one of the lions sitting on a piece of rock within the now closed circle of men. Mebálwe fired at him before I could, and the ball struck the rock on which the animal was sitting. He hit at the spot struck, as a dog does at a stick or stone thrown at him; then leaping away, broke through the opening circle and escaped unhurt. The men were afraid to attack him, perhaps on account of their belief in witchcraft. When the circle was re-formed, we saw two other lions in it; but we were afraid to fire lest we should strike the men, and they allowed the beasts to burst through also. If the Bakatla had acted according to the custom of the country, they would have speared the lions in their attempt to get out. Seeing we could not get them to kill one of the lions, we bent our footsteps towards the village; in going round the end of the hill, however, I saw one of the beasts sitting on a piece of rock as before, but this time he had a little bush in front. Being about thirty yards off, I took a good aim at his body through the bush, and fired both barrels into it. The men then called out, "He is shot, he is shot!" Others cried, "He has been shot by another man too; let us go to him!" I did not see any one else shoot at him, but I saw the lion's tail erected in anger behind the bush, and, turning to the people, said, "Stop a little till I load again." When in the act of ramming down the bullets I heard a shout. Starting, and looking half round, I saw the lion just in the act of springing upon me. I was upon a little height; he caught my shoulder as he sprang, and we both came to the ground below together. Growling horribly close to my ear, he shook me as a terrier dog does a rat. The shock produces a stupor similar to that which seems to be felt by a mouse after the first shake of the cat. It caused a sort of dreaminess, in which there was no sense of pain nor feeling of terror, though quite conscious of all that was happening. It was like what patients partially under the influence of chloroform describe, who see all the operation, but feel not the knife. This singular condition was not the result of any mental process. The shake annihilated fear, and allowed no sense of horror in looking round at the beast. This peculiar state is probably produced in all animals killed by the carnivora; and if so, is a merciful provision by our benevolent Creator for lessening the pain of death. Turning round to relieve myself of the weight, as he had one paw on the back of my head, I saw his eyes directed to Mebalwe, who was trying to shoot him at a distance of ten or fifteen yards. His gun, a flint one, missed fire in both barrels; the lion immediately left me, and, attacking Mebalwe, bit his thigh. Another man, whose life I had saved before, after he had been tossed by a buffalo, attempted to spear the lion while he was biting Mebalwe. He left Mebalwe and caught this man by the shoulder, but at that moment the bullets he had received took effect, and he fell down dead. The whole was the work of a few moments, and must have been his paroxysm of dying rage. In order to take out the charm from him, the Bakatla on the following day made a huge bonfire over the carcase, which was declared to be that of the largest lion they had ever seen. Besides crunching the bone into splinters, he left eleven teeth wounds on the upper part of my arm.

A wound from this animal's tooth resembles a gun-shot wound; it is generally followed by a great deal of sloughing and discharge, and pains are felt in the part periodically ever afterwards. I had on a tartan jacket on the occasion, and I believe that it wiped off all the virus from the teeth that pierced the flesh, for my two companions in this affray have both suffered from the peculiar pains, while I have escaped with only the inconvenience of a false joint in my limb.

A DEADLY EXPEDITION THROUGH UNKNOWN AFRICA

SIR HENRY M. STANLEY

(British-American explorer)

Raised in poverty in Wales before turning his hand to soldiering and journalism, legendary explorer Sir Henry M. Stanley is these days best known for his famous question, "Dr. Livingstone, I presume?", made in 1871 after completing an arduous 700-mile, 236-day search for Dr. Livingstone, whom he finally located in what is now Tanzania. Stanley explored Africa during the period when Western civilization was just rising above slavery and, although Westerners were learning more about other cultures through the works of explorers like him, many prejudices were still unfortunately strong. This is most apparent when Stanley (who had, in fact, briefly fought for the Confederacy in the American Civil War) refers to Africans he encounters as "savages." In the spirit of the age, Stanley assumed the superiority of his race and felt he was bringing enlightenment to a place whose people and civiliza-tion he saw as patently inferior. This aside, he certainly did introduce the Western world to an unknown side of this vast continent and his dangerous adventures amongst the warring tribes on his second expedition—which lasted nearly three years and during which all three of his white companions died—make for truly thrilling reading.

I gazed long on the grand encircling prospect. A halcyon calm brooded on the lake, eastward, northward, and southward, until the clear sky and stainless silver water met, the clear bounds of both veiled by a gauzy vapour, suggesting infinity. In a bold, majestic mass to the south-east rose Alice Island, while a few miles south-east of it appeared the Bumbireh group. Opposite me, to the west, and two miles from where I stood, was the long cliffy front of the plateau of Usongora, its slowly rising summit gemmed with patches of ever-green banana, until it became banked in the distance by lines of hazy blue mountains.

It is a spot from which, undisturbed, the eye may rove over one of the strangest yet fairest portions of Africa—hundreds of square miles of beautiful lake scenes— a great length of grey plateau wall, upright and steep, but indented with exquisite inlets, half surrounded by embowering plantains—hundreds of square miles of pastoral upland dotted thickly with villages and groves of banana. From my lofty eyrie I can see herds upon herds of cattle, and many minute specks, white and black, which can be nothing but flocks of sheep and goats. I can also see pale blue columns of ascending smoke from the fires, and upright thin figures moving about. Secure on my lofty throne, I can view their movements, and laugh at the ferocity of the savage hearts which beat in those thin dark figures; for I am a part of Nature now, and for the present as invulnerable as itself. As little do they know that human eyes survey their forms from the summit of this lake-girt isle as that the eyes of the Supreme in heaven are upon them.[...]

What a land they possess! and what an inland sea! How steamers afloat on the lake might cause Ururi to shake hands with Usongora, and Uganda with Usukuma, make the wild Wavuma friends with the Wazinza, and unite the Wakerewé with the Wagana! A great trading port might then spring up on the Shimeeyu, whence the coffee of Usongora, the ivory, sheep, and goats of Ugeyeya, Usoga, Uvuma, and Uganda, the cattle of Uwya, Karagwé, Usagara, Ihangiro, and Usukuma, the myrrh, cassia, and furs and hides of Uganda and Uddu, the rice of Ukerewé, and the grain of Uzinza, might be exchanged for the fabrics brought from the coast; all the land be redeemed from wildness, the industry and energy of the natives— stimulated, the havoc of the slave-trade stopped, and all the countries round about permeated with the nobler ethics of a higher humanity. But at present the hands of the people are lifted—murder in their hearts—one against the other;

ferocity is kindled at sight of the wayfarer; piracy is the acknowledged profession of the Wavuma; the people of Ugeyeya and Wasoga go stark naked; Mtesa [the emperor of Uganda] impales, burns, and maims his victims; the Wirigedi lie in wait along their shores for the stranger, and the slingers of the islands practise their art against him; the Wakara poison anew their deadly arrows at sight of a canoe; and each tribe, with rage and hate in its heart, remains aloof from the other. "Verily, the dark places of the earth are full of the habitations of cruelty."

Oh for the hour when a band of philanthropic capitalists shall vow to rescue these beautiful lands, and supply the means to enable the Gospel messengers to come and quench the murderous hate with which man beholds man in the beautiful lands around Lake Victoria!

I descended from the lofty height, the summit of Musira Island, by another way, which disclosed to me the character of the rocky island, and exposed to my view the precipitous walls of shale, rifted and indebted by ages of atmospheric influences, that surround the island upon all sides but the western. After great difficulty I succeeded in getting upon the top of a portion of an upper ledge that had fallen on the north-east corner and now formed a separate projection about 30 feet high. In a cavernous recess upon the summit of it, I discovered six human bodies in a state of decomposition, half covered with grass and débris of rock. One of the skulls showed the mark of a hatchet, which made me suspect that a tragedy had occurred here but a short time before. No doubt the horrible event took place on the island on the ground occupied by our camp, for there was no other spot where such a deed could have been wrought, and probably the victims were taken in canoes, and deposited in this hidden recess, that strangers might not be alarmed at the sight of the bodies, or of such evidence of violence as the hatchet cleft skull. Probably, also, these strangers were murdered for their cargo of coffee or of butter by the natives of the mainland, or by a later arrival of strangers like my own Waganda, who because of their numerical superiority had begun their molestation and robbery of the coffee traders, without other cause than that they were strong and the traders weak.

About 5 P.M., having long before returned to camp, I saw on the horizon Magassa's fleet of canoes, and counted fourteen. I despatched Safeni and some of the Waganda in a canoe to the small islands we passed just before reaching

Makongo, begging Magassa to hasten and join me early next morning, as we were short of provisions, and starvation would ensue if we were delayed in our voyage. Safeni returned about 9 P.M. with a request from Magassa that I would go on as early as I wished, and a promise that he would follow me to camp.

I waited, however, for Magassa until 10 A.M., and as Alice Island—which Sentum and Sentageya advised me was the best place to touch at in order to make a short course for Usukuma—was about thirty miles from Musira, I could delay no longer. It was then agreed that Sentum should stay at Musira Island until Magassa arrived, and inform him of the direction which Sentageya and I had taken.

We had proceeded on our voyage but three miles when Sentageya turned back with all speed towards Musira, waving his hand to me to continue my journey. Imagining that he had merely forgotten something, I did as he directed.

We reached Alice Island about 9 P.M., for we had been delayed by a strong head wind since 4 P.M. As it was pitch-dark, we were guided to a camping-place by a flickering light which we saw on the shore. The light for which we steered was that of a fire kindled by two men and a boy, who were drying fish in a cavern the entrance of which opened on the lake. Though the fishermen were rather frightened at first, they were discreet enough to remain passive; and to calm their fears, I assumed an air of extreme blandness and amiability. It being late, I prepared to rest in the stern-sheets of my boat, but as I was about to lie down, I heard the natives expostulating. I knew by this that the boat's crew must be committing depredations on their fish stores; so I sprang out—and only just in time to save them a serious loss. Murab had already made himself master of half a dozen large fish, when I came up with naked feet behind him, announcing my arrival by a staggering blow, which convinced the fishermen better than any amount of blandness and affectation of amiability could have done that I was sincere, and convinced the Wangwana also that injustice would not be permitted. The fishermen received a handful of beads as an atonement for the attempted spoliation, and to secure the Wangwana against further temptation, I gave them double rations.

The next morning, when I awoke, I found that we were camped under the shadow of a basaltic cliff, about 50 feet high, at the base of which was the fishermen's cavern, extending about 15 feet within. The island was lofty, about 400 feet

THE FAMOUS MEETING OF STANLEY AND LIVINGSTONE

David Livingston had become quite a celebrity by the time he made his last expedition into Africa. After rumors began circulating that he was dead, an American newspaper sent journalist Henry Stanley to search for him. After a long, dangerous journey, Stanley finally found him. Stanley described the encounter saying, "As I advanced slowly towards him, I noticed he was pale, looked weakened, had a gray beard, wore a bluish cap with a faded gold band round it, had on a red-sleeved waistcoat and a pair of gray tweed trousers. I would have run to him, only I was a coward in the presence of such a mob—would have embraced him, only, he being an Englishman, I did not know how he would receive me. So I did what cowardice and false pride suggested was the best thing—walked deliberately up to him, took off my hat and said, 'Dr. Livingstone, I presume?' 'Yes,' said he with a kind smile, lifting his cap slightly. I replace my hat on my head, and he puts on his cap, and we both grasp hands, and I then say aloud—

'I thank God, Doctor, I have been permitted to see you.' He answered, 'I feel thankful that I am here to welcome you.'"

Of this meeting, Livingston wrote, "The American flag at the head of the caravan told of the nationality of the stranger. Bales of goods, baths of tin, huge kettles, cooking-pots tents, etc., made me think, 'This must be a luxurious traveller and not one at his wits' end like me.' It was Henry Moreland [sic, Morton] Stanley, the travelling correspondent of the *New York Herald*, sent by James Gordon Bennett, junior, at the expense of more than £4,000, to obtain accurate information about Dr. Livingstone if living, and if dead to bring home my bones....I really do feel extremely grateful."

Livingston died eighteen months after this meeting. Stanley was the last white person to see him alive. Stanley launched several other expeditions into Africa and was soon considered to be the greatest living explorer of that time.

above the lake at its highest part, nearly four miles in length, and a mile and a half across at its greatest breadth. The inhabitants consisted of about forty families from Ukerewé, and owned King Lukongeh as their liege lord.

The summit of Alice Island is clothed with an abundance of coarse grass, and the ravines and hollows are choked with a luxuriance of vegetable life—trees, plants, ferns, ground orchids, and wild pine-apple: along the water's edge there waves a thin strip of water cane. The people became fast friends with us, but their keen trading instincts impelled them to demand such exorbitant prices for every article that we were unable to purchase more than a few ears of corn. I obtained a view from the summit with my field-glass, but I could distinguish nothing east or south-east. South-west we saw the Bumbireh group, and to purchase food we were compelled to proceed thither—disagreeably convinced that we had lost a whole day by calling at Alice Island, whereas, had we kept a direct course to the south, we might have reached the Bumbireh group in a few hours.

As we started only at noon from Alice Island, being delayed by expectations of seeing Magassa, and also by the necessity for purchasing something even at high prices to prevent starvation, we did not reach Barker's Island—the eastern-most of the Bunibireh group—until night, which we passed most miserably in a little cove surrounded by impenetrable brushwood. It was one downpour of rain throughout the whole night, which compelled us to sit up shivering and supper-less, for to crown our discomforts, we had absolutely nothing to eat. No more abject objects can be imagined than the human beings that occupied the boat through the hours of darkness. There were my crew all sitting as closely as possible, back to back or side by side, on the oars and boards which they had arranged like a plat-form on the thwarts, and I sitting alone under the awning in the stern sheets, wearily trying to outline their figures, or vaguely taking mental notes of the irregularities of the bush, with occasional hasty glances at the gloomy sky, or at Bumbireh, whose black mass looked grim and lofty in the dark, and all the time the rain kept pouring down with a steady malignant impetuosity. I doubt if even the happiest hours which may fall to my lot in the future will ever obliterate from my memory that dismal night of discomfort and hunger.

> "We were becoming exhausted. Yet we were still only on the middle line of the continent! We were also being weeded out by units and twos and threes. There were not thirty in the entire Expedition that had not received a wound. To continue this fearful life was not possible. Some day we should lie down, and offer our throats like lambs to the cannibal butchers."
>
> —*Sir Henry M. Stanley*

"Sechele had by right of chieftainship the breast of every animal slaughtered either at home or abroad, and he most obligingly sent us a liberal share during the whole period of our sojourn. But these supplies were necessarily so irregular, that we were sometimes fain to accept a dish of locusts. These are quite a blessing in the country; so much so, that the rain-doctors sometimes promised to bring them by their incantations. The locusts are strongly vegetable in taste, the flavour varying with the plants on which they feed. There is a physiological reason why locusts and honey should be eaten together. Some are roasted and pounded into meal, which eaten with a little salt is palatable. It will keep thus for months. Boiled they are disagreeable; but when they are roasted, I should much prefer locusts to shrimps, though I would avoid both if possible."

—explorer REV. DR. DAVID LIVINGSTONE

But as it generally happens, the dismal night was followed by a beautiful bright morning. Every inch of nature that we could scan seemed revivified, refreshed, and gay, except the little world which the boat contained. We were eager to renew our acquaintance with humanity, for only by contact with others could we live. We accordingly sailed for Bumbireh, which lay about two miles from Barker's Island, and ran down the coast in search of a cove and haven for our boat, while we should be bartering our beads, for edibles.

Bumbireh Island is about eleven miles in extreme length by two miles greatest breadth. It is in appearance a hilly range, with a tolerably even and softly rolling summit line clothed with short grass. Its slopes are generally steep, yet grassy or cultivated. It contains probably fifty small villages, averaging about twenty huts to a village, and if we calculate four souls to each hut, we have a population of about 4000, including all ages.

Herds of cattle grazed on the summit and slopes; a tolerably large acreage here and there showed a brown soil upturned for planting, while extensive banana groves marked most of the village sites. There was a kindly and prosperous aspect about the island.

As soon as we had sailed a little distance along the coast, we caught sight of a few figures which broke the even and smooth outline of the grassy summit, and heard the well-known melodious war-cries employed by most of the Central African tribes, "Hehu-a hehu-u-u-u!" loud, long-drawn, and ringing.

The figures increased in number, and fresh voices joined in the defiant and alarming note. Still, hungry wretches as we were, environed by difficulties of all kinds, just beginning to feel warm after the cold and wet of the night before, with famine gnawing at our vitals, leagues upon leagues of sea between us and our friends at Usukuma, and nothing eatable in our boat, we were obliged to risk something, reminding ourselves "that there are no circumstances so desperate which Providence may not relieve."

At 9 A.M. we discovered a cove near the south-east end of the long island, and pulled slowly into it. Immediately the natives rushed down the slopes, shouting war-cries and uttering fierce ejaculations. When about 50 yards from the shore, I bade the men cease rowing, but Safeni and Baraka [two chiefs from Zanzibar] became eloquent, and said, "It is almost always the case, master, with savages. They cry out, and threaten, and look big, but you will see that all that noise will cease as soon as they hear us speak. Besides, if we leave here without food, where shall we obtain it?"

The last argument was unanswerable, and though I gave no orders to resume their oars, four of the men impelled the boat on slowly, while Safeni and Baraka prepared themselves to explain to the natives, who were now close within hearing, as they came rushing to the water's edge. I saw some lift great stones, while others prepared their bows.

We were now about 10 yards from the beach, and Safeni and Baraka spoke, earnestly pointing to their mouths, and by gestures explaining that their bellies were empty. They smiled with insinuating faces; uttered the words "brothers," "friends," "good fellows," most volubly; cunningly interpolated the words Mtesa— the *Kabaka*—Uganda, and Antari king of Ihangiro, to whom Bumbireh belongs. Safeni and Baraka's pleasant volubility seemed to have produced a good effect, for the stones were dropped, the bows were unstrung, and the lifted spears lowered to assist the steady, slow-walking pace with which they now advanced.

Safeni and Baraka turned to me triumphantly and asked, "What did we say, master?" and then, with engaging frankness, invited the natives, who were now about two hundred in number, to come closer. The natives consulted a little while, and several—now smiling pleasantly themselves—advanced leisurely into the

water until they touched the boat's prow. They stood a few seconds talking sweetly, when suddenly with a rush they ran the boat ashore, and then all the others, seizing hawser and gunwale, dragged her about 20 yards over the rocky beach high and dry, leaving us almost stupefied with astonishment!

Then ensued a scene which beggars description. Pandemonium—all its devils armed—raged around us.[1] A forest of spears was levelled; thirty or forty bows were drawn taut; as many barbed arrows seemed already on the wing; thick, knotty clubs waved above our heads; two hundred screaming black demons jostled with each other and struggled for room to vent their fury, or for an opportunity to deliver one crushing blow or thrust at us.

In the meantime, as soon as the first symptoms of this manifestation of violence had been observed, I had sprung to my feet, each hand armed with a loaded self-cocking revolver, to kill and be killed. But the apparent hopelessness of inflicting

---

[1] Pandemonium is another name for Hell. Stanley's reference to "devils" and "demons" are another extension of his metaphor.

much injury upon such a large crowd restrained me, and Safeni turned to me, though almost cowed to dumbness by the loud fury around us, and pleaded with me to be patient. I complied, seeing that I should get no aid from my crew; but, while bitterly blaming myself for my imprudence in having yielded—against my instincts—to placing myself in the power of such savages, I vowed that, if I escaped this once, my own judgment should guide my actions for the future.

I assumed a resigned air, though I still retained my revolvers. My crew also bore the first outburst of the tempest of shrieking rage which assailed them with almost sublime imperturbability. Safeni crossed his arms with the meekness of a saint. Baraka held his hands palms outward, asking with serene benignity, "What, my friends, ails you? Do you fear empty hands and smiling people like us? We are friends, we came as friends to buy food, two or three bananas, a few mouthfuls of grain, or potatoes, or muhogo (cassava), and, if you permit us, we shall depart as friends."

Our demeanour had a great effect. The riot and noise seemed to be subsiding, when some fifty newcomers rekindled the smouldering fury. Again the forest of spears swayed on the launch, again the knotty clubs were whirled aloft, again the bows were drawn, and again the barbed arrows seemed flying. Safeni received a push which sent him tumbling, little Kirango received a blow on the head with a spear-staff, Saramba gave a cry as a club descended on his back.

I sprang up this time to remonstrate, with the two revolvers in my left hand. I addressed myself to an elder, who seemed to be restraining the people from proceeding too far. I showed him beads, cloth, wire, and invoked the names of Mtesa, and Antari their king.

The sight of the heaps of beads and cloth I exposed awakened, however, the more deliberate passions of selfishness and greed in each heart. An attempt at massacre, they began to argue, would certainly entail the loss of some of themselves. "Guns might be seized and handled with terrible effect even by dying men, and who knows what those little iron things in the white man's hands are?" they seemed to be asking themselves. The elder, whatever he thought, responded with an affectation of indignation, raised his stick, and to right and left of him drove back the demoniac crowd. Other prominent men now assisted this elder, whom we subsequently discovered to be Shekka, the king of Bumbireh.

Shekka then, having thus bestirred himself, beckoned to half a dozen men and walked away a few yards behind the mass. It was the "shauri," dear to a free and independent African's heart, that was about to be held. Half the crowd followed the king and his council, while the other half remained to indulge their violent, vituperative tongues on us, and to continually menace us with either club or spear. An audacious party came round the stern of the boat and, with superlatively hideous gestures, affronted me; one of them even gave a tug at my hair, thinking it was a wig. I revenged myself by seizing his hand, and suddenly bending it back almost dislocated it, causing him to howl with pain. His comrades swayed their lances, but I smilingly looked at them, for all idea of self-preservation had now almost fled.

The issue had surely arrived. There had been just one brief moment of agony when I reflected how unlovely death appears in such guise as that in which it then threatened me. What would my people think as they anxiously waited for the never returning master! What would [Frank] Pocock and [Frederick] Barker [who were leading the part of the expedition that was travelling by land] say when they heard of the tragedy of Bumbireh! And my friends in America and Europe! "Tut, it is only a brief moment of pain, and then what can the ferocious dogs do more? It is a consolation that, if anything, it will be short, sharp, sudden—a gasp, and then a silence—for ever and ever!" And after that I was ready for the fight and for death.

"Now, my black friends, do your worst; anything you choose; I am ready."

A messenger from the king and the council arrives, and beckons Safeni. I said to him, "Safeni, use your wit." "Please God, master," he replied.

Safeni drew nearly all the crowd after him, for curiosity is strong in the African. I saw him pose himself. A born diplomatist was Safeni. His hands moved up and down, outward and inward; a cordial frankness sat naturally on his face; his gestures were graceful; the man was an orator, pleading for mercy and justice.

Safeni returned, his face radiant. "It is all right, master, there is no fear. They say we must stop here until to-morrow."

"Will they sell us food?"

"Oh, yes, as soon as they settle their shauri."

While Safeni was speaking, six men rushed up and seized the oars.

Safeni, though hitherto politic, lost temper at this, and endeavoured to prevent them. They raised their clubs to strike him. I shouted out, "Let them go, Safeni."

A loud cheer greeted the seizure of the oars. I became convinced now that this one little act would lead to others; for man is the same all over the world. Set a beggar on horseback, and he will ride to the devil; give a slave an inch, and he will take an ell; if a man submit once, he must be prepared to submit again.

The "shauri" proceeded. Another messenger came, demanding five cloths and five fundo of necklaces. They were delivered. But as it was now near noon, and they were assured we could not escape, the savages withdrew to their nearest village to refresh themselves with wine and food.

After the warriors had departed, some women came to look at us. We spoke kindly to them, and in return they gave us the consoling assurance that we should be killed; but they said that if we could induce Shekka to make blood-brotherhood, or to eat honey with one of us, we should be safe. If we failed, there was only flight or death. We thanked them, but we would wait.

About 3 P.M. we heard a number of drums beaten. Safeni was told that if the natives collected he must endeavour to induce Shekka with gifts to go through the process of blood-brotherhood.

A long line of natives in full war costume appeared on the crest of the terrace, on which the banana grove and village of Kajurri stood. Their faces were smeared with black and white pigments. Almost all of them bore the peculiar shields of Usongora. Their actions were such as the dullest-witted of us recognized as indicating hostilities.

Even Safeni and Baraka were astounded, and their first words were, "Prepare, master. Truly, this is trouble."

"Never mind me," I replied, "I have been ready these three hours. Are you ready, your guns and revolvers loaded, and your ears open this time?"

"We are," they all firmly answered.

"Don't be afraid; be quite cool. We will try, while they are collecting together, the women's suggestion. Go frankly and smilingly, Safeni, up to Shekka, on the top of that hill, and offer him these three fundo of beads, and ask him to exchange blood with you."

Safeni proceeded readily on his errand, for there was no danger to him bodily while we were there within 150 yards, and their full power as yet unprepared. For ten minutes he conversed with them, while the drums kept beating, and numbers of men bepainted for war were increasing Shekka's force. Some of them entertained us by demonstrating with their spears how they fought; others whirled their clubs like tipsy Irishmen at Donnybrook fair. Their gestures were wild, their voices were shrill and fierce, they were kindling themselves into a fighting fever.

Safeni returned. Shekka had refused the pledge of peace. The natives now mustered over 300.

Presently fifty bold fellows came rushing down, uttering a shrill cry. Without hesitation they came straight to the boat, and, hissing something to us, seized our Kiganda drum. It was such a small affair, we did not resist; still the manner in which it was taken completely undeceived us, if any small hope of peace remained. Loud applause greeted the act of gallantry.

Then two men came down towards us, and began to drive some cows away that were grazing between us and the men on the hill. Safeni asked of one of them, "Why do you do that?"

"Because we are going to begin fighting presently, and if you are men, you may begin to prepare yourselves," he said scornfully.

"Thanks, my bold friend," I muttered to myself. "Those are the truest words we have heard to-day."

The two men were retiring up the hill. "Here, Safeni," I said, "take these two fine red cloths in your hand; walk slowly up after them a little way, and the minute you hear my voice run back; and you, my boys, this is for life and death, mind; range yourselves on each side of the boat, lay your hands on it carelessly, but with a firm grip, and when I give the word, push it with the force of a hundred men down the hill into the water. Are you all ready, and do you think you can do it? Otherwise we might as well begin fighting where we are."

"Yes, Inshallah Master," they cried out with one voice.

"Go, Safeni!"

I waited until he had walked fifty yards away, and saw that he acted precisely as I had instructed him.

"Push my boys; push for your lives!"

The crew bent their heads and strained their arms; the boat began to move, and there was a hissing, grinding noise below me. I seized my double-barrelled elephant rifle and shouted, "Safari! Safeni, return!"

The natives were quick-eyed. They saw the boat moving, and with one accord they swept down the hill uttering the most fearful cries.

My boat was at the water's edge. "Shoot her into the lake, my men; never mind the water"; and clear of all obstructions she darted out upon the lake.

Safeni stood for an instant on the water's edge, with the cloths in his hand. The foremost of a crowd of natives was about twenty yards from him. He raised his spear and balanced himself.

"Spring into the water, man, head first," I cried.

The balanced spear was about to fly, and another man was preparing his weapon for a deadly cast, when I raised my gun and the bullet ploughed through him and through the second. The bowmen halted and drew their bows. I sent two charges of duck-shot into their midst with terrible effect. The natives retreated from the beach on which the boat had lately lain.

Having checked the natives, I assisted one of my men into the boat, and ordered him to lend a hand to the others, while I reloaded my big guns, keeping my eyes on the natives. There was a point about 100 yards in length on the east, which sheltered the cove. Some of the natives made a rush for this, but my guns commanded the exposed position, and they were obliged to retire.

The crew seized their rifles, but I told them to leave and to tear the bottom-boards out of the boat and use them as paddles; for there were two hippopotami advancing upon us open-mouthed, and it seemed as if we were to be crushed in the water after such a narrow escape from the ferocious people ashore. I permitted one of the hippos to approach within ten yards, and, aiming between his eyes, perforated his skull with a three-ounce ball, and the second received such a wound that we were not molested by him.

Meanwhile the savages, baffled and furious at seeing their prey escape, had rushed, after a short consultation, to man two canoes that were drawn up on the beach at the north-west corner of the cove. Twice I dropped men as they endeavoured to launch the boats; but they persisted, and finally, launching them,

pursued us vigorously. Two other canoes were seen coming down the coast from the eastern side of the island.

Unable to escape, we stopped after we had got out of the cove, and waited for them.

My elephant rifle was loaded with explosive balls for this occasion. Four shots killed five men and sank two of the canoes. The two others retired to assist their friends out of the water. They attempted nothing further, but some of those on shore had managed to reach the point, and as we resumed our paddles, we heard a voice cry out, "Go and die in the Nyanza!" and saw them shoot their arrows, which fell harmlessly a few yards behind us. We were saved!

It was 5 P.M. We had only four bananas in the boat, and we were twelve hungry men. If we had a strong fair breeze, a day and a night would suffice to enable us to reach our camp. But if we had head-winds, the journey might occupy a month. Meanwhile, after the experience of Makongo, Alice Island, and Bumbireh, where should we apply for food? Fresh water we had them alone, in abundance, sufficient to satisfy the thirst of all the armies of the world for a century. But food? Whither should we turn for it?

A gentle breeze came from the island. We raised the lug sail, hoping that it would continue fair for a south-east course. But at 7 P.M. it fell a dead calm. We resumed our extemporized paddles—those thin weak bottom-boards. Our progress was about three quarters of a mile per hour!

Throughout the night we laboured, cheering one another. In the morning not a speck of land was visible: all was a boundless circle of grey water.

On the 14th September the Emperor of Uganda [Mtesa] decided to give battle to the Wavuma, who were daily becoming bolder and more boastful. In the morning, in accordance with Mtesa's orders, forty Waganda canoes sallied out from the

> "I needed but to hear the distant strains of a dirge to cause me to imagine that one of Kakuri's canoes out yonder on the windless lake was a funereal barge, slowly gliding with its freight of dead explorers to the gloomy bourne from whence never an explorer returned."
> —*explorer* HENRY STANLEY

beach in front of our camps to Nakaranga Point, where they formed in line of battle before the causeway, with the sterns of their canoes fronting Ingira, and their bows towards Nakaranga Point.

Mtesa was followed by about three-fourths of his army when he proceeded to the point to view the battle, and with him went the great war-drums, to the number of fifty or thereabouts, and fifes about a hundred, and a great number of men shaking gourds filled with pebbles, and the court criers and mad charmers against evil were not wanting to create din and noise, and celebrate victory.

A hut of ample size had been erected on the mountain slope overlooking the strait, into which Mtesa and his favourite women retired. When the Emperor was seated, the "prophets of Baal," or the priests and priestesses of the Muzimu, or witchcraft, came up, more than a hundred in number, and offered the charms to Mtesa one after another in a most tedious ceremonious way, and to all of them Mtesa condescended to point his imperial forefinger.

The chief priest was a most fantastically dressed madman. It is customary before commencing a battle to carry all the potent medicines or charms of Uganda (thus propitiating the dreadful Mizimu or evil spirits) to the monarch, that he may touch or point his forefinger at them. They consist of dead lizards, bits of wood, hide, nails of dead people, claws of animals, and beaks of birds, a hideous miscellany, with mysterious compounds of herbs and leaves carefully enclosed in vessels ornamented with varicoloured beads.

> "Unlawful intercourse with the women of a neighboring tribe or village is the cause of nearly all the 'Palavers,' and wars, and fights in Africa. If a tribe wants to fight, they make this the cause by getting one of their women to intrigue with a man of the other tribe or village; and even if they do not want to fight, they are often forced into it.
>
> "Then the system of intermarrying involves half a dozen tribes in the quarrel of two. Each chief calls on his fathers-in-law to assist, and thus the country is thrown into uproar; property is unsafe, and becomes almost valueless to them; agricultural operations are impeded, and whole villages gradually disappear from the scene of contention, either by migrating, starving out, or being killed out."
>
> —explorer PAUL DU CHAILLU

During the battle these wizards and witches chant their incantations, and exhibit their medicines on high before the foe, while the gourd-and-pebble bearers sound a hideous alarum, enough to cause the nerves of any man except an African to relax at once.

Mtesa and his army were in full war-paint, and the principal men wore splendid leopard-skins over their backs, but the Wastage bore the palm for splendour of dress and ornate equipments.

Ankori the chief, and his officers were wonderfully gay. Snow-white ostrich plumes decorated their heads, and lion and leopard-skins covered their backs, while their loins were girded with snow-white, long-haired monkey and goat skins; even the staves of their lances were ornamented with feathers and rings of white monkey-skin.

There was ample time afforded to observe all these things, and to be exceedingly amused and interested in what promised to be an animating scene, before all attention was drawn to and engaged by the battle.

The spectators were seated, safe from harm or danger, on the slope of Nakaranga mountain, from the water's edge to the mountain summit, tier above tier, and rank above rank, in thousands upon thousands.

The canoes, having formed line, slowly moved stern-wise towards Ingira. The Wavuma were not inactive spectators of this manœuvre, but as yet their warriors had not embarked. They were busy mustering, while those appointed to garrison the island, with the women and children, several thousands in number, sat down on the slopes of the opposite mountain of Ingira Island. The rushes and weeds lining the water's edge were too tall and thick to enable us to estimate exactly the number of the enemy's war-canoes, but the brown-coloured prows, long and curving, of a great many were seen thrust out from among the vivid green banana plantations, or arranged on the rising beach of the island beyond its reedy margin.

Having advanced with the utmost regularity of line, near enough to the island to make their "Brown Bess" muskets effective, the Waganda began to open fire in a steady, deliberate manner, and succeeded after awhile in annoying the foe and arousing him to action. At a given signal from their chiefs, forth from the reeds and rushes shot the prows of the Wavuma canoes; and then, giving utterance to most shrill war-cries, the rowers impelled them from all quarters, to the number

of 194, with an extraordinary velocity upon the Waganda line, which now began to retire slowly towards the causeway.

On the causeway at its farthest extremity were assembled a force of a hundred musketeers and four small boat howitzers under the command of the Katekiro and Mtesa's factotum Tori.

The furious advance of the Wavuma soon caused the Waganda to hurry their movements, and on approaching the causeway they parted their line, rushing on either side of it, giving the Katekiro and Tori ample opportunity to wreak their will on the pursuers. But owing to the want of skill of the cannoniers, and the nervousness of the musketeers, very little damage was inflicted on the Wavuma, but the noise and whirring of lead and iron sufficed to check them, and caused them to withdraw with much of the baffled aspect of hungry crocodiles cheated of their prey. This was all the battle—but, short as it was, it had sufficed to prove to me that Mtesa would be unable to take Ingira Island, garrisoned and defended as it was by such a determined foe. After a while Mtesa withdrew from the scene, the army returned to its quarters, and the canoes of the Waganda, closely hugging the Nakaranga shore, went back to their rendezvous, leaving the Wavuma masters of the situation.

During the afternoon of this day Mtesa held a grand levee, and when all were assembled, he addressed them publicly to the effect that in a few days another battle would be fought, but as he had heard very important news, he intended to wait a while to ascertain if it was true.

Work progressed but languidly at the causeway. It was very tedious waiting, but my time was principally occupied in teaching Mtesa and his principal chiefs, and in gleaning such information as might enable me to understand the complicated politics of the Empire.

Suddenly on the 18th September, at early dawn, orders were communicated to the chiefs to prepare for battle. The first intelligence of it that I received was from the huge war-drums which summoned both sailors and warriors to action.

But first a burzah, or council, was held. Though eager to learn the news, I dared not appear too much interested in the war. Sabadu, who would be present on guard, would be sure to relate to me all the details of whatever transpired.

At night, though I interpolate it here for the benefit of the narrative, gossipy Sabadu, whose retentive brain I knew I could trust, conveyed to me a faithful report of the proceedings; and I cannot do better than give it to the reader in Sabadu's language.

"Ah! master, you have missed a sight. I never saw Mtesa as he was to-day. Oh, it was awful! His eyes were as large as my fists. They jumped from their sockets, and they were glowing as fire. Didn't the chiefs tremble! They were as children, whimpering and crying for forgiveness. He said to them, 'Wherein have I been unkind to you, that you will not fight for me, for my slaves who were sent to Usoga have returned saying there was not a man but either had joined me or had already joined the Wavuma? Who gave you those clothes that you wear? Who gave you those guns you have? Was it not I? Did Suna my father give his chiefs such fine things as I give? No; yet they fought for him, and the boldest of them would not have dared to advise him to fly, as you have done me. Am I not *Kabaka*? Is this not Uganda, as well as my capital? Have I not my army here? And you, Katekiro, were you not a peasant before I dressed you and set you up as a chief of Uddu? And you, Chambarango, who made you a chief? And you, Mkwenda, and you, Sekebobo, and you, Kimbugwe,

Kitunzi, Kaeema, Kangau, Kagu, speak, was it not Mtesa who made you chiefs? Were you princes, that you came to be made chiefs, or peasants whom it was my pleasure to make chiefs? Ah, ha! I shall see to-day who will not fight; I will see to-day who dares to run away from the Wavuma. By the grave of my father, I will burn the man over a slow fire who runs away or turns his back, and the peasant who distinguishes himself to-day shall eat his land. Look out for yourselves, chiefs. I will sit down to-day and watch for the coward, and the coward I will burn. I swear it.' Instantly the Katekiro fell on his face to the ground, and rubbed his face in the earth, and cried, 'Kabaka' (emperor), I send me to-day to fight, watch my flag, and if I turn my back to the Wavuma, then take and burn me or cut me to little pieces.' The example of the Katekiro was followed by the other chiefs, and they all swore to be desperately brave."

About 8.30 A.M. while I was at the point of Nakaranga, the sound of drums approached me, and I knew that the council was ended, and that the battle would soon begin. Mtesa appeared anything but a Christian, judging from his looks. Fires of fury shot from his eyes; and pages, women, chiefs, and all seemed awe-stricken. I was then ignorant of what had taken place, but when I observed the absence of Chambarango and several of the great Wakungu, or generals, I felt assured that Mtesa had lately been in the midst of a scene.

Presently other drums sounded from the water-side, and soon the beautiful canoes of Uganda appeared in view. The entire war-fleet of 230 vessels rode gracefully on the calm grey waters of the channel.

The line of battle, I observed, was formed by Chambarango, in command of the right flank, with fifty canoes; Sambuzi, Mukavya, Chikwata, and Saruti, all sub-chiefs, were ranged with 100 canoes under the command of Kauta, the imperial steward to form the centre; the left flank was in charge of the gallant Mkwenda, who had eighty canoes. Tori commanded a force of musketeers, and with his four howitzers was stationed on the causeway, which was by this time 200 yards from the shore.

In the above manner the fleet of vessels, containing some 16,000 men, moved to the attack upon Ingira. The centre, defended by the flanks, which were to menace the rear of the Wavuma should they approach near the causeway, resolutely advanced to within thirty yards of Ingira, and poured in a most murderous fire among the slingers of the island, who, imagining that the Waganda meant to carry the island by storm, boldly stood exposed, resolved to fight. But they were unable to maintain that courageous behaviour long. Mkwenda then moved up from the left, and attacked with his musketeers the Wavuma on the right, riddling their canoes, and making matters specially hot for them in that quarter.

The Wavuma, seeing matters approaching a crisis, and not wishing to die tamely, manned their canoes, and 196 dashed impetuously, as at first, from the rushes of Ingira with loud shrill yells, and the Waganda lines moved backward to the centre of the channel, where they bravely and coolly maintained their position. As the centre of the Uganda line parted in front of the causeway and disclosed the hotly advancing enemy, Tori aimed the howitzers and fired at a group of about twenty canoes, completely shattering more than half of them, and re-loading one quickly, he discharged several bolts of iron three inches long among them with terrible effect. Before this cool bearing of the Waganda, the Wavuma retired to their island again, and we saw numbers of canoes discharging their dead and wounded, and the Waganda were summoned to Nakaranga shore to receive the congratulations of the Emperor and the applause of the vast multitude. Mtesa went down to the water's edge to express his satisfaction at their behaviour.

"Go at them again," said he, "and show them what fighting is." And the line of battle was again formed, and again the Wavuma darted from the cover of the reeds and water-cane with the swiftness of hungry sharks, beating the water into foam with their paddles and rending the air with their piercing yells. It was one of the most exciting and animating scenes I ever beheld; but, owing to the terror of the stake with which their dread monarch had threatened them, the Waganda distinguished themselves for coolness and method, and the Wavuma, as on a former occasion, for intrepidity and desperate courage.

A third time the Waganda were urged to the battle, and a third time the unconquerable and desperate enemy dashed on them, to be smitten and wounded sore in a battle where they had not the least chance of returning blow for blow without danger of being swept by the cannon and muskets on the causeway.

A third battle was fought a few days after between 178 Wavuma canoes and 122 Waganda; but had the Waganda possessed the spirit and dash of their enemies, they might have decided the war on this day, for the Wavuma were greatly dispirited.

A fourth battle was fought the next day by 214 Waganda canoes and 203 Wavuma canoes, after the usual delay and premonitory provocation. The Wavuma obtained the victory most signally, chasing the Waganda within 40 yards of Nakaranga Cape, and being only driven from their prey by the musketeers and the howitzers on the causeway, which inflicted great execution on them at such close quarters. The Waganda did not attempt a second trial this day, for they were disorganized and dispirited after the signal defeat they had experienced.

The fleet of the Waganda returned to their rendezvous with the jeers and scoffs of the intrepid Wavuma ringing in their cars. On enquiring into the cause of the disaster, I learned that Mtesa's gunpowder was almost exhausted, and that he had scarcely a round left for each musket. This fact alarmed him, and compelled him to request me to lend him my powder in the camp at Dumo, which was refused in such a decided tone that he never repeated the request.

It was now the 5th October, and I had left my camp on the 12th August. It was necessary that I should participate in some manner in the war and end it. Yet I scarcely knew how I should act effectively to produce results beneficial to all parties. For though my own interests and the welfare of the Expedition were involved and in a manner staked on the success of the Waganda, and though a passive partisan of Mtesa, yet the brave Wavuma, by their magnificent daring and superb courage, had challenged my fullest sympathies. My energies and thoughts were bent, therefore, upon discovering a solution of the problem how to injure none, yet satisfy all.

It was clear that the Wavuma would not surrender without a frightful waste of life; it was equally evident that Mtesa would not relax his hold upon them without some compensation or satisfaction, nor assist me in my projects of exploration unless I aided him in some manner.

At length I devised a plan which I thought would succeed; but before I was enabled to perfect my scheme an incident occurred which called for my immediate intervention.

Mtesa, by means of his scouts, had succeeded in capturing one of the principal chiefs of the Wavuma, and his Wakungu and principal strangers had been invited to be present to witness the execution of this chief at the stake.

When I arrived at the scene, a large quantity of faggots had already been collected to burn him. By this mode of punishment, Mtesa thought he would be able to strike terror into the souls of the Wavuma.

Mtesa was in high glee when I entered the council: he was unable to hide the triumph he felt at the terrible vengeance he was about to take for the massacre of Webba, his favourite page, and the peace party.

"Now Stamlee," he said, "when the chief is at the stake"—he was an old man of sixty or thereabouts—"you shall see how a chief of Uvuma dies. He is about to be burnt. The Wavuma will tremble when they hear of the manner of his death."

"Ah, Mtesa," I said, "have you forgotten the words of the good book which I have read to you so often? 'If thy brother offend thee, thou shalt forgive him many times.' 'Love thy enemies.' 'Do good to them that hate you.' 'Thou shalt love thy neighbour as thyself.' 'Forgive us our trespasses, as we forgive them that trespass against us.'"

"But this man is a native of Uvuma, and the Wavuma are at war with me. Have you forgotten Webba?"

"No, I remember poor little Webba. I saw him die, and I was very sorry."

"Shall this man not die, Stamlee? Shall I not have blood for him, Stamlee?"

"No."

"But I shall, Stamlee. I will burn this man to ashes. I will burn every soul I catch. I will have blood! blood! the blood of all in Uvuma."

"No, Mtesa! no more blood. It is time the war was ended."

"What!" said Mtesa bursting into one of those paroxysms of fury which Sabadu had so graphically described. "I will slay every soul in Uvuma, will cut down every plantain, and burn every man, woman, and child on that island. By the grave of my father Suna, I will."

"No, Mtesa, you must stop this wild pagan way of thinking. It is only a pagan who always dreams of blood and talks of shedding blood as you do. It is only the pagan boy Mtesa who speaks now. It is not the man Mtesa whom I saw, and whom I made a friend. It is not 'Mtesa the Good,' whom you said your people loved. It is not Mtesa the Christian, it is the savage. Bah! I have had enough of you, I know you now."

"Stamlee! Stamlee! Wait a short time, and you will see. What are you waiting for?" he said, suddenly turning round to the executioners, who were watching his looks.

Instantly the poor old man was bound; but, suddenly rising, I said to Mtesa, "Listen to one word. The white man speaks but once. Listen to me for the last time.

You remember the tale of Kintu which you told me the other day. He left the land of Uganda because it stank with blood. As Kintu left Uganda in the old, old days, I shall leave it, never to return. To-day Kintu is looking down upon you from the spirit-land, and as he rebuked Ma´anda for murdering his faithful servant, so is he rebuking you to-day through me. Yes, kill that poor old man, and I shall leave you to-day, unless you kill me too, and from Zanzibar to Cairo I shall tell every Arab I meet what a murderous beast you are, and through all the white man's land I shall tell with a loud voice what wicked act I saw Mtesa do, and how the other day he wanted to run away because he heard a silly old woman say the Wasoga were marching upon him. How grand old Kamanya must have wept in the spirit-land when he heard of Mtesa about to run away. How the lion-hearted Suna must have groaned when he saw Mtesa shiver in terror because an old woman had had a bad dream. Goodbye, Mtesa. You may kill the Mvuma chief, but I am going, and shall not see it."

Mtesa's face had been a picture wherein the passions of brutish fury and thirsty murder were portrayed most faithfully; but at the mention of Suna and Kamanya in the spirit-land looking down upon him, the tears began to well in his eyes, and finally, while they rolled in large drops down his face, he sobbed loudly like a child, while the chiefs and executioners, maintaining a deathly silence, looked very uncomfortable. Tori the cannonier and Kauta the steward, however, sprang up, and, unrolling their head-dresses, officiously wiped Mtesa's face, while the poor wayward man murmured audibly as I walked away from the scene:—

"Did not Stamlee talk about the spirit-land, and say that Suna was angry with me? Oh, he speaks too true, too true! O father, forgive me, forgive me." After which, I was told he suddenly broke away from the council.

An hour afterwards I was summoned by a page to his presence, and Mtesa said:—

"Stamlee will not say Mtesa is bad now, for he has forgiven the Mvuma chief, and will not hurt him. Will Stamlee say that Mtesa is good now? And does he think Suna is glad now?"

"Mtesa is very good," and I clasped his hand warmly. "Be patient, all shall come out right, and Kintu and Suna must be glad when they see that Mtesa is kind to his guests. I have something to tell you. I have thought over your trouble here, and I want to finish this war for your good without any more trouble. I will build a structure which shall terrify the Wavuma, and make them glad of a peace, but you must give me plenty of men to help me, and in three days I shall be ready. Meantime shout out to the Wavuma from the causeway that you have something which will be so terrible that it will finish the war at once."

"Take everybody, do anything you like; I will give you Sekebobo and all his men."

The next morning Sekebobo brought about 2000 men before my quarters, and requested to know my will. I told him to despatch 1000 men to cut long poles 1 inch thick, 300 to cut poles 3 inches thick and 7 feet long, 100 to cut straight long trees 4 inches thick, and 100 to disbark all these, and make bark rope. Himself and 500 men I wished to assist me at the beach. The chief communicated my instructions and urged them to be speedy, as it was the Emperor's command, and himself accompanied me to the canoe fleet.

I selected three of the strongest-built canoes, each 70 feet long and 6½ feet wide, and, after preparing a space of ground near the water's edge, had them drawn up parallel with one another, and 4 feet apart from each other. With these three canoes I began to construct a floating platform, laying the tall trees across the canoes, and lashing them firmly to the thwarts, and as fast as the 7-foot poles came, I had them lashed in an upright position to the thwarts of the outer canoes, and as fast as the inch poles arrived, I had them twisted in among these uprights, so that when completed, it resembled an oblong stockade, 70 feet long by 27 feet wide, which the spears of the enemy could not penetrate.

On the afternoon of the second day, the floating fort was finished, and Mtesa and his chiefs came down to the beach to see it launched and navigated for a trial trip. The chiefs, when they saw it, began to say it would sink, and communicated their fears to Mtesa, who half believed them. But the Emperor's women said to him: "Leave Stamlee alone; he would not make such a thing if he did not know that it would float."

On receiving orders to launch it, I selected sixty paddlers and 150 musketeers of the bodyguard to stand by to embark as soon as it should be afloat, and appointed Tori and one of my own best men to superintend its navigation, and told them to close the gate of the fort as soon as they pushed off from the land. About 1000 men were then set to work to launch it, and soon it was floating in the water, and when the crew and garrison, 214 souls, were in it, it was evident to all that it rode the waves of the lake easily and safely—

"The invention all admired, and each how he
　To be the inventor missed, so easy it seemed
　Once found, which yet unfound most would have thought
Impossible"—

and a burst of applause from the army rewarded the inventor.

Several long blue Kaniki and white and red cloths were hoisted above this curious structure, which, when closed up all round, appeared to move of its own accord in a very mysterious manner, and to conceal within its silent and impenetrable walls some dread thing, well calculated to strike terror into the mind of the ignorant savage.

At eight o'clock on the morning of the 13th October the army was assembled at Nakaranga with unusual display, and it was proclaimed across the strait from the extremity of the causeway that a terrible thing was approaching which would blow them into atoms if they did not make peace at once and acknowledge the power of Mtesa; and I believe that they declared that all the Muzimus and the charms of Uganda were within, for I heard something said about Muzimu and Uganda. The old Mvuma chief was also placed in prominent view, and induced to urge them to accept the terms which Mtesa offered, viz. pardon to all, provided they went through the form of submission. After this announcement, which was made with all gravity, the awful mysterious structure appeared, while the drums beat a tremendous sound, and the multitude of horns blew a deafening blast.

It was a moment of anxiety to me, for manifold reasons. The fort, perfectly defensible in itself against the most furious assaults by men armed with spears, steadily approached the point, then steered direct for the island of Ingira, until it was within fifty yards.

"Speak," said a stentorian voice amid a deathly silence within. "What will you do? Will you make peace and submit to Mtesa, or shall we blow up the island? Be quick and answer."

There was a moment's consultation among the awe-stricken Wavuma. Immediate decision was imperative. The structure was vast, totally unlike anything that was ever visible on the waters of their sea. There was no person visible, yet a voice spoke clear and loud. Was it a spirit, the Wazimu of all Uganda, more propitious to their enemy's prayers than those of the Wavuma? It might contain some devilish, awful, thing, something similar to the evil spirits which in their hours of melancholy and gloom their imagination invoked.

There was an audacity and confidence in its movements that was perfectly appalling.

"Speak," repeated the stern voice; "we cannot wait longer."

Immediately, to our relief, a man, evidently a chief, answered, "Enough; let Mtesa be satisfied. We will collect the tribute to-day, and will come to Mtesa. Return, O spirit, the war is ended!" At which the mysterious structure solemnly began its return back to the cove where it had been constructed, and the quarter of a million of savage human beings, spectators of the extraordinary scene, gave a shout that seemed to split the very sky, and Ingira's bold height repeated the shock of sound back to Nakaranga.

Three hours afterwards a canoe came from Ingira Island, bearing fifty men, some of whom were chiefs. They brought with them several tusks of ivory, and two young girls, daughters of the two principal chiefs of Uvuma. These were the tribute. The ivory was delivered over to the charge of the steward, and the young girls were admitted to the harem of Mtesa, into the mystery of which no man dare penetrate and live. The old Mvuma chief was surrendered to his tribe, and thus the long war terminated on the evening of the 13th October 1875.

We had hoped to pass our first day in the Wenya land in kindly interchange of gifts, and engaging the wild hearts of the natives by ostentatious liberality. But lo! when we searched in the morning for the aborigines they were gone!

Many a village stood in the neighbourhood of the main landing, embowered in the thick shade of tamarind and bombax, teak, iron-wood, and elais palm, but the inhabitants were fled! Each village street had its two rows of bleached trophies of eaten humanity, with an attempt at a ghastly decoration similar to "rockery." The canoes were all left at the landing-place; the fruit of the banana and the plantain hung on the stalks, and the crimson palm-nuts swayed in clusters above our heads, but word was given to our people that nothing should be touched on penalty of fearful punishment.

It was absolutely necessary that our introduction to the Wenya tribe should be heralded by peaceful intercourse. We therefore rested, and sent people round about with shells to purchase food for their respective messes. Only Kachéché and Murabo, one of the boat-boys, succeeded in reaching an inhabited village, but no sooner were they seen than they had to run for their lives back to camp.

Leaving everything untouched, we departed from this first village of the Wenya. My boat floated down river with thirty-three people on board according to agreement, with Frank [Pocock], Tippu-Tib [a notorious Arab slaver from Zanzibar], and the land party following the river-bank, until we should arrive at a village where we might purchase food.

From the villages below, at least from many, long before we had floated abreast of them, rang out the strange war-cries, "Ooh-hu-hu! Ooh-hu-hu!" and the natives decamped into the bush, leaving everything they possessed *in situ.* This was only to lure us to our destruction, for had we been tempted to capture their goat, and black pigs, they would no doubt have rushed from the bushes on the unwary. We, however, were not to be thus tempted to felony and our destruction, and quietly floated down past them.

We then came abreast of a forest, uninhabited, and about three miles in length, and after that sighted a plantation of bananas. We could see the tops of the low gable-roofed houses, but none of the natives descried us until we were within a hundred yards of a large and wealthy village. Then a little child, coming down the high banks to fetch water, suddenly lifting her head, saw us close to the landing, and screamed out, "Mama, the Wasambye! the Wasambye are coming!"

At the name, which seemed to be a dreaded one—no doubt because of Mtagamoyo and his uncircumcised Wanyamwezi—the people, who, it seemed, were holding a market, scattered immediately, the women screaming "Wasambye! Wasambye!" and the banana stalk and bushes shaking violently, as everybody in a panic flew into the jungle, like a herd of buffaloes stung to frenzy by a fly pest. By the time we had glided down a few paces beyond the landing there was a deathly silence.

We passed by three or four other villages, but, the inhabitants simply responded to our attempts at intercourse by protruding their heads from the bushes and shouting "Ooh-hu-hu! Ooh-hu-hu! Ooh-hu-hu!

At 3 P.M. we came to the Ruiki river, which at the mouth was about 100 yards wide, a black and sluggish stream, with an average depth of about twelve feet. As the land division would be unable to cross this stream without the aid of a boat, we camped at a point between the right bank and the left bank of the Livingstone, in east longitude 25° 33′ and south latitude 3° 26′.

We halted on the 23rd November, awaiting the arrival of the land division, and meanwhile built a strong camp. We saw several forms on the opposite side of the Ruiki, in the village of chief Kasongo, but they would not deign to answer us, though our interpreter made frequent attempts to induce them to converse. Our party was only thirty-six in number, including myself, and we had but a few bananas, which had been obtained at Kampunzu. Before we could hope to purchase anything from the natives an intercourse of some kind had to be opened. But the aborigines, for some reason, persisted in their distrustful reserve. However, we waited patiently for the land force until sunset, and all night maintained a strict watch lest our boat should be stolen.

Early on the 24th, no news having as yet arrived of our friends, I manned the boat and rowed some ten miles up the Ruiki river, hoping to find them encamped on the bank waiting for us. The general course of the river, though very winding, was from south-west to north-east. A few miles above its mouth it is filled with snags, and becomes narrow, crooked, and swift, and of an inky colour, from a particular tree, whose branches droop in dense masses into the stream.

About 2 P.M. we began to return, and, after rowing hard for about an hour and a half, were approaching our lonely camp when we heard guns being fired rapidly. Unless as a measure of defence there could be no earthly reason why the men in the camp should fire their guns. We therefore urged the crew to full speed, and in a short time were astonished to see the mouth of the Ruiki blocked with canoes filled with savages, launching spears and shooting arrows.

With a loud shout we dashed down the last straight reach of the Ruiki, which attracted the attention of the savages, who immediately turned and fled down stream, uttering in harmonious but weird concord their strange war-cries.

After first learning that no one was wounded, though there were several sheaves of iron-headed and wooden spears, besides reed arrows, in the camp, we inquired the cause of the attack, and heard with astonishment that the people of Kasongo's had signalled to all the neighbouring villages that the "Nwema" (white chief) was gone away, and had invited them to arm and man their canoes to get meat before he should return. About thirty canoes, manned by a great number of savages, had entered the Ruiki, and, without listening to warning, had persisted in advancing on the camp, until fired upon. They had been engaged only a few minutes before I appeared.

Billali, the youth in charge of the heavy rifle, and my factotum on hunting excursions, had shot a man, who lay dead in the stream. When asked how he dared to use my guns to shoot people, he replied with alarm, "I could not help it, sir, indeed I could not. If I had waited but a little minute, he would have killed me, for he was aiming with his spear only a few feet off!"

Night came, but with it no tidings of the land party. We listened all through the dark hours for the sound of signal gun-shots, but none cheered us. In the early morning I despatched Uledi, the coxswain, and five of the younger boatmen, through the jungles, with a caution to observe the villages, and by no means to risk an unequal contest with people, who would dog them through the bushes like leopards. Uledi, with a calm smile, bade me rest assured: he was confident he would soon find them. They set out, leaving us alone to indulge in gloomy thoughts.

At 4 P.M. we heard the roar of a musket-shot through the forest, and soon Uledi emerged from the jungle behind us, his face all aglow with triumph. "They are coming, master, close by," he said.

True enough, the advanced-guard appeared in a few seconds, and presently the column, weary, haggard, sick, and low-spirited. The people had been wandering. Having found a road, they followed it, till they came upon a tribe, who attacked them with arrows, and killed three of them. They retaliated, and the advanced guard captured one of the assailants, and asked what tribe he belonged to. "The Bakusu," he had said, "and the great river is a long way east of you."

They compelled him to show the way, and, after some fifteen hours' marching from the place of the fight, they had met with gallant Uledi and his scouting party, and had hurried after him.

Within four hours the boat had transported the entire party to the left bank of the Ruiki. I was here compelled to relax the rigour of the command that no one should appropriate food without payment, for the suffering of the people was excessive.

On the 26th, we floated down river to Nakanpemba, the land division on this day keeping close to the river, and though it was buried frequently in profound depths of jungle, we were able to communicate with it occasionally by means of drum-taps.

The river had widened gradually to 1700 yards, and was studded with large tree-clad islands, both banks presenting dense masses of tall woods and undergrowth.

Not a soul had been seen in any of the villages passed through; now and then we heard screams of "Wasambye! Wasambye!" and sometimes we heard voices crying out something about Bwana Muhala, or Mtagamoyo, the notorious land-pirate and kidnapper. Nakanpemba possessed also its dreadful relics, arranged in ghastly lines, along the streets—relics of many a feast, as Professor Huxley has now taught us, on dead humanity.

The march through the jungles and forests, the scant fare, fatigue, and consequent suffering, resulted in sickness. Small-pox and dysentery attacked the land division. Thorns had also penetrated the feet and wounded the legs of many of the people, until dreadful ulcers had been formed, disabling them from travel. In the course of two days' journey we found six abandoned canoes, which, though unsound, we appropriated and repaired, and, lashing them together, formed a floating hospital.

Four miles below Nakanpemba, as we were gliding down at the rate of 1½ knot per hour, we heard the dull murmur of rapids, and from the opposite bank eight canoes were seen to dash swiftly down river, disappearing most mysteriously from view. There being no necessity for us to seek acquaintance with people who appeared to think it undesirable, we did not attempt to disturb them, but, clinging to the left bank, cautiously approached the rapids of Ukassa. These were caused by a ledge of greenish shale, mixed with ironstone and pudding rock, projecting from the Ukassa Hills on the right bank. The hospital was warned in-shore, while I dropped down, as near as possible, to the rapids and there landed.

The land division was requested to encamp for the day abreast the rapids, while, selecting ten stout young fellows, in addition to the boat's crew, I proceeded to explore along the river; but, before departing, I gave the strictest orders to Frank and Manwa Sera that upon no account should any one be permitted to move from the camp until I returned.

The rapids were parted by a couple of two long rocky islets running parallel and separated from each other and the left bank by two narrow streams, which descended into a quiet, creek-like portion of the river after a fall of 10 feet within half a mile, but on the eastern side the river was of a breadth of 800 yards, and descended with a furious whirl for the distance of a mile and a half, where it was joined by the quiet flowing creek on the left or western side.

We continued our inspection of the shore and river for about two miles, where we very nearly fell into an ambuscade. In a little creek, hidden by high overhanging banks, densely clothed, were some forty or fifty small canoes, the crews all seated, silent, and watching the river. We instantly retreated without disturbing their watchful attitude, and hurried to camp.

On arriving at the boat I was alarmed at hearing that Frank had permitted Manwa Sera, the chief, and five others, to detach two of the hospital canoes, and to descend the great rapids. As this was a suicidal act, I felt my blood run cold, and then recollecting the ambuscade in the creek, I lost no time in selecting fifty men and retracing our steps.

When we reached the creek, we ascertained it to be empty. I then offered high rewards to the first scout who sighted the Wangwana. Uledi and Shumari, his brother, gave wild yells, and dashed forward like antelopes through the jungle, Saywa (their cousin) and Murabo hard after them. With startling echoes some gun-shots soon rang through the forest. Away we tore through the jungle in the direction of the sounds. We came in sight of the river, and heard the rifles close to us, in mid-stream were the five Wangwana riding on the keels of the upset canoes, attacked by half a dozen native canoes. Uledi and his comrades had without hesitation opened fire upon them, and thus saved the doomed men. We soon had the gratification of receiving them on shore, but four Snider rifles were lost. The party, it appeared, had been swept into a whirlpool, drawn down, and ejected out of it several feet below the dreadful whirl. This disobedience to orders, which had entailed on me such a loss of valuable rifles, when I was already so weakly armed, on themselves such a narrow escape, besides bringing us into collision with the natives, was punished by well-merited reproaches—so keenly felt moreover that Manwa Sera proceeded to Tippu-Tib's camp, and sent word to me that he would not serve me any longer. I laughed, and returned word to him that I was sure he would. To Frank I solemnly protested against such breach of duty, as life or death now depended on the faithful execution of instructions.

Tippu-Tib and the Arabs advanced to me for a shauri. They wished to know whether I would not now abandon the project of continuing down the river—now that things appeared so gloomy, with rapids before us, natives hostile, cannibalism rampant, small-pox raging, people dispirited, and Manwa Sera sulky. "What prospects," they asked, "lie before us but terrors, and fatal collapse and ruin? Better turn back in time." I told them to be resigned until the morning. They returned to their camp, which was about half a mile from the vicinity of the rapids.

Early next day the Wangwana were mustered. They lifted the boat out of the water above their heads, and cautiously conveyed her in about an hour below the rapids, and launched her on the quiet waters of the creek. Then a messenger was despatched to order Safeni to push the four remaining canoes into the rapids. Within an hour the rapids of Ukassa had been passed.[...]

On the 30th the journey was resumed. The river ran with sharp bends, with many dangerous whirls, and broad patches of foam on its face, and was narrow, not above eight hundred yards in width, for a distance of three miles and a half, when it suddenly widened to 1700 yards. Two fine wooded islands stood in mid-stream. On the northern side of a little tributary we camped at the market-place of Usako Ngongo, Ukassa Hills bearing south-south-west. The southern end of the largest of the two islands, Nionga, bore east by north from camp.

These market-places on the banks of the Livingstone, at intervals of three or four miles, are central resorts of the aborigines from either bank, and considered as neutral ground, which no chief may claim, nor any individual assert claims or tribute for its use. Many of them are wide grassy spaces under the shade of mighty spreading trees, affording admirable river scenes for an artist. In the background is the deeply black forest, apparently impenetrable in its density; here and there a taller giant, having released itself from acquaintance and familiarity, overlooks its neighbours. Its branches are favoured by the white-collared eagle and the screaming ibis. Here and there rise the feathery and graceful fronds of the elais palm. In the foreground flows the broad brown river.

In the morning, on market days, the grassy plots are thronged. From the depths of the forest, and from isolated clearings, from lonely islands, and from the open country of the Bakusu, come together the aborigines with their baskets of cassava, their mats of palm-fibre and sedge, their gourds of palm-wine, their beans and maize, millet and sugar-cane, crockery and the handiwork of their artisans in copper and iron and wood, the vermilion camwood, their vegetables, and fruit of banana and plantain, their tobacco and pipes and bangles, their fishnets and baskets, fish, and a multitude of things which their wants and tastes have taught them to produce. All is animation and eager chaffer, until noon, when the place becomes silent again and untenanted, a prey to gloom and shade, where the hawk and the eagle, the ibis, the grey parrot, and the monkey, may fly and scream and howl, undisturbed.[...]

On the 4th December we halted, because of a rainstorm and, also, to forage for food, in which we were only partially successful. No conflicts resulted, fortunately.

The next day, the river flowing a little cast of north, we came to Muriwa Creek, on the northern bank of which was a remarkably long village, or rather a series of villages, from fifty to a hundred yards apart, and a broad, uniform street, thirty feet wide, and two miles in length! Behind the village were the banana and the palm groves, which supplied the inhabitants with fruit, wine, and oil.

This remarkable town was called Ikondu, and was situated in south latitude 2° 53′. The huts were mere double cages, made very elegantly of the Panicum grass cane, 7 feet long by 5 feet wide and 6 feet high, separated, as regards the main building, but connected by the roof, so that the central apartments were common to both cages, and in these the families meet and perform their household duties, or receive their friends for social chat. Between each village was the burial-place or vault of their preceding kings, roofed over with the leaves of the *Phrynium ramosissimum,* which appears to be as useful a plant for many reasons as the banana to the Waganda. These cane cages are as cosy, comfortable, and dry as ships' cabins, as we found in the tempests of rain that every alternate day now visited us.

The town of Ikondu was quite deserted, but food was abundant; the wine-pots were attached to the palm-trees, bananas were hanging in clusters, in the gardens were fine large melons, luxuriant plantations of cassava, extensive plots of ground-nuts, and great tracts of waving sugar-cane.

We were very much dispirited, however. This desertion of their villages, without an attempt on the part of the natives to make terms, or the least chance of communicating with them, showed a stern contempt for the things of this life that approached the sublime. Whither had such a large population fled? For assuredly the population must have exceeded two thousand.

We were dispirited for other reasons. The small-pox was raging, dysentery had many victims, over fifty were infected with the itch, some twenty suffered from ulcers, many complained of chest-diseases, pneumonic fever, and pleurisis: there was a case or two of typhoid fever, and others suffered from prolapsus ani and umbilical pains; in short, there was work enough in the stricken Expedition for a dozen physicians. Every day we tossed two or three bodies into the deep waters of the Livingstone. Frank and I endeavoured our utmost to alleviate the misery, but when the long caravan was entering camp I had many times to turn my face away lest the tears should rise at sight of the miserable victims of disease who reeled and staggered through the streets. Poor creatures, what a life! wandering, ever wandering, in search of graves.

At Ikondu, left high and dry by some mighty flood years ago, there was a large condemned canoe with great holes in its keel, and the traces of decay both at bow and stem, yet it was capacious enough to carry sixty sick people, and by fastening cables to it the boat might easily take it in tow. I, therefore, called my carpenters, Uledi the coxswain, Saywa, his cousin, and Salaam Allah, and offered 12 yards of cloth to each if they would repair it within two days. They required twelve men and axes. The men were detailed, and day and night the axes and hatchets were at work trimming poles into narrow planking. The carpenters fitted the boards, and secured them with wooden pins, and with the bruised pulp of banana and bark cloth they caulked it. Then the Wangwana were called to launch the monster, and we presently had the satisfaction of seeing it float. It leaked a good deal, but some of the sick were not so ailing but that they might bale it sufficiently to keep themselves afloat.

The success of the repairs which we had made in this ancient craft proved to me that we possessed the means to construct a flotilla of canoes of sufficient capacity to float the entire Expedition. I resolved, therefore, should Tippu-Tib still persist in his refusal to proceed with us, to bribe him to stay with us until we should have constructed at least a means of escape.

About noon of the next day, while we were busy repairing the canoe, a native was found in the bushes close to the town with a small bow and a quiver of minia-ture arrows in his hand, and, it being a suspicious circumstance, he was secured and brought to me. He was a most remarkable specimen for a warrior, I thought, as I looked at the trembling diminutive figure. He stood, when measured, 4 feet 6½ inches, round the chest 30 inches, and at the waist 24 inches. His head was large, his face decked with a scraggy fringe of whiskers, and his complexion light chocolate. As he was exceedingly bow-legged and thin-shanked, I at first supposed him to be a miserable abortion cast out by some tribe, and driven to wander through the forest, until he mentioned the word "Watwa." Recollecting that the Watwa were well-known to be dwarfs, I asked Bwana Abed, the guide, if this man resembled those Watwa dwarfs Muhala's people had fought with. He replied that the Watwa he had met were at least a head shorter, though the man might be a member of some tribe related to those he had seen! His complexion was similar, but the dwarfs west of Ukuna, in the West Lumami country, had very long beards, and bushy whiskers. His weapons were also the same—the short bow, and tiny reed arrows, a foot long, with points smeared over with a dark substance, with an odour resembling that of cantharides. Everybody seemed to be particularly care-ful, as they examined the arrows, not to touch the points, and, as many of them were folded in leaves, it appeared to me that the native had some reason for this precaution. In order to verify this opinion, I uncovered one of the leaf-guarded points, and, taking hold of one of his arms, I gravely pretended to be about to inoculate the muscle with the dark substance on the arrow. His loud screams, visible terror, and cries of "Mabi! Mabi!" ("Bad, bad"), with a persuasive eloquence of gesture, left no doubt in my mind that the arrows were poisoned.

But the native possessed the talent of pronunciation in an eminent degree. For the first time I heard the native name of the Livingstone, as known to the Manyema and Wenya, pronounced as distinctly and deliberately as though Haji Abdallah himself was endeavouring to convey to my interested ears the true word RU-A´R-OW-A, emphasizing the ante-penultimate syllable. I requested several Wangwana, Wanyamwezi, and Arabs to pronounce the word after him. Only the principal Arabs were able to articulate distinctly "Rua´rowa"; the black people transformed the word instantly into "Lualawa."

The ugly, prognathous-jawed creature, among other information he gave us, related that just below Ikondu there was an island called Maturu, whose people the "Kirembo-rembo" (lightning) had completely destroyed.

"Who sent the Kirembo-rembo, my friend?" I asked.

"Ah, who knows? Perhaps 'Firi Niambi' "—the deity.

"Were they all killed?"

"All—men, women, children, goats, bananas, everything."

He also told us that the chief of Ikondu, with all his people, was on the opposite side; that from the wooded bluffs fronting the Urindi river extended the powerful tribe of the Wabwiré, or Wasongora Mono ("the people of the filed teeth").

On the 8th December we moved down river to Unya-N´singé, another large town, a mile in length, on the north side of a creek, about thirty yards wide. On the south side, on the summit of bluffs, 125 feet high, was a similar town called Kisui-cha-Uriko.

About four miles up the river from Unya-N´singé, the Lira river entered the Livingstone. At the mouth it was 300 yards wide and 30 feet deep, but two miles above it narrowed to 250 yards, of deep and tolerably clear water. A hostile movement on the part of the natives, accompanied by fierce demonstrations on shore, compelled us, however, to relinquish the design of penetrating farther up and to hurry back to camp at Unya-N´singé.

We had not been long there before we heard the war horns sounding on the right bank, and about 4 P.M. we saw eight large canoes coming up river along the islands in mid-stream, and six along the left bank. On approaching the camp they formed in line of battle near a small grassy island about four hundred yards from us, and shouted to us to come and meet them in mid-river. Our interpreters were told to tell them that we had but one boat, and five canoes loaded with sick people; and that as we had not come for the purpose of fighting, we would not fight.

A jeering laugh greeted the announcement, and the next minute the fourteen canoes dashed towards us with wild yells. I disposed my people along the banks, and waited. When they came within thirty yards, half of the men in each canoe began to shoot their poisoned arrows, while the other half continued to paddle in-shore. Just as they were about to land, the command to fire was given to about thirty muskets, and the savages fell back, retiring to the distance of about a hundred and fifty yards, whence they maintained the fight. Directing the people on shore to keep firing, I chose the boat's crew, including Tippu-Tib, and Bwana Abdallah, and dashed out into mid-stream. The savages appeared to be delighted, for they yelled triumphantly as they came towards us; only for a short time, however, for we were now only some fifty yards from them and our guns were doing terrible execution. In about a minute the fight was over, and our wild foes were paddling down river; and we returned to our camp, glad that this first affair with the Wasongora Meno had terminated so quickly. Three of our people had been struck by arrows, but a timely application of caustic neutralized the poison and, excepting painful swellings, nothing serious occurred.[...]

Here we dismissed our dwarf to his home, with a handful of shells and four necklaces of beads for his very intelligent geographical knowledge and his civilized pronunciation. He could not comprehend why we did not eat him; and though we shook hands with him and smiled, and patted him on the shoulder, I doubt whether he felt himself perfectly safe until he had plunged out of sight into his native woods once more.

Tippu-Tib determined to journey on land, and Frank and Sheikh Abdallah were invited to the boat. Eight more victims to small-pox were admitted into the hospital canoes, among them being three young girls, the favourites of Tippu-Tib's harem. For the accommodation of the raving and delirious sick, we constructed a shed over the hospital-canoe. Before we moved from Unya-N´singé, we had thrown eight corpses into the Livingstone.

On the 14th, gliding down river without an effort on our part, we reached Kisui Kachiambi, another large town about a mile in length, and consisting of about three hundred long houses—situated on the left bank, in south latitude 2° 35'. Opposite Mutako the natives made a brilliant and well-planned attack on us, by suddenly dashing upon us from a creek; and had not the ferocious nature of the people whom we daily encountered taught us to be prepared at all times against assault, we might have

> "Jabu, our cook, somewhat indisposed, was sitting in the stern of a canoe while the crew was on shore about forty feet from him, hauling it past a bit of rapids. A bold and crafty native, with fixed arrow before him, steadily approached the vessel and shot a poisoned wooden dart, which penetrated the arm near the shoulders and pierced the base of the throat. The wound was a mere needle-hole puncture, but Jabu had barely time to say 'Mahommed!' when he fell back dead. "
>
> —*explorer* HENRY STANLEY

suffered considerable injury. Fortunately, only one man was slightly punctured with a poisoned arrow, and an immediate and plentiful application of nitrate of silver nullified all evil effects.

During our halt at Kisui-Kachiambi, two of the favourite women of Tippu-Tib died of small-pox, and three youths also fell victims; of the land division only one perished.

On the 18th, after floating down a few miles, we came to a broad channel which ran between the populous island of Mpika and the left bank, and arriving at a market green, under the shade of fine old trees, halted for breakfast. The aborigines of Mpika at once gathered opposite, blew war-horns, and mustered a large party, preparing to attack us with canoes. To prevent surprise from the forest while the porridge for the sick was being cooked, I had placed scouts on either side of each of the roads that penetrated inland from the market green, at about a couple of hundred yards' distance from the camp. It happened that, while drums were beating and horns were blowing on the island, and everybody seemed mustering for a grand attack on us, a party of ten people (among whom were three very fine-looking women), who had been on a trading excursion to a village inland, and were returning to their island home, had been waiting to be ferried across from the market-place when we occupied it. The scouts surrounded them, and, seeing there was no escape, they came into the market-place. The interpreters were called to calm their fears, and to tell them that we were simply travellers going down river, with no intention of hurting anybody.

By means of these people we succeeded in checking the warlike demonstrations of the islanders, and in finally persuading them to make blood-brotherhood, after which we invited canoes to come and receive their friends. As they hesitated to do so, we embarked them in our own boat, and conveyed them across to the island.

The news then spread quickly along the whole length of the island that we were friends, and as we resumed our journey, crowds from the shore cried out to us, "Mwendé Kivuké-vuké." ("Go in peace!")

The crest of the island was about eighty feet above the river, and was a marvel of vegetation, chiefly of plantain and banana plantations. On our left rose the other bank with similar wooded heights, dipping occasionally into small creeks and rising into ridges, with slopes though steep, clothed with a perfect tangle of shrubs and plants.

After a descent of ten miles by this channel, we found the river increased in width to 2000 yards. While rowing down, close to the left bank, we were suddenly surprised by hearing a cry from one of the guards of the hospital canoes, and, turning round, saw an arrow fixed in his chest. The next instant, looking towards the bank, we saw the forms of many men in the jungle, and several arrows flew past my head in extremely unpleasant proximity.

We sheered off instantly, and, pulling hard down stream, came near the landing-place of an untenanted market-green. Here we drew in-shore, and, sending out ten scouts to lie in wait in the jungle, I mustered all the healthy men, about thirty in number, and proceeded to construct a fence of brushwood, inspired to unwonted activity by a knowledge of our lonely, defenceless state.

Presently a shriek of agony from another of my men rang out through the jungle, followed immediately by the sharp crack of the scouts' Sniders, which again was responded to by an infernal din of war-horns and yells, while arrows flew past us from all directions. Twenty more men were at once sent into the jungle to assist the scouts, while, with might and main, we laboured to surround our intended camp with tall and dense hedges of brushwood, with sheltered nooks for riflemen.

After an hour's labour the camp was deemed sufficiently tenable, and the recall was sounded. The scouts retreated on the run, shouting as they approached, "Prepare! prepare! they are coming!"

About fifty yards of ground outside our camp had been cleared, which, upon the retreat of the scouts who had been keeping them in cheek, was soon filled by hundreds of savages, who pressed upon us from all sides but the river, in the full expectation that we were flying in fear. But they were mistaken, for we were at bay, and desperate in our resolve not to die without fighting. Accordingly, at such close quarters the contest soon became terrific. Again and again the savages hurled themselves upon our stockade, launching spear after spear with deadly force into the camp, to be each time repulsed. Sometimes the muzzle of our guns almost touched their breasts. The shrieks, cries, shouts of encouragement, the rattling volleys of musketry, the booming war-horns, the yells and defiance of the combatants, the groans and screams of the women and children in the hospital camp, made together such a medley of hideous noises as can never be effaced from my memory. For two hours this desperate conflict lasted. More than once, some of the Wangwana were about to abandon the struggle and run to the canoes, but Uledi, the coxswain, and Frank threatened them with clubbed muskets, and with the muzzles of their rifles drove them back to the stockade. At dusk the enemy retreated from the vicinity of the clearing; but the hideous alarums produced from their ivory horns, and increased by the echoes of the close forest, still continued; and now and again a vengeful poison-laden arrow flew by with an ominous whizz to quiver in the earth at our feet, or fall harmlessly into the river behind us.

Sleep, under such circumstances, was out of the question; yet there were many weak, despairing souls whom even the fear of being eaten could not rouse to a sense of manliness and the necessity for resistance. Aware of this, I entrusted the task of keeping the people awake to Frank Pocock, Sheikh Abdallah, and Wadi Rebani, the "treasurer" of the Expedition, who were ordered to pour kettles of cold water over their heads upon the least disposition to go to sleep.

About 11 P.M. a dark form was seen creeping from the bush on all fours towards our stockade. I moved quietly to where vigilant Uledi was maintaining watch and ward, and whispered to him to take two men and endeavour to catch him. Uledi willingly consented, and burrowed out through a slight opening in the fence. The eyes of those in the secret became fastened upon the dim shadows of the hostile forms, so similar, it seemed to me, in their motions to a crocodile which I had seen on a rock near Kisorya in Ukerewé, as it endeavoured to deceive a large diver into the belief that it was asleep while actually meditating its murder.

Soon we saw Uledi's form leap upon that of the prostrate savage and heard him call out for help, which was at once given him by his two assistants; but an ominous rustling in the bushes behind announced that the cunning enemy were also on the alert, and, as they rushed to the rescue, Uledi snatched his captive's spears, and with his two friends retreated into the camp, while our guns again awoke the echoes of the forest and the drowsy men in the camp to a midnight action as brisk as it was short.

Twit, twit, fell the arrows once more in showers, piercing the brush fence, perforating the foliage, or smartly tapping the trunks and branches, while we, crouching down on the ground, under the thick shadows of the brushwood, replied with shot, slugs, and bullets, that swept the base of the jungle.

Silence was soon again restored and the strict watch renewed. From a distance the poisoned reeds still pattered about us, but, protected by our snug stockade and lying low in our covert, they were harmless, though they kept us awake listening to the low whizz and reminding one another that the foe was still near.

Morning dawned upon the strange scene. The cooks proceeded to make fires, to cook some food, under the shelter of the high banks, that we might break our long fasts. Frank and I made a sufficient meal out of six roasted bananas and a few cups of sugarless coffee.

After which, giving strict orders to Frank and Sheikh Abdallah to be vigilant in my absence, the boat was manned, and I was rowed to a distance of 500 yards from the camp towards the right bank. There, stopping, to examine the shores, I was surprised to see, only a quarter of a mile below our camp, a large town, consisting, like those above, of a series of villages, in a uniform line along the high bank, while a perfect wealth of palm-trees and banana plantations proved unquestionably the prosperity of the populous district. I recollected then that the intelligent dwarf already mentioned had spoken of a powerful chief, whose district, called Vinya-Njara, possessed so many men that it would be utterly impossible to pass him.

My plans were soon made. It was necessary that we should occupy the southern-most village, in order to house the sick, to obtain food for ourselves, and to keep up communication with the land division when it should announce its presence.

We rowed back to the camp, by this time the observed of a thousand heads which projected from the jungle between our camp and the first village. As nothing had been unpacked from the boat and the hospital-canoes, and only the defenders of the camp had disembarked, every soul was in a few seconds seated in his place, and, pulling swiftly over that intervening quarter of a mile down to the landing of the first village—targets, it is true, for several arrows for a short time, but no one could stop to reply. Arriving at the landing, two men were detailed off to each canoe and the boat, and we rushed up the high and steep bank. The village was empty, and, by cutting some trees down to block up each end, became at once perfectly defensible.

We were not long left unmolested. The savages recovered their wits, and strove desperately to dislodge us, but at each end of the village, which was about three hundred yards long, our muskets blazed incessantly. I also caused three or four sharpshooters to ascend tall trees along the river banks, which permitted them, though unseen, to overlook the tall grasses and rear of the village, and to defend us from fire. Meanwhile, for the first time for twenty-four hours, the sick (seventy-two in number) were allotted one-fourth of the village for themselves, as over one-half of them were victims of the pest, of which three had died in the canoes during the fearful hours of the previous night.

The combat lasted until noon, when, mustering twenty-five men, we made a sally, and succeeded in clearing the skirts of the village for the day. Uledi caught one of the natives by the foot, and succeeded in conveying him within the village, where he was secured as a most welcome prize, through whom we might possibly, if opportunities offered, bring this determined people to reason.

Then while the scouts deployed in a crescent form from beyond the ends of the village into the forest, the rest of our force formed in line, and commenced to cut down all weeds and grass within a distance of a hundred yards. This work consumed three hours, after which the scouts were withdrawn, and we rested half an hour for another scant meal of bananas. Thus refreshed after our arduous toil, we set about building marksmen's nests at each end of the village 15 feet high, which, manned with ten men each, commanded all approaches. For our purpose there were a number of soft-wood logs, already prepared in the village, and bark rope and cane fibre were abundant in every hut, for the inhabitants of Vinya-Njara devoted themselves, among other occupations, to fishing, and the manufacture of salt from the Pistia plants.

By evening our labours were nearly completed. During the night there was a slight alarm, and now and then the tapping on the roofs and the pattering among the leaves informed us that our enemies were still about, but we did not reply to them.

The next morning an assault was attempted, for the enemy emerged from the bush on the run into the clearing; but our arrangements seemed to surprise them, for they retreated again almost immediately into the gloomy obscurities of the jungle, where they maintained, with indomitable spirit, horn-blowing and a terrific "bo-bo-boing."

We had, it seems—though I have not had time to mention it before—passed the tribes which emitted cries of "Ooh-hu-hu, ooh-hu, ooh-hu-hu," for ever since our arrival at Vinya-Njara we had listened with varied feelings to the remarkable war-strains of "Bo-bo, bo-bo, bo-bo-o-o-oh," uttered in tones so singular as to impress even my African comrades with a sense of its eccentricity.

About noon a large flotilla of canoes was observed ascending the river close to the left bank, manned by such a dense mass of men that any number between five hundred and eight hundred would be within the mark. We watched them very carefully until they had ascended the river about half a mile above us, when, taking advantage of the current, they bore down towards us, blowing their war-horns, and drumming vigorously. At the same moment, as though this were a signal in concert with those on land, war-horns responded from the forest, and I had scarcely time to order every man to look out when the battle-tempest of arrows broke upon us from the woods. But the twenty men in the nests at the corners of the village proved sufficient to resist the attack from the forest side, Frank Pocock being in charge of one, and Sheikh Abdallah of the other, while I, with twenty men lining the bushes along the water line, defended the river side.

This was a period when every man felt that he must either fight or resign himself to the only other alternative, that of being heaved a headless corpse into the river. Our many successful struggles for a precarious existence had begun to animate even the most cowardly with that pride of life that superiority creates, and that feeling of invulnerability that frequent lucky escapes foster. I was conscious, as I cast my eyes about, that my followers were conspicuously distinguishing themselves, and were at last emerging from that low level of undeveloped manhood which is the general state of men untried and inexperienced. With a number of intelligent whites, that acquisition of courageous qualities would have been assisted by natural good sense, and a few months' hard service such as we had undergone would have sufficed to render them calm and steady in critical times; but with such people as I had, who had long shown—with the exception of a few—a wonderful inaptitude for steadiness, the lesson had taken two years. These last few days on the Livingstone river had been rapidly perfecting that compact band for the yet more dangerous times and periods to come.

Therefore, though the notes of the war-horns were dreadful, our foe numerous and pertinacious, and evidently accustomed to victory, I failed to observe one man amongst my people then fighting who did not seem desirous to excel even Uledi, the coxswain.

The battle had continued half an hour with a desperate energy, only qualified by our desperate state. Ammunition we possessed in abundance, and we made use of it with deadly effect, yet what might have become of us is doubtful, had not the advanced-guard of Tippu-Tib and our land division arrived at this critical juncture, causing dismay to the savages in the forest, who announced the reinforcement by war-horns to the savages in the canoes, many of whom were, at the moment, making most strenuous efforts to effect a landing. The river savages, upon hearing these signals, withdrew, but as they were paddling away they proclaimed their intention of preventing all escape, either up river or down river, and expressed their enormous contempt for us by throwing water towards us with their paddles. We saw all the canoes mysteriously disappear behind an island, situated about 1600 yards off, and opposite to our camp.

It was a great pleasure to greet all our people once more, though they were in a wretched plight. Bad food, and a scarcity of even that during three days in the jungle, constantly losing the road, wandering aimlessly about, searching for thinly grown spots through which they might creep more easily, had reduced their physical strength so much that it was clear at a glance that several days must elapse before they would be able to resume their journey.

When all had arrived, I called the forty defenders of the camp together, and distributing cloth to each of them, told them that as the enemy had taken their canoes behind the island opposite, they very probably intended to resume the fight; that it was, therefore, our duty to prevent that if possible, by making a night expedition, and cutting the canoes adrift, which would leave them under the necessity of abandoning the project of attacking us; "besides," said I, "if we can do the job in a complete way, the enormous loss of canoes will have such an effect on them that it will clear our progress down river."

Frank Pocock was requested to take his choice of crews and man the four little canoes, which would carry about twenty men and, proceeding to the south end of the islet, to spread his canoes across the mouth of the channel, between the islet and the right bank, while I proceeded in the boat to the north end of the islet, and, bearing down the channel, sought out the enemy's canoes, and cut them adrift which floating down were to be picked up by him.

It was a rainy, gusty night, and dark; but at 10 P.M., the hour of deepest sleep, we set out with muffled oars, Frank to his appointed position, and I up river, along the left bank, until, having ascended nearly opposite the lower end of Mpika Island, we cut rapidly across river to the right bank. Then, resting on our oars, we searched the bank narrowly, until seeing a fire on the bank we rowed cautiously in, and discovered eight large canoes, each tied by a short cable of rattan to a stake, driven deep into the clay. Uledi, Bwana Hamadi, and myself, soon set these free, and giving each a push successively far into the stream, waited a short time, and then followed them in our boat. Four other canoes were cut adrift a few hundred yards below. On coming into the channel between the islet and the bank, numerous bright fires informed us that the largest number of the enemy was encamped on it, and that their canoes must be fastened below the several camps. We distinctly heard the murmur of voices, and the coughing of shivering people, or of those who indulged in the pernicious *bhang*; but gliding under the shadows of the tall banks and in the solemn blackness of the trees, we were unperceived, and canoe after canoe, each with its paddles and scoops within, was pushed into the swift stream, which conveyed it down river to where we felt assured Frank was ready with his sharp and quick-eyed assistants. In this manner thirty-six canoes, some of great size, were sent adrift; and not being able to discover more, we also followed them noiselessly down stream, until we came to Frank's canoes, which were being borne down stream by the weight of so many. However, casting the great stone anchor of the boat, canoe after canoe was attached to us, and leaving twenty-six in charge of Frank, we hoisted sail and rowed up stream, with twelve canoes in tow. Arriving at camp, the canoes were delivered in charge to the Wangwana, and then the boat hastily returned to lend assistance to Frank, who made his presence known to us by occasionally blowing the trumpet. After relieving him of eight more canoes, he was able almost to keep up with us to camp, where we all arrived at 5 A.M. after a most successful night expedition.

At 9 A.M. the boat was manned again, and we rowed to the scene of our midnight labours. The island was all but abandoned! Only a few persons were left, and to them, with the aid of our interpreters, we communicated our terms, viz., that we would occupy Vinya-Njara, and retain all the canoes unless they made peace. We also informed them that we had one prisoner, who would be surrendered to them if they availed themselves of our offer of peace: that we had suffered heavily, and they had also suffered; that war was an evil which wise men avoided; that if they came with two canoes with their chiefs, two canoes with our chiefs should meet them in mid-stream, and make blood-brotherhood; and that on that condition some of their canoes should be restored, and we would purchase the rest.

They replied that what we had spoken was quite true, but as their chiefs were some distance away in the woods they must have time to communicate with them, but that they would announce their decision next day. We then left them, not, however, without throwing packets of shells towards them, as an earnest of our wish to be friends, and rowed to our camp at Vinya-Njara.

The forests for a distance of ten miles around Vinya-Njara were clear of enemies. The friendly natives of Mpika Island came down to our assistance in negotiating a peace between us and the surly chiefs, who had all withdrawn into the forests on the right bank.

On the 22nd December, the ceremony of blood-brotherhood having been formally concluded, in mid-river, between Safeni and the chief of Vinya-Njara, our

captive and fifteen canoes were returned, and twenty-three canoes were retained
by us for a satisfactory equivalent, and thus our desperate struggle terminated.
Our losses at Vinya-Njara were four killed and thirteen wounded.

*　　*　　*

The next day at dawn we embarked all the men, women, and children, 149 souls
in all, and the riding-asses of the Expedition, and, telling Tippu-Tib we should
on the morrow pull up stream and descend the river close to the village of Vinya-
Njara for a last farewell, we pulled across to the islet near the right bank, where
we constructed a rude camp for the only night we should remain. When I ascertained, after arrival, that every soul connected with the Expedition was present,
my heart was filled with a sense of confidence and trust such as I had not enjoyed
since leaving Zanzibar.

In the evening, while sleep had fallen upon all save the watchful sentries in
charge of the boat and canoes, Frank and I spent a serious time.

Frank was at heart as sanguine as I that we should finally emerge somewhere,
but, on account of the persistent course of the great river towards the north, a
little uneasiness was evident in his remarks.

"Before we finally depart, sir," said he, "do you really believe, in your inmost
soul, that we shall succeed? I ask this because there are such odds against us—not
that I for a moment think it would be best to return, having proceeded so far."

"Believe? Yes, I do believe that we shall all emerge into light again some time.
It is true that our prospects are as dark as this night. Even the Mississippi presented
no such obstacles to De Soto as this river will necessarily present to us.[…]

"Though I love life as much as you do, or any other man does, yet on the success
of this effort I am about to stake my life, my all. To prevent its sacrifice foolishly I
have devised numerous expedients with which to defy wild men, wild nature, and
unknown terrors. There is an enormous risk, but you know the adage, 'Nothing
risked, nothing won.'"

*　　*　　*

"Now look at this, the latest chart which Europeans have drawn of this region. It
is a blank, perfectly white. We will draw two curves just to illustrate what I mean.

One shows the river reaching the Equator and turning westward. Supposing there are no cataracts, we ought to reach 'Tuckey's Furthest' by the 15th February; but if the river takes that wider sweep from 2° north of the Equator, we may hope to reach by the 15th March, and, if we allow a month for cataracts or rapids, we have a right to think that we ought to see the ocean by either the middle or the end of April 1877.

"I assure you, Frank, this enormous void is about to be filled up. Blank as it is, it has a singular fascination for me. Never has white paper possessed such a charm for me as this has, and I have already mentally peopled it, filled it with most wonderful pictures of towns, villages, rivers, countries, and tribes—all in the imagination—and I am burning to see whether I am correct or not. *Believe?* I see us gliding down by tower and town, and my mind will not permit a shadow of doubt. Good night, my boy! Good night! and may happy dreams of the sea, and ships, and pleasure, and comfort and success attend you in your sleep! To-morrow, my lad, is the day we shall cry—'Victory or death!'"

*   *   *

About 2 P.M. we dropped down river again a few miles, and at 4:30 P.M. halted to camp at an old clearing on the right bank. Had we dared, we might have continued our journey by night, but prudence forbade the attempt, as cataracts might have been more disastrous than cannibals.

Near sunset we were once more alarmed by finding arrows dropping into the camp. Of course there was a general rush to guns; but, upon noting the direction whence the arrows came, I ordered the people simply to go on about their duties as though nothing had occurred, while I sent twenty men in two canoes down the river with instructions to advance upon the enemy from behind, but by no means to fire unless they were overwhelmed in numbers.

Just at dark our canoes came back with three prisoners bound hand and foot. Except the poor dwarf at Ikondu up river, I had not seen any human creatures so unlovable to look at. There was no one feature about them that even extravagant charity could indicate as elevating them into the category of noble savages. I do not think I was prejudiced; I examined their faces with eyes that up to that time had gazed into the eyes of over five hundred thousand black men. They were

> "It seemed to me so absurd to be angry with people who looked upon one only as an epicure would regard a fat capon. Sometimes also a faint suspicion came to my mind that this was all but a part of a hideous dream. Why was it that I should be haunted with the idea that there were human beings who regarded me and my friends only in the light of meat? Meat! We? Heavens! what an atrocious idea!"
>
> —SIR HENRY M. STANLEY

intolerably ugly. I would not disturb them, however, that evening, but releasing their feet, and relaxing the bonds on their arms, appointed Katembo and his friend to keep them company and feed them, and Wadi Rehani to stimulate the keepers to be hospitable.

By the morning they were sociable, and replied readily to our questions. They were of the Wanongi—an inland tribe—but they had a small fishing village about an hour's journey below our camp called Katumbi. A powerful tribe called the Mwana Ntaba occupied a country below Katumbi, near some falls, which they warned us would be our destruction. On the left side of the river, opposite the Mwana Ntaba, were the Wavinza, south of a large river called the Rumami or Lumami. The great river on which we had voyaged was known to them as the Lowwa.

As we stepped into our canoes we cut their bonds and permitted the unlovable and unsympathetic creatures to depart, a permission of which they availed themselves gladly.

The banks were from 10 to 30 feet high, of a grey-brown clay, and steep with old clearings, which were frequent at this part until below Katumbi. Half an hour afterwards we arrived at a channel which flowed in a sudden bend to the north-east, and, following it, we found ourselves abreast of a most populous shore, close to which we glided. Presently several large canoes appeared from behind an island to our right, and seemed to be hesitating as to whether they should retreat or advance.

The "Open Sesame"—"Sen-nen-neh!"—was loudly uttered by Katembo with his usual pathetic, bleating accent, and to our joy the word was repeated by over a hundred voices. "Sen-nen-neh! Sennenneh! Sennenneh!"—each voice apparently vying with the other in loudness. The river bore us down, and as they would not shorten the distance, we thought it better to keep this condition of things, lest the movement might be misconstrued, and we might be precipitated into hostilities.

For half an hour we glided down in this manner, keeping up a constant fire of smiling compliments and pathetic Sennennehs. Indeed, we were discovering that there was much virtue in a protracted and sentimental pronunciation of Sen-nen-neh! The men of the Expedition, who had previously ridiculed with mocking Ba-a-a-as, the absurd moan and plaintive accents of Sen-nen-neh, which Katembo had employed, now admired him for his tact. The good natives with whom we were now exchanging these suave, bleating courtesies proved to us that the true shibboleth of peace was to prolong each word with a quavering moan and melancholic plaint.

We came to a banana grove, of a delicious and luxuriant greenness which the shadowy black green of the antique forest behind it only made more agreeable and pleasant. Beyond this grove, the bank was lined by hundreds of men and women, standing or sitting down, their eyes directed towards our approaching flotilla.

"Sen-nen-neh!" was delivered with happy effect by one of the boat-boys. A chorus of Sen-nen-nehs, long-drawn. loud, and harmonious, quickly following the notes of the last syllable, burst from the large assembly, until both banks of the great river re-echoed it with all its indescribable and ludicrous pathos.

The accents were peaceful, the bearing of the people and the presence of the women were unmistakably pacific, so the word was given to drop anchor.

The natives in the canoes, who had hitherto preceded us, were invited to draw near, but they shrugged their shoulders, and declined the responsibility of beginning any intercourse with the strangers. We appealed to the concourse on the banks, for we were not a hundred feet from them. They burst out into a loud laughter, yet with nothing of scorn or contempt in it, for we had been so long accustomed to the subtle differences of passion that we were by this time adepts in discovering the nicest shades of feeling which wild humanity is capable of expressing. We held out our hands to them with palms upturned, heads sentimentally leaning on one side, and, with a captivating earnestness of manner, begged them to regard us as friends, strangers far from their homes who had lost their way, but were endeavouring to find it by going down the river.

The effect is manifest. A kind of convulsion of tenderness appears to animate the entire host. Expressions of pity break from them, and there is a quick interchange of sympathetic opinions.

DRINKING POISON

On an expedition into Africa, English explorer Richard Lemon Lander raised the ire of a local ruler and was arrested. He later wrote:

"The news of the white man's arrest, and approaching trial, spread like wild-fire through the town, and the inhabitants, assembling from all parts, armed with axes, spears, clubs, and bows and arrows, followed the procession to the dismal spot. On entering the hut, I beheld a number of priests and elders of the people, seated in a circle, who desired me to stand in the midst of them. When I had complied with their request, one of the priests arose, and presenting me with a bowl, containing about a quart of a clear liquid, scarcely distinguishable from water, cried out in a loud voice, and with much emphasis, "You are accused, white man, of designs against our king and his government, and are therefore desired to drink the contents of this vessel, which, if the reports to your prejudice be true, will surely destroy you; whereas, if they be without foundation, you need not fear, Christian; the fetish will do you no injury, for our gods will do that which is right."

I took the bowl in my trembling hand, and gazed for a moment on the sable countenances of my judges; but not a single look of compassion shone upon any of them; a dead silence prevailed in the gloomy sanctuary of skulls; every eye was intently fixed upon me; and seeing no possibility of escape, or of

"Ah," thought I, "how delighted Livingstone would have been had he been here to regard this scene! Assuredly he would have been enraptured, and become more firmly impressed than ever with the innocence and guilelessness of true aborigines," and I am forced to admit it is exceedingly pleasant, but—I wait.

We hold up long necklaces of beads of various colours to view: blue, red, white, yellow, and black.

"Ah-h-h," sigh a great many, admiringly, and heads bend toward heads in praise and delight of them.

"Come, my friends, let us talk. Bring one canoe here. These to those who dare to approach us." There is a short moment of hesitation, and then some forms disappear, and presently come out again bearing gourds, chickens, bananas, and vegetables, &c., which they place carefully in a small canoe. Two women step in and boldly paddle towards us, while a deathly silence prevails among my people as well as among the aborigines on the bank.

evading the piercing glance of the priests and elders, I offered up, internally, a short prayer to the Throne of Mercy,—to the God of Christians,—and hastily swallowed the fetish, dashing the poison-chalice to the ground. A low murmur ran through the assembly; they all thought I should instantly have expired, or at least have discovered symptoms of severe agony, but detecting no such tokens, they arose simultaneously, and made way for me to leave the hut. On getting into the open air, I found my poor slaves in tears; they had come, they said, to catch a last glimpse of their master; but when they saw me alive and at liberty, they leaped and danced for joy, and prepared a path for me through the dense mass of armed people.

These set up an astounding shout at my unexpected appearance, and seemed greatly pleased (if I might be allowed to judge) that I had not fallen a victim to the influence of their fearful fetish. On arriving at my dwelling, I took instant and powerful means to eject the venomous potion from my stomach, and happily succeeded in the attempt.

I was told that the liquid I had swallowed was a decoction of the bark of a tree abounding in the neighbourhood, and that I was the only individual who, for a long season, had escaped its poisonous qualities. It had a disagreeably bitter taste, but I experienced no other ill effects from it than a slight dizziness, which wore off completely a few hours after the conclusion of the trial.

I observed one or two coquettish airs on the part of the two women, but though my arm was getting tired with holding out so long in one position those necklaces of glorious beads, I dared not withdraw them, lest the fascination might be broken. I felt myself a martyr in the cause of public peace, and the sentiment made me bear up stoically.

"Boy," I muttered, in an undertone, to Mabruki, my gun-bearer, "when the canoe is alongside, seize it firmly and do not let it escape."

"Inshallah, my master."

Nearer the canoe came, and with its approach my blandness increased, and further I projected my arm with those beads of tempting colours.

At last the canoe was paddled alongside. Mabruki quietly grasped it. I then divided the beads into sets, talking the while to Katembo—who translated for me—of the happiness I felt, at the sight of two such beautiful women coming out to see the white chief, who was so good, and who loved to talk to beautiful women.

"There! these are for you—and these are for you," I said to the steerswoman and her mate.

They clapped their hands in glee, and each woman held out her presents in view of the shore people; and hearty hand-claps from all testified to their grateful feelings.

The women then presented me with the gourds of malofu—palm-wine—the chickens, bananas, potatoes and cassava they had brought, which were received by the boat's crew and the interested members of the Expedition with such a hearty clapping of hands that it sent the shore people into convulsions of laughter. Mabruki was told now to withdraw his hand, as the women were clinging to the boats themselves, and peace was assured. Presently the great native canoes drew near and alongside the boat, forming dense walls of strange humanity on either side.

"Tell us, friends," we asked, " why it is you are so friendly, when those up the river are so wicked."

Then a chief said, "Because yesterday some of our fishermen were up the river on some islets near Kibombo Island, opposite the Amu-Nyam villages; and when we heard the war-drums of the Amu-Nyam we looked up, and saw your canoes coming down. You stopped at Kibombo Island and we heard you speak to them, saying you were friends. But the Amu-Nyam are bad; they eat people, we don't. They fight with us frequently, and whomsoever they catch they eat. They fought with you, and while you were fighting our fishermen came down and told us that the Wajiwa" [we] "were coming; but they said that they heard the Wajiwa say that they came as friends, and that they did not want to fight. To-day we sent a canoe, with a woman and a boy up the river, with plenty of provisions in it. If you had been bad people, you would have taken that canoe. We were behind the bushes of that island watching you; but you said, 'Sen-nen-neh' to them, and passed into the channel between the island and our villages. Had you seized that canoe, our drums would have sounded for war, and you would have had to fight us, as you fought the Amu-Nyam. We have left our spears on one of those islands. See, we have nothing."

It was true, as I had already seen, to my wonder and admiration. Here, then, I had opportunities for noting what thin barriers separated ferocity from amiability. Only a couple of leagues above lived the cannibals of Amu-Nyam, who had advanced towards us with evil and nauseous intentions; but next to them was a tribe which detested the unnatural custom of eating their own species, with whom we had readily formed a pact of peace and goodwill!

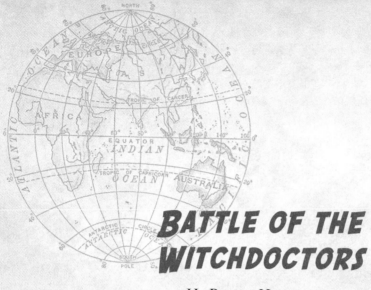

BATTLE OF THE WITCHDOCTORS

H. RIDER HAGGARD

(novelist)

Among the Kaffirs was an old fellow named Indaba-zimbi, which, being translated, means "tongue of iron." I suppose he got this name from his strident voice and exhaustless eloquence. This man was a great character in his way. He had been a noted witch-doctor among a neighbouring tribe, and I met him under the following circumstances[...]

Two years before my father's death I had occasion to search the country round for some lost oxen. After a long and useless quest it occurred to me that I had better go to the place where the oxen were bred by a Kaffir chief, whose name I forget, but whose kraal was about fifty miles from our station. There I journeyed, and found the oxen safe at home. The chief entertained me handsomely, and on the following morning I went to pay my respects to him before leaving, and was somewhat surprised to find a collection of some hundreds of men and women sitting round him anxiously watching the sky in which the thunder-clouds were banking up in a very ominous way.

"You had better wait, white man," said the chief, "and see the rain-doctors fight the lightning."

I inquired what he meant, and learned that this man, Indaba-zimbi, had for some years occupied the position of wizard-in-chief to the tribe, although he was not a member of it, having been born in the country now known as Zululand. But a son of the chiefs, a man of about thirty, had lately set up as a rival in supernatural powers. This irritated Indaba-zimbi beyond measure, and a quarrel ensued between the two witch-doctors that resulted in a challenge to trial by lightning being given and accepted. These were the conditions. The rivals must await the coming of a serious thunderstorm, no ordinary tempest would serve their turn. Then, carrying assegais in their hands, they must take their stand within fifty paces of each other upon a certain patch of ground where the big thunderbolts were observed to strike continually, and by the exercise of their occult powers and invocations to the lightning, must strive to avert death from themselves and bring it on their rival. The terms of this singular match had been arranged a month previously, but no storm worthy of the occasion had arisen. Now the local weatherprophets believed it to be brewing.

I inquired what would happen if neither of the men were struck, and was told that they must then wait for another storm. If they escaped the second time, however, they would be held to be equal in power, and be jointly consulted by the tribe upon occasions of importance.

The prospect of being a spectator of so unusual a sight overcame my desire to be gone, and I accepted the chief's invitation to see it out. Before mid-day I regretted it, for though the western heavens grew darker and darker, and the still air heralded the coming of the storm, yet it did not come. By four o'clock, however, it became obvious that it must burst soon—at sunset, the old chief said, and in the company of the whole assembly I moved down to the place of combat. The kraal was built on the top of a hill, and below it the land sloped gently to the banks of a river about half a mile away. On the hither side of the bank was the piece of land that was, the natives said, "loved of the lightning." Here the magicians took up their stand, while the spectators grouped themselves on the hillside about two hundred yards away—which was, I thought, rather too near to be pleasant. When we had sat there for a while my curiosity overcame me, and I asked leave of the chief to go down and inspect the arena. He said I might do so at my own risk. I told him that the fire from above would not hurt white men, and went to find that the spot was a bed of iron ore, thinly covered with grass, which of course accounted for its attracting the lightning from the storms as they travelled along the line of the river. At each end of this iron-stone area were placed the combatants, Indaba-zimbi facing the east, and his rival the west, and before each there burned a little fire made of some scented root. Moreover they were dressed in all the paraphernalia of their craft, snakeskins, fish bladders, and I know not what beside, while round their necks hung circlets of baboons' teeth and bones from human hands. First I went to the western end where the chief's son stood. He was pointing with his assegai towards the advancing storm, and invoking it in a voice of great excitement.

"Come, fire, and lick up Indaba-zimbi!

"Hear me, Storm Devil, and lick Indaba-zimbi with your red tongue! Spit on him with your rain!

"Whirl him away in your breath!

"Make him as nothing—melt the marrow in his bones!

"Run into his heart and burn away the lies!

"Show all the people who is the true Witch Finder!

"Let me not be put to shame in the eyes of this white man!"

Thus he spoke, or rather chanted, and all the while rubbed his broad chest— for he was a very fine man—with some filthy compound of medicine or *mouti*.

After a while, getting tired of his song, I walked across the iron-stone to where Indaba-zimbi sat by his fire. He was not chanting at all, but his perform-ance was much more impressive. It consisted in staring at the eastern sky, which was perfectly clear of cloud, and every now and again beckoning at it with his finger, then turning round to point with the assegai towards his rival. For a while I looked at him in silence. He was a curious wizened man, apparently over fifty years of age, with thin hands that looked as tough as wire. His nose was much sharper than is usual among these races, and he had a queer habit of holding his head sideways like a bird when he spoke, which, in addition to the humour that lurked in his eye, gave him a most comical appearance. Another strange thing about him was that he had a single white lock of hair among his black wool. At last I spoke to him:

"Indaba-zimbi, my friend," I said, "you may be a good witch-doctor, but you are certainly a fool. It is no good beckoning at the blue sky while your enemy is getting a start with the storm."

"You may be clever, but don't think you know everything, white man," the old fellow answered, in a high, cracked voice, and with something like a grin.

"They call you Iron-tongue," I went on; "you had better use it, or the Storm Devil won't hear you."

"The fire from above runs down iron," he answered, "so I keep my tongue quiet. Oh, yes, let him curse away, I'll put him out presently. Look now, white man."

I looked, and in the eastern sky there grew a cloud. At first it was small, though very black, but it gathered with extraordinary rapidity.

This was odd enough, but as I had seen the same thing happen before it did not particularly astonish me. It is by no means unusual in Africa for two thunderstorms to come up at the same time from different points of the compass.

"You had better get on, Indaba-zimbi," I said, "the big storm is coming along fast, and will soon eat up that baby of yours," and I pointed to the west.

"Babies sometimes grow to giants, white man," said Indaba-zimbi, beckoning away vigorously. "Look now at my cloud-child."

I looked; the eastern storm was spreading itself from earth to sky, and in shape resembled an enormous man. There was its head, its shoulders, and its legs; yes, it was like a huge giant travelling across the heavens. The light of the setting sun escaping from beneath the lower edge of the western storm shot across the intervening space in a sheet of splendour, and, lighting upon the advancing figure of cloud, wrapped its middle in hues of glory too wonderful to be described; but beneath and above this glowing belt his feet and head were black as jet. Presently, as I watched, an awful flash of light shot from the head of the cloud, circled it about as though with a crown of living fire, and vanished.

"Aha," chuckled old Indaba-zimbi, "my little boy is putting on his man's ring," and he tapped the gum ring on his own head, which natives assume when they reach a certain age and dignity. "Now, white man, unless you are a bigger wizard than either of us you had better clear off, for the fire-fight is about to begin."

I thought this sound advice.

"Good luck go with you, my black uncle," I said. "I hope you don't feel the iniquities of a misspent life weighing on you at the last."

"You look after yourself, and think of your own sins, young man," he answered, with a grim smile, and taking a pinch of snuff, while at that very moment a flash of lightning, I don't know from which storm, struck the ground within thirty paces of me. That was enough for me, I took to my heels, and as I went I heard old Indaba-zimbi's dry chuckle of amusement.

I climbed the hill till I came to where the chief was sitting with his indunas, or headmen, and sat down near to him. I looked at the man's face and saw that he was intensely anxious for his son's safety, and by no means confident of the young man's powers to resist the magic of Indaba-zimbi. He was talking in a low voice to the induna next to him. I affected to take no notice and to be concentrating my attention on the novel scene before me; but in those days I had very quick ears, and caught the drift of the conversation.

"Hearken!" the chief was saying, "if the magic of Indaba-zimbi prevails against my son I will endure him no more. Of this I am sure, that when he has slain my son he will slay me, me also, and make himself chief in my place. I fear Indaba-zimbi. *Ou!*"

"Black One," answered the induna, "wizards die as dogs die, and, once dead, dogs bark no more."

"And once dead," said the chief, "wizards work no more spells," and he bent and whispered in the induna's ear, looking at the assegai in his hand as he whispered.

"Good, my father, good!" said the induna, presently. "It shall be done tonight, if the lightning does not do it first."

"A bad lookout for old Indaba-zimbi," I said to myself. "They mean to kill him." Then I thought no more of the matter for a while, the scene before me was too tremendous.

The two storms were rapidly rushing together. Between them was a gulf of blue sky, and from time to time flashes of blinding light passed across this gulf, leaping from cloud to cloud. I remember that they reminded me of the story of the heathen god Jove and his thunderbolts. The storm that was shaped like a giant and ringed with the glory of the sinking sun made an excellent dove, and I am sure that the bolts which leapt from it could not have been surpassed even in mythological times. Oddly enough, as yet the flashes were not followed by thunder. A deadly stillness lay upon the place, the cattle stood silently on the hillside, even the natives were awed to silence. Dark shadows crept along the bosom of the hills, the river to the right and left was hidden in wreaths of cloud, but before us and beyond the combatants it shone like a line of silver beneath the narrowing space of open sky. Now the western tempest was scrawled all over with lines of intolerable light, while the inky head of the cloud-giant to the east was continually suffused with a white and deadly glow that came and went in pulses, as though a blood of flame was being pumped into it from the heart of the storm.

The silence deepened and deepened, the shadows grew blacker and blacker, then suddenly all nature began to moan beneath the breath of an icy wind. On sped the wind; the smooth surface of the river was ruffled by it into little waves, the tall grass bowed low before it, and in its wake came the hissing sound of furious rain.

Ah! the storms had met. From each there burst an awful blaze of dazzling flame, and now the hill on which we sat rocked at the noise of the following thunder. The light went out of the sky, darkness fell suddenly on the land, but not for long. Presently the whole landscape grew vivid in the flashes, it appeared and disappeared, now everything was visible for miles, now even the men at my side vanished in the blackness. The thunder rolled and cracked and pealed like the trump of doom, whirlwinds tore round, lifting dust and even stones high into the air, and in a low, continuous undertone rose the hiss of the rushing rain.

I put my hand before my eyes to shield them from the terrible glare, and looked beneath it towards the lists of iron-stone. As flash followed flash, from time to time I caught sight of the two wizards. They were slowly advancing towards one another, each pointing at his foe with the assegai in his hand. I could see their every movement, and it seemed to me that the chain lightning was striking the iron-stone all round them.

Suddenly the thunder and lightning ceased for a minute, everything grew black, and, except for the rain, silent.

"It is over one way or the other, chief," I called out into the darkness.

"Wait, white man, wait!" answered the chief, in a voice thick with anxiety and fear.

Hardly were the words out of his mouth when the heavens were lit up again till they literally seemed to flame. There were the men, not ten paces apart. A great flash fell between them, I saw them stagger beneath the shock. Indaba-zimbi recovered himself first—at any rate when the next flash came he was standing bolt upright, pointing with his assegai towards his enemy. The chief's son was still on his legs, but he was staggering like a drunken man, and the assegai had fallen from his hand.

Darkness! then again a flash, more fearful, if possible, than any that had gone before. To me it seemed to come from the east, right over the head of Indaba-zimbi. At that instant I saw the chief's son wrapped, as it were, in the heart of it. Then the thunder pealed, the rain burst over us like a torrent, and I saw no more.

The worst of the storm was done, but for a while the darkness was so dense that we could not move, nor, indeed, was I inclined to leave the safety of the hillside where the lightning was never known to strike, and venture down to the ironstone. Occasionally there still came flashes, but, search as we would, we could see no trace of either of the wizards. For my part, I believed that they were both dead. Now the clouds slowly rolled away down the course of the river, and with them went the rain; and now the stars shone out in their wake.

"Let us go and see," said the old chief, rising and shaking the water from his hair. "The fire-fight is ended, let us go and see who has conquered."

I rose and followed him, dripping as though I had swum a hundred yards with my clothes on, and after me came all the people of the kraal.

We reached the spot; even in that light I could see where the ironstone had been split and fused by the thunderbolts. While I was staring about me, I suddenly heard the chief, who was on my right, give a low moan, and saw the people cluster round him. I went up and looked. There, on the ground, lay the body of his son. It was a dreadful sight. The hair was burnt off his head, the copper rings upon his arms were fused, the assegai handle which lay near was literally shivered into threads, and, when I took hold of his arm, it seemed to me that every bone of it was broken.

The men with the chief stood gazing silently, while the women wailed.

"Great is the magic of Indaba-zimbi!" said a man, at length. The chief turned and struck him a heavy blow with the kerrie in his hand.

"Great or not, thou dog, he shall die," he cried, "and so shalt thou if thou singest his praises so loudly."

I said nothing, but thinking it probable that Indaba-zimbi had shared the fate of his enemy, I went to look. But I could see nothing of him, and at length, being thoroughly chilled with the wet, starting back to my waggon to change my clothes. On reaching it, I was rather surprised to see a strange Kaffir seated on the driving-box wrapped up in a blanket.

"Hullo! come out of that," I said.

The figure on the box slowly unrolled the blanket, and with great deliberation took a pinch of snuff.

"It was a good fire-fight, white man, was it not?" said Indaba-zimbi, in his high, cracked voice. "But he never had a chance against me, poor boy. He knew nothing about it. See, white man, what comes of presumption in the young. It is sad, very sad, but I made the flashes fly, didn't I?"

"You old humbug," I said, "unless you are careful you will soon learn what comes of presumption in the old, for your chief is after you with an assegai, and it will take all your magic to dodge that."

"Now you don't say so," said Indaba-zimbi, clambering off the waggon with rapidity; "and all because of his wretched upstart. There's gratitude for you, white man. I expose him, and they want to kill me. Well, thank you for the hint. We shall meet again before long," end he was gone like a shot, and not too soon, for just then some of the chief's men came up to the waggon.

On the following morning I started homewards. The first face I saw on arriving at the station was that of Indaba-zimbi.

"How do you do, Macumazahn?" he said, holding his head on one side and nodding his white lock. "I hear you are Christians here, and I want to try a new religion. Mine must be a bad one seeing that my people wanted to kill me for exposing an impostor."

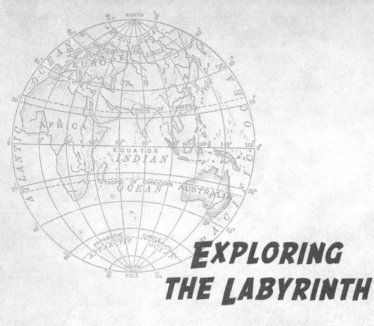

EXPLORING THE LABYRINTH

JOHN LLOYD STEPHENS
(American diplomat, explorer, and archeologist)

John Lloyd Stephens was a New York lawyer who became fascinated by accounts of ruined ancient cities in Mesoamerica. His chance to search for the ruins came in 1839 when President Martin Van Buren commissioned him as Special Ambassador to negotiate a treaty with the Federal Republic of Central America. However, his planned negotiations were soon derailed when the Federal Republic collapsed into civil war. Stephens' explorations first brought him to the Mayan ruins at Copán, which he amazingly purchased for $50 and hoped to ship back to the United States. This never happened, but he went on to extensively explore dozens of lost cities. His books fired the general public's imagination and generated a tremendous amount of interest in Mayan history. It's probably fair to say he single-handedly launched the field of Mesoamerican archeology.

T he road was broad, even, and level. It was the *camino real* between Mérida and Campeche, and would pass in any country for a fair carriage-road. All along we passed parties of Indians returning from the fair. In an hour we came in sight of the sierra which traverses at that point the whole peninsula of Yucatán from east to west. The sight of hills was cheering, and with the reflection of the setting sun upon them, they presented almost the first fine scenery I had encountered in the country. In an hour and ten minutes we reached Maxcanú, twelve miles distant, being by far the greatest speed at which I ever travelled in Yucatán.

The hacienda of Don Lorenzo was in this neighborhood, and he had a large house in the village, at which we stopped. My object in coming to this place was to visit La Cueva de Maxcanú, or the Cave of Maxcanú. In the evening, when notice was given of my intention, half the village was ready to join me, but in the morning my volunteers were not forthcoming, and I was reduced to the men procured for me by Don Lorenzo. From the time consumed in getting the men together and procuring torches, cord, &c., I did not get off till after nine o'clock. Our direction was due east till we reached the sierra, ascending which through a passage overgrown with woods, at eleven o'clock we arrived at the mouth, or rather door, of the *cueva*, about a league distant from the village.

I had before heard so much of caves and had been so often disappointed that I did not expect much from this; but the first view satisfied me in regard to the main point, viz., that it was not a natural cave, and that, as had been represented to me, it was *hecha a mano*, or made by hand.

La Cueva de Maxcanú, or the Cave of Maxcanú, has in that region a marvellous and mystical reputation. It is called by the Indians "Satun Sat," which means in Spanish *El Laberinto* or *El Perdedero*, the Labyrinth, or place in which one may be lost. Notwithstanding its wonderful reputation and a name which alone, in any other country, would induce a thorough exploration, it is a singular fact, and exhibits more strikingly than anything I can mention the indifference of the people of all classes to the antiquities of the country, that up to the time of my arrival at the door, this *laberinto* had never been examined. My friend Don Lorenzo Peón would give me every facility for exploring it except joining me himself. Several persons had penetrated to some distance with a string held outside, but had turned back, and the universal belief was that it contained passages without number and without end.

Under these circumstances, I certainly felt some degree of excitement as I stood in the doorway. The very name called up those stupendous works in Crete and on the shores of the Mœritic Lake which are now almost discredited as fabulous.

My retinue consisted of eight men, who considered themselves in my employ, besides three or four supernumeraries, and all together formed a crowd around the door. Except the *mayoral* of Uxmal, I had never seen one of them before, and as I considered it important to have a reliable man outside, I stationed him at the door with a ball of twine. I tied one end round my left wrist, and told one of the men to light a torch and follow me, but he refused absolutely, and all the rest, one after the other, did the same. They were all ready enough to hold the string; and I was curious to know, and had a conference with them on the interesting point, whether they expected any pay for their services in standing out of doors. One expected pay for showing me the place, others for carrying water, another for taking care of the horses, and so on, but I terminated the matter abruptly by declaring that I should not pay one of them a *medio*; and, ordering them all away from the door, which they were smothering, and a little infected with one of their apprehensions of starting some wild beast, which might be making his lair in the recesses of the cave, I entered with a candle in one hand and a pistol in the other.

The entrance faces the west. The mouth was filled up with rubbish, scrambling over which I stood in a narrow passage or gallery, constructed, like all the apartments above ground, with smooth walls and triangular arched ceiling. This passage was about four feet wide and seven feet high to the top of the arch. It ran due east, and at the distance of six or eight yards opened into another, or rather was stopped by another crossing it and running north and south. I took first that on the right hand, running south. At the distance of a few yards, on the right side of the wall, I found a door, filled up, and at the distance of thirty-five feet the passage ended, and a door opened at right angles on the left into another gallery running due east. Following this, at the distance of thirteen feet I found another gallery on the left, running north, and beyond it, at the end, still another, also on the left, and running north, four yards long, and then walled up, with only an opening in it about a foot square.

Turning back, I entered the gallery which I had passed and which ran north eight or ten yards; at the end was a doorway on the right, opening into a gallery that ran east. At the end of this were six steps, each one foot high and two wide, leading to another gallery, which ran north twelve yards. At the end there came another gallery on the left, which ran west ten yards, and at the end of this another on the right, running north about sixty feet. This passage was walled up at the north end, and at the distance of five yards from this end another doorway led into a passage running to the east. At the distance of four yards a gallery crossed this at right angles, running north and south, forty-five feet long, and walled up at both ends; and three or four yards farther on another gallery crossed it, also running north and south. This last was walled up at the south, and on the north led to still another gallery, which ran east, three yards long. This was stopped by another gallery crossing it, running to the south three yards, when it was walled up, and to the north eight yards, when it turned to the west.

In utter ignorance of the ground, I found myself turning and doubling along these dark and narrow passages, which seemed really to have no end, and justly to entitle the place to its name of El Laberinto.

I was not entirely free from the apprehension of starting some wild animal, and moved slowly and very cautiously. In the meantime, in turning the corners, my twine would be entangled, and the Indians, moved by the probability of getting no pay entered to clear it, and by degrees all came up with me in a body. I got a glimpse of their torches behind me just as I was turning into a new passage, and at the moment I was startled by a noise which sent me back rather quickly and completely routed them. It proceeded from a rushing of bats, and, having a sort of horror of these beastly birds, this was an ugly place to meet them in, for the passage was so low, and there was so little room for a flight over head that in walking upright there was great danger of their striking the face. It was necessary to move with the head bent down, and protecting the lights from the flapping of their wings. Nevertheless, every step was exciting, and called up recollections of the Pyramids and tombs of Egypt, and I could not but believe that these dark and intricate passages would introduce me to some large saloon, or perhaps some royal sepulchre. [Egyptologist Giovanni] Belzoni and the tomb of Cephrenes and its alabaster sarcophagus were floating through my brain, when all at once I found the passage choked up and effectually stopped. The ceiling had fallen in, crushed by a great mass of superincumbent earth, and farther progress was utterly impossible.

I was not prepared for this abrupt termination. The walls and ceiling were so solid and in such good condition that the possibility of such a result had not occurred to me. I was sure of going on to the end and discovering something, and I was arrested without knowing any better than when I entered to what point these passages led, or for what purposes they had been constructed. My first impulse was not to turn back, but to begin immediately and dig a way through; but the impossibility of accomplishing anything in this way soon presented itself. For the Indians to carry out the earth on their backs through all these passages would be a never ending work; besides, I had no idea how far the destruction extended, and, for the present at least, nothing could be done.

In [...] my disappointment I began to feel most sensibly the excessive heat and closeness of the place, which I had hardly perceived before, and which now became almost insufferable from the smoke of the torches and the Indians choking the narrow passage.

> "I was much entertained last summer with a tame bat, which would take flies out of a person's hand. If you gave it anything to eat, it brought its wings round before the mouth, hovering and hiding its head in the manner of the birds of prey when they feed. The adroitness it showed in shearing off the wings of the flies, which were always rejected, was worthy, of observation, and pleased me much. Insects seemed to be most acceptable, though it did not refuse raw flesh when offered [...]"
>
> —*naturalist* GILBERT WHITE

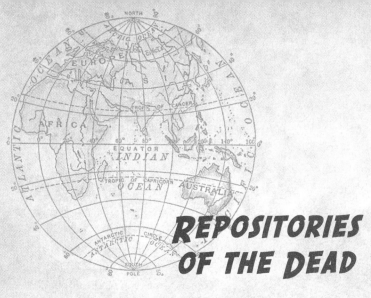

REPOSITORIES OF THE DEAD

JOHN LLOYD STEPHENS
(American diplomat, explorer, and archeologist)

I had seen thousands of Egyptian mummies, and the catacombs of Kiev, the holy city of Russia, where the bodies of the saints are laid in rows, in open coffins, clothed in their best apparel, and adorned with gold and jewels; and in that extraordinary burial-place I had seen, too, a range of small glasses in a dead stone wall, where wild and desperate fanatics had made their own tombs, with their own hands building themselves in an upright position against the walls, leaving a small hole open in front by which to receive their bread and water; and when they died, the small opening was closed with a piece of glass, and the body of the saint was left thus buried. I had seen the catacombs of the Capuchin convent at Syracuse, where the bodies of the monks are dried and laid in open coffins, or fixed in niches in the walls, with their names labeled on their breasts; and in the vault of the convent at Palermo I had seen the bodies of nobles and ladies, the men arranged upright along the walls, dressed as in life, with canes in their hands and swords by their sides; and the noble ladies of Palermo lying in state, their withered bodies clothed in silks and satins, and adorned with gold and jewels; and I remember one among them, who, if then living, would have been but twenty, who two years before had shone in the bright constellation of Sicilian beauty, and, lovely as a light from heaven, had led the dance in the royal palace; I saw her in the same white dress which she had worn at the ball, complete even to the white slippers, the belt around her waist, and the jeweled mockery of a watch hanging at her side, as if she had not done with time forever; her face was bare, the skin dry, black, and shriveled, like burnt paper; the cheeks sunken; the rosy lips a piece of discolored parchment; the teeth horribly projecting; the nose gone; a wreath of roses around her head; and a long tress of hair curling in each hollow eye.

I had seen these things, and even these did not strike me so powerfully as the charnel-house at the convent of Mount Sinai. There was something peculiarly and terribly revolting in this promiscuous heaping together of mortal relics; bones upon bones; the old and young; wise men and fools; good men and bad; martyrs and murderers; masters and servants; bold, daring, and ambitious men—men who would have plucked bright honor from the moon, lying pell-mell with cowards and knaves. The superior told me that there were more than thirty thousand skeletons in the cemetery—literally an army of dead men's bones. Besides the pile of skulls and bones, in a chamber adjoining were the bones of the archbishops, in open boxes, with their names and ages labeled on them, and those of two sons of a king of Persia, who came hither on pilgrimage and died in the convent; their iron shirts, the only dress they wore on their long journey from their father's court, are in the same box. Other skeletons were lying about, some in baskets, and some arranged on shelves, and others tied together and hanging from the roof.

> "[Going down a corridor into the catacombs of Kiev, Russia,] the explorer has not proceeded far in it before he comes to a recess on the right hand containing a coffin without a lid, in which lies the mummied corpse of one of the saints, dressed, or rather swaddled, in silk, with an embroidered cap, and with the stiffened hands so placed as easily to receive the kisses of those visitors who are of the religion of the country. The other bodies seem to be similarly clad, and the kissing of hands is repeated in passing each of the bodies which is so placed as to admit the performance of this ceremony."
>
> —*an anonymous travel writer*

CAVES OF A
THOUSAND BUDDHAS

SIR M. AUREL STEIN

(Anglo-Hungarian archeologist and geographer)

While working for the government of India's Education Department, Aurel Stein became interested in tracing the Silk Road, an ancient series of trading routes that connected China to India, Persia, Syria, Cairo, Athens, and Rome. For centuries, caravans had hauled silks, spices, plants, livestock, exotic animals, slaves, and other commodities along these routes.

Stein's 1906–08 expedition crossed the Hindu Kush into China and traveled around the Taklimakan Desert—one of the most hostile environments on earth, known to locals as the "Land of Death." On the eastern edge of the desert, near the western rim of Chinese settlements, he reached Dunhuang, an oasis crossroads where the Silk Road divides in two directions. Near here he found the Caves of a Thousand Buddhas—a temple complex with 492 grotto openings carved into the face of a cliff, most of them stacked three high—some five high. Inside a small Buddhist monastery nearby, he came upon an immense hoard of 50,000 ancient manuscripts, silk banners, and embroideries dating from the 5th through the 10th centuries A.D.

These treasures were hidden there in the 11th century to protect
them from marauders. His find stunned scholars and revolutionized
what was known of ancient Chinese art and Buddhist history. One
of his contemporaries described his expeditions as "the most daring
and adventurous raid upon the ancient world that any archaeologist
has attempted."

The fine avenues of trees, apparently elms, which extended along the foot of the honeycombed cliffs, and the distant view of some dwellings farther up where the river bank widened, were evidence that the cave-temples had still their resident guardians. Yet there was no human being about to receive us, no guide to distract one's attention. In bewildering multitude and closeness the lines of grottoes presented their faces, some high, some low, perched one above the other without any order or arrangement in stories. In front of many were open verandah-like porches carved out of the soft rock with walls and ceilings bearing faded frescoes. Rough stairs cut into the cliff and still rougher wooden galleries served as approaches to the higher caves. But many of these seemed on the point of crumbling away, and high up in the topmost rows there were manifestly shrines which had become quite inaccessible.

There was nothing to guide me in my first rapid sightseeing. Some of the larger grottoes on the lowest floor had, indeed, elaborate wooden antechapels of unmistakably modern look to indicate restoration. But I soon found that even these shrines contained much that was manifestly old both in fresco work and statuary. [...]

It was in a large shrine farther north, bearing on its walls evidence of recent restoration, that the deposit of manuscripts had been discovered. The entrance to the cave-temple had been formerly blocked by fallen rock-débris and drift sand. After this had been cleared out, and while restorations were slowly proceeding in the temple cella and its antechapel, the workmen engaged had noticed a crack in the frescoed wall of the passage between them. Attracted by this they discovered an opening leading to a recess or small chamber hollowed out from the rock behind the stuccoed wall to the right.

It proved to be completely filled with manuscript rolls which were said to be written in Chinese characters, but in a non-Chinese language. The total quantity was supposed to make up some cart-loads. News of the discovery ultimately reached provincial headquarters, and after specimens had been sent to far-away Lan-chou, orders were supposed to have come from the Viceroy to restore the whole of the find to its original place of deposit. So now behind the carefully locked door with which the recess had been furnished, these strange undeciphered manuscripts were said to be kept. The shrine, though full of Buddhist frescoes and sculptures, was in charge of a Taoist priest, the small fraternity of Ho-shangs or Buddhist monks, to which our guide belonged, peacefully sharing with him the guardianship of the site.

The priest was away in the oasis, apparently on a begging tour with his acolytes. Chiang [Stein's secretary, assistant, and interpreter] had thus no chance to pursue his preliminary enquiries further. But, fortunately, the young Ho-shang's spiritual guide, a Sramana of Tibetan extraction, had borrowed one of the manuscripts for the sake of giving additional lustre to his small private chapel, and our cicerone was persuaded by the Ssŭ-yeh [Chinese secretary, i.e. Chiang] to bring us this specimen. It was a beautifully preserved roll of paper, about a foot high and perhaps fifteen yards long, which I unfolded with Chiang in front of the original hiding-place. The writing was, indeed, Chinese; but my learned secretary frankly acknowledged that to him the characters conveyed no sense whatever.

Was this evidence of a non-Chinese language, or merely an indication how utterly strange the phraseology of Chinese Buddhism is to the literatus brought up on a classical pabulum? However, a frequently repeated formula at once attracted our attention, containing the word "Pu-sa," the Chinese contraction of the Sanskrit term "Bodhisattva." This sufficed to show that the text must be Buddhist—enough to whet my appetite even more for the whole collection. The paper looked remarkably strong and fresh with its smooth surface and fine texture; but in a climate so dry and in a carefully sheltered hiding-place there was no judging of age from mere appearance. So I was obliged to put off all further speculation on this score until we should obtain access to the whole of the hidden library.

It was a novel experience for me to find these shrines, notwithstanding all apparent decay, still frequented as places of actual worship. But quite apart from the damage done by well-meant restorations, I reflected with some apprehension upon the difficulties which this continued sanctity of the site might raise against archaeological exploitation. Would the resident priests be sufficiently good-natured— and mindful of material interests—to close their eyes to the removal of any sacred objects? And, if so, could we rely on their spiritual influence to allay the scruples which might arise among the still more superstitious laity patronizing their pilgrimage place or "Tirtha," to use the familiar Indian term? Only experience and time could show.

Meanwhile I was glad enough to propitiate the young Buddhist priest with an appropriate offering. I always like to be liberal with those whom I may hope to secure as "my own" local priests or "Purohitas" at sites of ancient worship. But, unlike the attitude usually taken up by my Indian Pandit friends on such occasions, when they could—vicariously—gain "spiritual merit" for themselves, Chiang-ssŭ-yeh in his worldly wisdom advised moderation. A present too generous might arouse speculations about possible ulterior objects. Recognising the soundness of his reasoning, I restricted my "Dakshina," or offering, to a piece of hacked silver, equal to about three rupees or four shillings. The gleam of satisfaction on the young Ho-shang's face showed that the people of Tun-huang, whatever else their weaknesses, were not much given to spoiling poor monks. As to Chiang, I thought I could in his attitude detect something closely akin to that mingled regard for the cult and self-conscious pity for its ignorant representatives, which in the old days never allowed of easy relations between my learned associates in Kashmir and the local priests at pilgrimage places we used to visit together for archaeological purposes.

It was getting dusk before I could tear myself away from this wonderful beehive of temples in its setting of barren rocks and sands. The route we followed when returning clambered up the riverine terrace by a steep detritus-covered slope, and then crossed the bare gravel plateau which edges the foot of the outer hills. The west wind which now swept it was piercing, and in the dustladen atmosphere complete darkness soon overtook us. So there was nothing to interfere with the pictures full of vivid colour and grave pomp, all of ages long gone by, which that day's over-abundant sight-seeing had left impressed on my mind's eyes.

*   *   *

Next morning I started what was to be ostensibly the main object of my stay at the site, the survey of the principal grottoes, and the photographing of the more notable frescoes. Purposely I avoided any long interview with the Tao-shih, who had come to offer me welcome at what for the most of the year he might well regard his domain. He looked a very queer person, extremely shy and nervous, with an occasional expression of cunning which was far from encouraging. It was clear from the first that he would be a difficult person to handle.

But when later on I had been photographing in one of the ruined temple grottoes near the great shrine restored by him, where the manuscripts had been discovered, I could not forgo a glance at the entrance passage from which their place of deposit was approached. On my former visit I had found the narrow opening of the recess, locked with a rough wooden door; but now to my dismay it was completely walled up with brickwork. Was this a precaution to prevent the inquisitive barbarian from pining even a glimpse of the manuscript treasures hidden within? I thought of the similar device by which the Jain monks of Jesalmir, in their temple vault, had once attempted to keep Professor Bühler from access to their storehouse of ancient texts, and mentally prepared myself for a long and arduous siege.

The first task was to assure that I should be allowed to see the whole of the manuscripts, and in their original place of deposit. Only thus could I hope to ascertain the true character and approximate date of the collection which had lain hidden behind the passage wall. In order to effect this Chiang had been despatched in the morning to another restored cave-temple where the priest had his quarters, and proceeded to sound him in confidential fashion about the facilities which were to be given. It proved a very protracted affair. Backed up by the promise of a liberal donation for the main shrine, the Ssŭ-yeh's tactful diplomacy seemed at first to make better headway than I had ventured to hope for. The saintly guardian of the reputed treasure explained that the walling up of the door was intended for a precaution against the curiosity of the pilgrims who had recently flocked to the site in their thousands. But evidently wary and of a suspicious mind, he would not yet allow himself to be coaxed into any promise about showing the collection to us as a whole. All that he would agree to, with various meticulous reservations, was to let me see eventually such specimens of the collection as he might conveniently

lay his hands on. When Chiang, in his zeal momentarily forgetting the dictates of diplomatic reticence, was cautiously hinting at the possibility of my wishing, perhaps, to acquire "for future study" one or other of those specimens, the Tao-shih showed such perturbation, prompted equally, it seemed, by scruples of a religious sort and fear of popular resentment, that my sharp-witted secretary thought it best to drop the subject for a time.

But after hours of such diplomatic wrangling he did not leave the priest's smoke-filled chapel and kitchen combined without having elicited an important piece of information. Statements heard at Tun-huang seemed to indicate that the great find of manuscripts had been reported at the time to the Tao-t'ai at Su-chou and thence to the Viceroy of Kan-su. Expression had been given also to a belief, of which we had no means of testing the foundation, that the latter had given orders for the transmission of specimens and for the safe keeping of the whole collection. If such injunctions had really been issued and, perhaps, an official inventory taken, things would necessarily, from our point of view, become far more complicated.

Fortunately Chiang's apprehensions on this score were dispelled by what the priest, turning talkative at times like many nervous people, let drop in conversation.

A few rolls of Chinese texts, apparently Buddhist, had, indeed, been sent to the Viceregal Ya-mên at Lan-chou. But their contents had not been made out there, or else they had failed to attract any interest. Hence officialdom had rested satisfied with the rough statement that the whole of the manuscripts would make up about seven cartloads, and evidently dismayed at the cost of transport, or even of close examination, had left the whole undisturbed in charge of the Tao-shih as guardian of the temple.

But apart from this piece of information, the gist of Chiang-ssŭ-yeh's long report seemed far from justifying great hopes. In spite of the optimistic tinge which Chiang's ever-cheerful disposition was apt to impart to his observations, there was much reason to fear that the priest's peculiar frame of mind would prove a serious obstacle. To rely on the temptation of money alone as a means of overcoming his scruples was manifestly useless. So I thought it best to study his case in personal contact. Accompanied by Chiang I proceeded in the afternoon to pay my formal call to the Tao-shih, and asked to be shown over his restored cave-temple. It was the pride and the mainstay of his Tun-huang existence, and my request was fulfilled with alacrity. As he took me through the lofty antechapel with its substantial woodwork, all new and lavishly gilt and painted, and through the high passage or porch giving access and light to the main cella, I could not help glancing to the right where an ugly patch of unplastered brickwork then still masked the door of the hidden chapel. This was not the time to ask questions of my pious guide as to what was being guarded in that mysterious recess, but rather to display my interest in what his zeal had accomplished in the clearing of the cella and its sacred adornment.

The restoration had been only too thorough. In the middle of the large cella, some forty-six feet square, there rose on a horseshoe-shaped dais, ancient but replastered, a collection of brand-new clay images of colossal size, more hideous, I thought, than any I had seen in these caves. The seated Buddha in the centre, and the disciples, saints, and Guardians of the Regions symmetrically grouped on his sides, showed only too plainly how low sculptural art had sunk in Tun-huang. But neither for this nor for the painful contrast these statues presented to the tasteful and remarkably well preserved fresco decoration on the walls and ceiling of the cella could the worthy Tao-shih reasonably be held responsible. His devotion

"When I visited Angkor Vat [in Kampuchea], I had the shrine very much to myself. Perhaps the grand old ruin was the more impressive in that it showed no trace of human meddling for the last thousand years. The chaos of vegetation had penetrated to the inner courts of the temple; one could see the roots at grips with the masonry.[...]

"I slept two moonlight nights in the temple, alone save for a small company of yellow-robed Buddhist priests—a solitude probably unpurchasable to-day. The sound of one's footsteps in the deserted colonnades awoke myriads of bats. Every night, as the sun sinks, they sweep along the vaulted roofs with a rushing sound like a great wind. The smell of them is like some fœtid incense to age and decay. Then, when they were still, I could hear upon the gentle stir of the palms inside the walls. The moonlight patterned on the stones, silhouetting their plume-like fronds, is associated in my mind with an atmosphere of nirvanic calm and rest. Now and then an owl wailed plaintively from a tree by the moat, and I heard other strange noises nearer by, the labouring of the stones, rustlings as of snakes, sounds without reason, voices of the night.

"Sometimes the darkness of the corridors took tangible shape and a shadowy priest appeared out of the silence. A quiet old priest glided by me with noiseless feet like a shadow; he lit a taper at the end of the cloister; a little shrine before a Buddha was illumined by the flicker of a joss-stick; then he turned and passed me again, as silently as he had come, without a look or a word, devoutly incurious, walking in a trance. The flag-stones were haunted with pious feet."

—*traveler* EDMUND CHANDLER

to this shrine and to the task of religious merit which he had set himself in restoring it, was unmistakably genuine. As a poor, shiftless mendicant he had come from his native province of Shan-hsi some eight years before my visit, settled down at the ruined temple caves, and then set about restoring this one to what he conceived to have been its original glory.

The mouth of the passage was then blocked by drift sand from the silt deposits of the stream, and the original antechapel had completely decayed. When I thought of all the efforts, the perseverance, and the enthusiasm it must have cost this humble priest from afar to beg the money needed for the clearing out of the sand and the substantial reconstructions,—besides the antechapel there were several stories of temple halls built above in solid hard brick and timber, right to the top of the cliff,—I could not help feeling something akin to respect for the queer little figure by my side. It was clear from the way in which he lived with his two humble acolytes, and from all that Chiang had heard about him at Tun-huang, that he spent next to nothing on his person or private interests. Yet his list of charitable subscriptions and his accounts, proudly produced later on to Chiang-ssŭ-yeh, showed quite a respectable total, laboriously collected in the course of these years and spent upon these labours of piety.

It had not taken Chiang long to fathom Wang Tao-shih's profound ignorance of all that constitutes Chinese learning, and the very limited extent of his knowledge in general. So I knew that it would be futile to talk to him about my archaeological interests, about the need of firsthand materials for Chinese historical and anti-quarian studies, and the like, as I was accustomed to do on meeting educated Chinese officials, ever ready to be interested in such topics. But the presence of this quaint priest, with his curious mixture of pious zeal, naïve ignorance, and astute tenacity of purpose, forcibly called to my mind those early Buddhist pilgrims from China who, simple in mind but strong in faith and superstition, once made their way to India in the face of formidable difficulties.

More than once before, my well-known attachment to the memory of Hsüan-tsang, the greatest of those pilgrims, had been helpful in securing me a sympathetic hearing both among the learned and the simple. Wang Tao-shih, too, had probably heard about it. So surrounded by these tokens of lingering Buddhist worship, genuine though distorted, I thought it appropriate to tell Wang Tao-shih, as well as my poor Chinese would permit, of my devotion to the saintly traveller; how I had followed his footsteps from India for over ten thousand li across inhospitable mountains and deserts; how in the course of this pilgrimage I had traced to its present ruins, however inaccessible, many a sanctuary he had piously visited and described; and so on.

I confess it never cost me any effort to grow eloquent on the subject of my "Chinese patron saint," whose guidance had so often proved fruitful for my own work. But now it was made doubly easy by the gleam of lively interest which I caught in the Tao-shih's eyes, otherwise so shy and fitful. As Chiang, in reply to interjected questions, elaborated details and made the most of my familiarity with Hsüan-tsang's authentic records and the distant scenes of his travels, I

could read the impression made in the Taoist priest's generally puzzling countenance. Very soon I felt sure that the Tao-shih, though poorly versed in and
indifferent to things Buddhist, was quite as ardent an admirer in his own way
of "T'ang-seng" [i.e. Hsüan-tsang], the great "monk of the T'ang period," as I
am in another.

I had ocular proof of this when he took us outside into the spacious newly
built loggia in front of the temple, and showed us with pride how he had caused
all its walls to be decorated by a local Tun-huang artist with a series of quaint but
spirited frescoes representing characteristic scenes from the great pilgrim's adventures. They were those fantastic legends which have transformed Hsüan-tsang in
popular belief throughout China into a sort of saintly Munchausen. It is true they
are not to be found in the genuine memoirs and biography. But what did that
little difference in our respective conceptions of the hero matter? Gladly I let my
delightfully credulous cicerone expound in voluble talk the wonderful stories of
travel which each fresco panel depicted. Here the holy pilgrim was seen snatched
up to the clouds by a wicked demon and then restored again to his pious companions through the force of his prayer or magic. Two queer-looking figures—one
horse-, one bull-headed—were represented as his constant attendants. Elsewhere
he was shown forcing a ferocious dragon which had swallowed his horse to restore
it again, and so on.

But the picture in which I displayed particular interest showed a theme curiously adapted to our own case, though it was not till later that I appealed again
and again to the moral it pointed. There was T'ang-sêng standing on the bank
of a violent torrent, and beside him his faithful steed laden with big bundles of
manuscripts. To help in ferrying across such a precious burden a large turtle was
seen swimming towards the pilgrim. Here was clearly a reference to the twenty
pony-loads of sacred books and relics which the historical traveller managed to
carry away safely from India. But would the pious guardian read this obvious
lesson aright, and be willing to acquire spiritual merit by letting me take back to
the old home of Buddhism some of the ancient manuscripts which chance had
placed in his keeping? For the time being it seemed safer not to tackle that question. Yet when I took my leave of the Tao-shih I instinctively felt that a new and
more reliable link was being established between us.

I left the Ssŭ-yeh behind to make the most of the favourable impression produced, and to urge an early loan of the promised manuscript specimens. But the priest had again become nervous and postponed their delivery in a vague way "until later." There was nothing for me but to wait.

All doubt, however, disappeared in the end. Late at night Chiang groped his way to my tent in silent elation with a bundle of Chinese rolls which Wang Tao-shih had just brought him in secret, carefully hidden under his flowing black robe, as the first of the promised "specimens." The rolls looked unmistakably old as regards writing and paper, and probably contained Buddhist canonical texts; but Chiang needed time to make sure of their character. Next morning he turned up by daybreak and with a face expressing both triumph and amazement reported that these fine rolls of paper contained Chinese versions of certain "Sutras" from the Buddhist canon which the colophons declared to have been brought from India and translated by Hsüan-tsang himself. The strange chance which thus caused us to be met at the very outset by the name of my Chinese patron saint, and by what undoubtedly were early copies of his labours as a sacred translator, struck both of us as a most auspicious omen. Was it not "T'ang-sêng" himself, so Chiang declared, who at the opportune moment had revealed the hiding-place of that manuscript hoard to an ignorant priest in order to prepare for me, his admirer and disciple from distant India, a fitting antiquarian reward on the westernmost confines of China proper?

Of Hsüan-tsang's authorship, Wang Tao-shih in his ignorance could not possibly have had any inkling when he picked up that packet of "specimens." Chiang-ssŭ-yeh realized at once that this discovery was bound to impress the credulous priest as a special interposition on my behalf of the great traveller of sacred memory. So he hastened away to carry the news to the Tao-shih, and, backed up by this visible evidence of support from the latter's own cherished saint, to renew his pleading for free access to the hidden manuscript store. The effect was most striking. Before long Chiang returned to report that the portent could be trusted to work its spell. Some hours later he found the wall blocking the entrance to the recess of the temple removed, and on its door being opened by the priest, caught a glimpse of a room crammed full to the roof with manuscript bundles. I had purposely kept away from the Tao-shih's temple all the forenoon, but on getting this news

I could no longer restrain my impatience to see the great hoard myself. The day was cloudless and hot, and the "soldiers" who had followed me about during the morning with my cameras, were now taking their siesta in sound sleep soothed by a good smoke of opium. So accompanied only by Chiang I went to the temple.

I found the priest there evidently still combating his scruples and nervous apprehensions. But under the influence of that quasi-divine hint he now summoned up courage to open before me the rough door closing the narrow entrance which led from the side of the broad front passage into the rock-carved recess, on a level of about four feet above the floor of the former. The sight of the small room disclosed was one to make my eyes open wide. Heaped up in layers, but without any order, there appeared in the dim light of the priest's little lamp a solid mass of manuscript bundles rising to a height of nearly ten feet, and filling, as subsequent measurement showed, close on 500 cubic feet. The area left clear within the room was just sufficient for two people to stand in. It was manifest that in this "black hole" no examination of the manuscripts would be possible, and also that the digging out of all its contents would cost a good deal of physical labour.

A suggestion to clear out all the bundles into the large cellar of the cave-temple, where they might have been examined at ease, would have been premature; so much oppressed at the time was Wang Tao-shih by fears of losing his position—and patrons—by the rumours which any casual observers might spread against him in the oasis. So for the present I had to rest content with his offer to take out a bundle or two at a time, and to let us look rapidly through their contents in a less cramped part of the precincts. Fortunately the restorations carried out by him, besides the fine loggia already mentioned, included a kind of large ante-chapel, having on either side a small room provided with a door and paper-covered windows. So here a convenient "reading-room" was at hand for this strange old library, where we were screened from any inquisitive eyes, even if an occasional worshipper dropped in to "kotow" before the huge and ugly Buddha statue now set up in the temple.

While the Tao-shih was engaged in digging out a few bundles, I closely examined the passage wall behind which this great deposit of manuscripts had been hidden. The priest had told us that, when he first settled at the "Thousand Buddhas" some eight years before, he found the entrance to this cave-temple almost completely blocked by drift sand. Judging from the condition of the ocher caves near by and the relatively low level of this particular temple, it is probable that this accumulation of drift sand rose to ten feet or more at the entrance. Keeping only a few labourers at work from the proceeds of pious donations, at first coming driblet-like with lamentable slowness, our Tao-shih had taken two or three years to lay bare the whole of the broad passage, some forty feet deep. When this task had been accomplished, and while engaged in setting up new statues in place of the decayed old stucco images occupying the dais of the cellar, he had noticed a small crack in the frescoed wall to the right of the passage. There appeared to be a recess behind the plastered surface instead of the solid conglomerate from which the cells and its approach are hewn; and on widening the opening he discovered the small room with its deposit such as I now saw it.[...]

The first bundles which emerged from that "black hole" consisted of thick rolls of paper about one foot high, evidently containing portions of canonical Buddhist texts in Chinese translations. All were in excellent preservation and yet showed in paper, arrangement, and other details, unmistakable signs of great age. The jointed strips of strongly made and remarkably tough and smooth yellowish paper, often ten yards or more long, were neatly rolled up, after the fashion of Greek papyri, over small sticks of hard wood sometimes having carved or inlaid end knobs. All showed signs of having been much read and handled; often the protecting outer fold, with the silk tape which had served for tying up the roll, had got torn off. Where these covering folds were intact it was easy for the Ssŭ-yeh to read off the title of the Sutra, the chapter number, etc.

Buddhist literature lay wholly outside the range of Chiang's studies, as indeed it is nowadays beyond the ken of almost all Chinese literati. I myself, though familiar to some extent with Buddhist scriptures in their original Indian garb, laboured under a fatal disadvantage—my total ignorance of literary Chinese. So what Chiang could make out of the titles was of no guidance to me. But on one point his readings soon gave me assurance: the headings in the first bundles were all found to be different. So my apprehension of discovering here that inane repetition of a few identical texts in which modern Buddhism in Tibet and elsewhere revels, gradually vanished. I set the Ssŭ-yeh to work to prepare a rough list of titles; but as by and by the devout guardian of these treasures took more courage and began to drag out load after load of manuscript bundles, all attempt even at the roughest cataloguing had to be abandoned. It would have required a whole staff of learned scribes to deal properly with such a deluge.

Mixed up with the Chinese bundles there came to light Tibetan texts also written in roll form, though with clearly marked sections, as convenience of reading required in the case of a writing running in horizontal lines, not in vertical columns like Chinese. I could not doubt that they contained portions of the great canonical collections now known as the Tanjur and Kanjur. In the first rapid examination Chiang failed to discover colophons giving exact dates of the writing in any of the Chinese rolls, and owing to their length a complete unfolding would have required much time. So I had reason to feel doubly elated when, on the reverse of a Chinese roll, I first lighted upon a text written in that cursive form of Indian Brahmi script with which the finds of ancient Buddhist texts at sites of the Khotan region had rendered me familiar. Here was indisputable proof that the bulk of the manuscripts deposited went back to the time when Indian writing and some knowledge of Sanskrit still prevailed in Central-Asian Buddhism. With such evidence clearly showing the connection which once existed between these religious establishments and Buddhist learning as transplanted to the Tarim Basin, my hopes rose greatly for finds of direct importance to Indian and Western research.

All the manuscripts seemed to be preserved exactly in the same condition they were in when deposited. Some of the bundles were carelessly fastened with only rough cords and without an outer cloth wrapper; but even this had failed to injure the paper. Nowhere could I trace the slightest effect of moisture. And, in fact, what better place for preserving such relics could be imagined than a chamber carved in the live rock of these terribly barren hills, and hermetically shut off from what moisture, if any, the atmosphere of this desert valley ever contained? Not in the driest soil could relics of a ruined site have so completely escaped injury as they had here in a carefully selected rock chamber where, hidden behind a brick wall and protected by accumulated drift sand, these masses of manuscripts had lain undisturbed for centuries.

How grateful I felt for the special protection thus afforded when, on opening a large packet wrapped in a sheet of stout coloured canvas, I found it full of paintings on fine gauze-like silk and on linen, ex-votos in all kinds of silk and brocade, with a mass of miscellaneous fragments of painted papers and cloth materials. Most of the paintings first found were narrow pieces from two to three feet in length, and proved by their floating streamers and the triangular tops provided with strings for fastening to have served as temple banners. These mountings made them look much more imposing when hung up. Many of them were in excellent condition, and all exactly as they had been deposited, after longer or shorter use.[...]

Closely and often carelessly folded up at the time of their deposition, and much creased in consequence as they were, any attempt to open them out would have implied obvious risk of damage to the thin material which centuries of compression in the driest air had rendered terribly brittle. But by lifting a fold here and there I could see that the scenes represented were almost as elaborate as the fresco panels on the walls of the old grottoes. Greatly tempted as I was to search for votive inscriptions likely to contain dates, I had to leave the opening till later from fear of possible damage.

Nor was there time for any closer study, such as I should have loved to give there and then to these delicate, graceful paintings. My main care was how many of them I might hope to rescue from their dismal imprisonment and the risks attending their present guardian's careless handling. To my surprise and relief he evidently attached little value to these beautiful relics of pictorial art in the T'ang times. So I made bold to put aside rapidly "for further inspection," the best of the pictures on silk, linen, or paper I could lay my hands on, more than a dozen from the first bundle alone. I longed to carry away all its contents; for even among the fragments there were beautiful pieces, and every bit of silk would have its antiquarian and artistic value. But it would not have been wise to display too much *empressement*. So I restrained myself as well as I could, and put the rest away, with the firm resolve to return to the charge as soon as the ground was prepared for more extensive acquisitions.

To remains of this kind the priest seemed indifferent. The secret hope of diverting by their sacrifice my attention from the precious rolls of Chinese canonical texts or "Ching" made him now more assiduously grope for and hand out bundles of what he evidently classed under the head of miscellaneous rubbish. I had every reason to be pleased with this benevolent intention; for in the very first large packet of this kind I discovered, mixed up with Chinese and Tibetan texts, a great heap of oblong paper leaves in the variety of Indian script known as Central-Asian Brahmi.

They proved on arrangement to belong to half-a-dozen different manuscripts of the Pothi shape, some in Sanskrit, some in one or other of the "unknown" languages used by Turkestan Buddhism. Several of these manuscripts were of large size, with leaves up to twenty-one inches in length, and some have since on arrangement proved to be complete. None of my previous finds in Brahmi script equalled them in this respect or in excellence of preservation. So that first day Chiang and myself worked on without a break until quite late, picking out sometimes stray leaves in Indian script even from regular bundles of Chinese or Tibetan rolls, or else Chinese rolls bearing on the reverse texts in a cursive form of Central-Asian Brahmi.

Flushed as I was with delight at these unhoped-for discoveries, I could not lose sight of the chief practical task, all-important for the time being. It was to keep our priest in a pliable mood, and to prevent his mind being overcome by the trepidations with which the chance of any intrusion and of consequent hostile rumours among his patrons would fill him. With the help of Chiang-ssǔ-yeh's genial persuasion, and what reassuring display I could make of my devotion to Buddhist lore in general and the memory of my patron saint in particular, we succeeded better than I had ventured to hope. I could see our honest Tao-shih's timorous look changing gradually to one of contentment at our appreciation of all this, to him valueless, lore. Though he visibly grew tired climbing over manuscript heaps and dragging out heavy bundles, it seemed as if he were becoming resigned to his fate, at least for a time.

When the growing darkness in the cave compelled us to stop further efforts for the day, a big bundle of properly packed manuscripts and painted fabrics lay on one side of our "reading room" awaiting removal for what our diplomatic convention styled "closer examination." The great question was whether Wang Tao-shih would be willing to brave the risks of this removal, and subsequently to fall in with the true interpretation of our proceeding. It would not have done to breathe to him unholy words of sale and purchase; it was equally clear that any removal would have to be effected in strictest secrecy. So when we stepped outside the temple there was nothing in our hands or about our persons to arouse the slightest suspicion.

Then, tired as we all were, I took the occasion to engage the priest in another long talk about our common hero and patron saint, the great Hsüan-tsang. What better proof of his guidance and favour could I claim than that I should have been allowed to behold such a wonderful hidden store of sacred relics belonging to his own times and partly derived, perhaps, from his Indian wanderings, within a cave-temple which so ardent an admirer of "T'ang-sêng" had restored and was now guarding? Again I let the Tao-shih enlarge, as we stood in the loggia, upon the extraordinary adventures of his great saint as depicted in those cherished frescoes on its walls. The panel which showed Hsüan-tsang returning with his animal heavily laden with sacred manuscripts from India, was the most effective apologue I could advance for my eager interest in the relics the Tao-shih had discovered and was yet keeping from daylight.

The priest in his more susceptible moods could not help acknowledging that this fate of continued confinement in a dark hole was not the purpose for which the great scholar-saint had let him light upon these precious remains of Buddhist lore, and that he himself was quite incompetent to do justice to them by study or otherwise. Was it not evident, so Chiang pleaded with all the force of his soft reasoning, that by allowing me, a faithful disciple of Hsüan-tsang, to render accessible to Western students the literary and other relics which a providential discovery had placed so abundantly in his keeping, he would do an act of real religious merit? That this pious concession would also be rewarded by an ample donation for the benefit of the shrine he had laboured to restore to its old glory, was a secondary consideration merely to be hinted at.

Whatever impression such and similar talks produced on the mind of the good Tao-shih, constantly vacillating between fears about his saintly reputation and a business-like grasp of the advantages to be attained by accommodating me in the matter of useless old things, the day closed with a gratifying achievement. In accordance with his own advice, I had left the Ssŭ-yeh alone to tackle the question of how to secure quietly the manuscripts and paintings selected. It was late at night when I heard cautious footsteps. It was Chiang who had come to make sure that nobody was stirring about my tent. A little later he returned with a big bundle over his shoulders. It contained everything I had picked out during the day's work.

The Tao-shih had summoned up courage to fall in with my wishes, on the solemn condition that nobody besides us three was to get the slightest inkling of what was being transacted, and that as long as I kept on Chinese soil the origin of these "finds" was not to be revealed to any living being. He himself was afraid of being seen at night outside his temple precincts. So the Ssŭ-yeh, zealous and energetic as always, took it upon himself to be the sole carrier. For seven nights more he thus came to my tent, when everybody had gone to sleep, with the same precautions, his slight figure panting under loads which grew each time heavier, and ultimately required carriage by instalments. For hands accustomed only to wield pen and paper it was a trying task, and never shall I forget the good-natured case and cheerful devotion with which it was performed by that most willing of helpmates.

It would serve no useful purpose if I were to attempt to describe in detail how the search was continued day after day without remission, or to indicate in quasi-chronological order all the interesting finds with which this curious "digging" was rewarded. From the first it was certain that the contents of the hidden chapel must have been deposited in great confusion, and that any indications the original position of the bundles might have afforded at the time of discovery, had been completely effaced when the recess was cleared out, as the Tao-shih admitted, to search for valuables, and again later on for the purpose of removing the big inscribed slab from its west wall into the passage outside. It was mere chance, too, what bundles the Tao-shih would hand us out.

Nor was that hurried search the time for appreciating properly the import of all that passed through my hands. The systematic study of the materials I was most eager to secure was bound to take years of specialist labour, and what this has so far revealed as regards the main classes of relics, I shall endeavour to sketch in a subsequent chapter. Here I must content myself with a rapid review of those discoveries which at the time struck me most and helped me to form conclusions as to the history of this whole *cache* of antiquarian treasures.

After the experience of the first day it was easy to recognize the special value of those bundles filled with miscellaneous texts, painted fabrics, ex-votos, papers of all sorts, which had evidently been stored away as no longer needed for use.

By their irregular shape and fastening they could readily be distinguished from the uniform packets containing rolls of Buddhist texts in Chinese or Tibetan. Fortunately their very irregularity had caused the Tao-shih to put them on the top when he built up the wall-like array of what I may call "library bundles;" and the consequent case with which they could be reached induced him now to bring them out in steady succession.

It was from those "mixed" bundles chiefly that manuscripts and detached leaves in Indian script and of the traditional Pothi shape continued to emerge. By far the most important among such finds was a remarkably well preserved Sanskrit manuscript on palm leaves, some seventy in number, and no less than twenty inches long. The small but beautifully clear writing closely covering these leaves showed palaeographical features which seemed to leave little doubt as to the manuscript going back to the third or fourth century A.D. at the latest. This high age, not surpassed by any Sanskrit manuscript then known, made the text important, even though it has proved to be that of a work well known in the Northern Buddhist Canon. That the manuscript had been written in India itself was quite certain from its material. But who was the pilgrim who had brought it to the very confines of China? [. . .]

The Chinese, as people of culture and business habits, have always recognized the need of exact dates. So I soon was able to gather a considerable mass of dated documents, many quasi-official, from which to draw a definite conclusion as to the time when this great deposit of manuscripts and sacred relics was finally closed and forgotten. The great majority belonged to the ninth and tenth centuries of our era, and as those from the middle of the tenth century were frequent while only a few approached its end and none extended beyond the reign of the Emperor Chên Tsung (998–1022 A.D.), I was able to determine that the walling-up of the chamber must have taken place early in the eleventh century. There can be little doubt that the fear of some destructive invasion had prompted the act, and in view of the above chronological indication a connection naturally suggests itself with the conquest of Tun-huang by the rising power of the Hsi-hsia which took place between 1034 and 1037 A.D. The total absence of any manuscripts written in the special characters which the founder of the Hsi-hsia dynasty adopted in 1036 A.D., strongly supports this assumption.

But the small well-sheltered cave had in all probability served for a long time previously as a place of deposit for all kinds of objects sanctified by use but no longer needed in the various shrines. A clear indication of this was supplied by many small and carefully packed bags which I found containing tiny fragments of sacred texts, and ragged remnants of silk paintings. Such insignificant relics would certainly not have been collected and sewn up systematically in the commotion of a sudden emergency. So much was obvious from the first, that the objects deposited in this chapel must very often have been already of considerable antiquity at the time when the deposit was finally walled up. Yet it was to me a very gratifying assurance when in examining portions of our Chinese collection, a year later, Chiang-ssŭ-yeh found a series of manuscript rolls showing exact dates which seemed to extend as far back as the third century A.D. But even then I realized that it would take protracted scholarly labours in Europe before the date of the earliest pieces could be definitely established.

As I worked my way in great haste through the contents of the "mixed" bundles,—we never knew how long we might rely on the Tao-shih's indulgence— I felt elated and at the same time oppressed by the constant flow of fresh materials pouring down upon us. Even in the case of art relics and manuscripts which were neither Chinese nor Tibetan, and of which I was able to estimate the full interest, there was no chance of closer examination. All I could do was to make sure of their being put apart "for further study," as our polite convention called removal. But what obsessed me most at the time was my total want of Sinologist training. How gladly would I then have exchanged one-half of my Indian knowledge for a tenth of its value in Chinese! Even with Chiang's zealous help I could never be sure of not leaving behind documents and texts of historical or literary interest amidst the smothering mass of Buddhist canonical literature and the like.

Nevertheless in this tantalizing *embarras des richesses* I was able to catch a few encouraging glimpses. It was thus that, in a series of monastic records apparently issued under the seal of the abbot of the chief establishment, I lighted upon the old name of the Ch'ien-fo-tung site, which here figured as San-chieh-ssŭ, the "Temples of the Three Regions." Subsequently I found out that even now three divisions are distinguished among the cave-temples, though the old designation of the site seems quite forgotten. Then again I found complete rolls stamped with the die of the "Temples of the Three Regions," and thus clearly marked as having formed part of a general monastic library.

Greatly delighted was I when I found that an excellently preserved roll with a well-designed block-printed picture as frontispiece, had its text printed through-out, showing a date of production corresponding to 860 A.D. Here was conclusive evidence that the art of printing books from wooden blocks was practised long before the conventionally assumed time of its invention, during the Sung period, and that already in the ninth century the technical level had been raised practically as high as the process permitted. Then again there were spirited drawings and woodcuts to be found in the midst of the Chinese text rolls, needing no specialist experience to recognize their artistic merit.

Five days of strenuous work resulted in the extraction and rapid search of all "miscellaneous" bundles likely to contain manuscripts of special interest, paint-ings, and other relics which I was eager to rescue first of all. Fortunately when the Tao-shih had last stuffed back his treasures into their "black hole," these had

been put mostly on the top or in other more or less accessible places, being, of course, less convenient building material than the tight uniform packets of Chinese and Tibetan rolls. But my task was not ended while there still rose against the walls of the chamber that solid rampart of manuscript bundles. They would have to be cleared out, too, and rapidly looked through. It was bound to prove a troublesome undertaking in more than one sense, though discreet treatment and judiciously administered doses of silver had so far succeeded in counteracting the Tao-shih's relapses into timorous contrariness. The labour of clearing out the whole chapel might by itself have dismayed a stouter heart than that of our priestly "librarian;" and what with this and the increased risk of exposure involved, Wang Tao-shih became now altogether refractory. However, he had already been gradually led from one concession to another, and we took care not to leave him much time for reflection.

So at last with many a sigh and plaintive remonstrance, and behind the outer temple gates carefully locked, he set to this great toil, helped now by a sort of priestly famulus whose discretion could be relied on. Previously I had sometimes feared that the little Tao-shih might get smothered under a tumbling wall of manuscript. Now I wondered whether the toil of pulling them out would not cause his slender physique to collapse. But it held out all the same, and by the evening of May 28th the regular bundles of Chinese rolls, more than 1050 in all, and those containing Tibetan texts had been transferred to neat rows in the spacious main cella of the temple.

The bundles were almost all sewn up tightly in coarse covers of linen. But the ends were generally left open, and as Wang handed out bundle after bundle through the chapel door, Chiang and myself were just able to see hastily whether, amidst the usual rolls with Chinese texts, there were embedded any Pothi leaves from Brahmi manuscripts, folded-up pictures, or other relics of special attraction. Such we picked out and put aside rapidly. But there was no time even to glance at individual rolls and to see whether they bore anywhere within or without Indian or Central-Asian writing.

Perfunctory as the operation had to be in view of the Tao-shih's visibly growing reluctance, I had a gratifying reward for my insistence on this clearing in the discovery of several miscellaneous bundles at the very bottom. They had been used there by the Tao-shih to turn a low clay platform into a level foundation for the manuscript wall above. In spite of the crushing these bundles had undergone, I recovered from them a large number of exquisite silk paintings of all sizes, and some beautiful embroidered pieces. One of the latter was a magnificent embroidery picture, remarkable for design, colours, and fineness of material, and showing a Buddha between Bodhisattvas in life size, which I shall have occasion to discuss hereafter.

Perhaps it was a lively sensation of the toil he had undergone and now longed to see ended, or else the fear that we were now touching those precious Chinese Sutra texts to which alone he seemed to attach any real value. At any rate the Tao-shih at this stage came to business, so to speak, by asking for a substantial "subscription" (*pu-shih*) to his temple. At the same time he protested that any cession of sacred texts or "Chings" was impossible. I myself was glad to take up the theme; for I had recognized long before that it was my duty towards research to try my utmost to rescue, if possible, the whole of the collection from the risk of slow dispersion and loss with which it was threatened in such keeping.

But at the same time I could not close my eyes to the serious difficulties and objections. I was quite unable to form any definite estimate of the philological value of those masses of Chinese canonical texts which made up the bulk of the hidden library. Their contents were, no doubt, to be found in the complete editions of the Buddhist "Tripitaka," printed for centuries past in China, Korea, Japan. Still less was I able to select those texts which for one reason or other were possessed of antiquarian or literary interest. The removal of so many cart-loads of manuscripts would inevitably give publicity to the whole transaction, and the religious resentment this was likely to arouse in Tun-huang, even if it did not lead to more serious immediate consequences, would certainly compromise my chance of further work in Kan-su.

Nevertheless, I was prepared to face these risks rather than forgo the endeavour to rescue the whole hoard. Chiang-ssŭ-yeh, in spite of misgivings justified by his knowledge of the local conditions, loyally did his best to persuade the Tao-shih that removal of the collection to a "temple of learning in Ta-Ying-kuo," or England, would in truth be an act which Buddha and his Arhats might approve as pious. He also urged that the big sum I was prepared to pay (I hinted at 40 horse-shoes, about Rs.5000, and was resolved to give twice as much, if need be, whatever the excess over my sanctioned grant) would enable Wang to return to a life of peace in his native province, distant Shan-hsi, if Tun-huang should become too hot for him. Or else he could allay any scruples by using the whole sum for the benefit of the temple, which by his restoration he could claim to have annexed as his own with all its contents known or unknown.

But all in vain. The prospect of losing his precious "Chings" as a whole or in part profoundly frightened the good priest, who had before resignedly closed his eyes to my gathering whatever I thought of special artistic or antiquarian value. For the first time our relations became somewhat strained, and it required very careful handling and our suavest manners to obviate anything like a breach. What the Tao-shih urged with all signs of sincere anxiety was that any deficiency in those piles of sacred texts would certainly be noticed by his patrons, who had helped him with their publicly recorded subscriptions to clear and restore the temple; that in consequence the position he had built up for himself in the district by the pious labours of eight years would be lost for good, and his life-task destroyed. He even vaguely reproached himself for having given up sacred things over which his lay patrons ought to have as much right of control as he himself, and doggedly asserted the need of consulting them before moving a step further. And in the depth of my heart I could bear him no grudge for these scruples and recriminations, or even gainsay them.

For two long days these discussions had to be carried on intermittently with a view to gain time while my examination of the miscellaneous bundles was proceeding. I managed to complete this by the second evening. But on returning early next day to the temple in order to start the close search of the regular Chinese bundles for Central-Asian and other foreign text materials, I found to my dismay that the Tao-shih in a sudden fit of perturbation had shifted back overnight almost the whole of them to their gloomy prison of centuries. His sullen temper gave us further cause of anxiety. But the advantage we possessed by already holding loads of valuable manuscripts and antiques, and the Tao-shih's unmistakable wish to secure a substantial sum of money, led at last to what I had reason to claim as a substantial success in this diplomatic struggle.

He agreed to let me have fifty well-preserved bundles of Chinese text rolls and five of Tibetan ones, besides all my previous selections from the miscellaneous bundles. For all these acquisitions four horse-shoes of silver, equal to about Rs.500, passed into the priest's hands; and when I surveyed the archaeological value of all I could carry away for this sum, I had good reason to claim it a bargain. Of course, after so severe a struggle I lost no time in removing the heavy loads of Chinese and Tibetan rolls. Until now my devoted Ssŭ-yeh had struggled to my tent night by night with the loads of daily "selections;" but to this task his physical strength would not have been equal. So help had to be sought on this occasion from Ibrahim, Beg, and Tila, my trusted followers; and after two midnight trips to the temple, under the screening shadow of the steep river bank, the huge sackfuls were safely transferred to my store-room without any one, even of my own men, having received an inkling.

The Tao-shih's nervousness had been increased by prolonged absence from his clients in the oasis; and now he hastened to resume his seasonal begging tour in the Tun-huang district. But a week later he returned, reassured that the secret had not been discovered and that his spiritual influence, such as it was, had suf-fered no diminution. So we succeeded in making him stretch a point further, and allow me to add some twenty more bundles of manuscripts to my previous selections, against an appropriate donation for the temple. When later on it came to the packing, the manuscript acquisitions needed seven cases, while the paintings, embroideries, and other miscellaneous relics filled five more. The packing of these was a very delicate task and kept me busy on the days when photographic work was impossible in the caves. There was some little trouble about getting enough boxes without exciting suspicion at Tun-huang. Luckily I had foreseen the chance and provided some "empties" beforehand. The rest were secured in disguise and by discreet instalments. So everything passed off without a hitch.

The good Tao-shih now seemed to breathe freely again, and almost ready to recognize that I was performing a pious act in rescuing for Western scholarship those relics of ancient Buddhist literature and art which local ignorance would allow to lie here neglected or to be lost in the end. When I finally said good-bye to the "Thousand Buddhas," his jovial sharp-cut face had resumed once more its look of shy but self-contented serenity. We parted in fullest amity. I may anticipate here that I received gratifying proof of the peaceful state of his mind when, on my return to An-hsi four months later, he agreed to let depart for that "temple of learning" in the distant West another share of the Chinese and Tibetan manuscripts in the shape of over two hundred compact bundles. But my time for feeling true relief came when all the twenty-four cases, heavy with manuscript treasures rescued from that strange place of hiding, and the five more filled with paintings and other art relics from the same cave, had been deposited safely in the British Museum.

THE STRANGE RIDE OF MORROWBIE JUKES

RUDYARD KIPLING

(novelist)

Alive or dead—there is no other way.
—NATIVE PROVERB

There is no invention about this tale. Jukes by accident stumbled upon a village that is well known to exist, though he is the only Englishman who has been there. A somewhat similar institution used to flourish on the outskirts of Calcutta, and there is a story that if you go into the heart of Bikanir, which is in the heart of the great Indian desert, you shall come across not a village but a town where the dead who did not die but may not live have established their headquarters. And since it is perfectly true that in the same desert is a wonderful city where all the rich money-lenders retreat after they have made their fortunes (fortunes so vast that the owners cannot trust even the strong hand of the government to protect them, but take refuge in the waterless sands), and drive sumptuous Cee-spring barouches, and buy beautiful girls, and decorate their palaces with gold and ivory and Minton tiles and mother-o'-pearl, I do not see why Jukes's tale should not be true. He is a civil engineer, with a head for plans and distances and things of that kind, and he certainly would not take the trouble to invent imaginary traps. He could earn more by doing his legitimate work. He never

169

varies the tale in the telling, and grows very hot and indignant when he thinks of the disrespectful treatment he received. He wrote this quite straightforwardly at first, but he has touched it up in places and introduced moral reflections; thus:

In the beginning it all arose from a slight attack of fever. My work necessitated my being in camp for some months between Pakpattan and Mubarakpur—a desolate sandy stretch of country, as everyone who has had the misfortune to go there may know. My coolies were neither more nor less exasperating than other gangs, and my work demanded sufficient Attention to keep me from moping, had I been inclined to so unmanly a weakness.

On the 23rd December, 1884, I felt a little feverish. There was a full moon at the time, and in consequence, every dog near my tent was baying it. The brutes assembled in twos and threes and drove me frantic. A few days previously I had shot one loud-mouthed singer and suspended his carcass *in terrorem* about fifty yards from, my tent door, but his friends fell upon, fought for, and ultimately devoured the body, and as it seemed to me, sang their hymns of thanksgiving afterwards with renewed energy.

The light-headedness which accompanies fever acts differently on different men. My irritation gave way after a short time to a fixed determination to slaughter one huge black-and-white beast who had been foremost in song and first in flight throughout the evening. Thanks to a shaking hand and a giddy head, I had already missed him twice with both barrels of my shotgun, when it struck me that my best plan would be to ride him down in the open and finish him off with a hog-spear. This, of course, was merely the semi-delirious notion of a fever patient, but I remember that it struck me at the time as being eminently practical and feasible.

I therefore ordered my groom to saddle Pornic and bring him round quietly to the rear of my tent. When the pony was ready, I stood at his head prepared to mount and dash out as soon as the dog should again lift up his voice. Pornic, by the way, had not been out of his pickets for a couple of days; the night air was crisp and chilly; and I was armed with a specially long and sharp pair of persuaders with which I had been rousing a sluggish cob that afternoon. You will easily believe, then, that when he was let go he went quickly. In one moment, for the brute bolted as straight as a die, the tent was left far behind, and we were flying over the smooth sandy soil at racing speed. In another we had passed the wretched dog, and I had almost forgotten why it was that I had taken horse and hog-spear.

The delirium of fever and the excitement of rapid motion through the air must have taken away the remnant of my senses. I have a faint recollection of standing upright in my stirrups, and of brandishing my hog-spear at the great white moon that looked down so calmly on my mad gallop, and of shouting challenges to the camel-thornbushes as they whizzed past. Once or twice, I believe, I swayed forward on Pornic's neck, and literally hung on by my spurs—as the marks next morning showed.

The wretched beast went forward like a thing possessed, over what seemed to be a limitless expanse of moonlit sand. Next, I remember, the ground rose suddenly in front of us, and as we topped the ascent I saw the waters of the Sudej shining like a silver bar below. Then Pornic blundered heavily on his nose, and we rolled together down some unseen slope.

I must have lost consciousness, for when I recovered I was lying on my stomach in a heap of soft white sand, and the dawn was beginning to break dimly over the edge of the slope down which I had fallen. As the light grew stronger I saw I was at the bottom of a horseshoe-shaped crater of sand opening on one side directly on to the shoals of the Sutlej. My fever had altogether left me, and with the exception of a slight dizziness in the head, I felt no bad effects from the fall overnight.

Pornic, who was standing a few yards away, was naturally a good deal exhausted but had not hurt himself in the least. His saddle, a favourite polo one, was much knocked about and had been twisted under his belly. It took me some time to put him to rights, and in the meantime I had ample opportunities of observing the spot into which I had so foolishly dropped.

At the risk of being considered tedious, I must describe it at length, inasmuch as an accurate mental picture of its peculiarities will be of material assistance in enabling the reader to understand what follows.

Imagine then, as I have said before, a horseshoe-shaped crater of sand with steeply graded sand walls about thirty-five feet high. (The slope, I fancy, must have been about sixty-five degrees.) This crater enclosed a level piece of ground about fifty yards long by thirty at its broadest part, with a rude well in the centre. Round the bottom of the crater, about three feet from the level of the ground proper, ran a series of eighty-three semicircular, ovoid, square, and multilateral holes, all about three feet at the mouth. Each hole on inspection showed that it was carefully shored internally with driftwood and bamboos, and over the mouth a wooden drip-board projected, like the peak of a jockey's cap, for two feet. No sign of life was visible in these tunnels, but a most sickening stench pervaded the entire amphitheatre—a stench fouler than any which my wanderings in Indian villages have introduced me to.

Having remounted Pornic, who was as anxious as I to get back to camp, I rode round the base of the horseshoe to find some place whence an exit would be practicable. The inhabitants, whoever they might be, had not thought fit to put in an appearance, so I was left to my own devices. My first attempt to "rush" Pornic up the steep sand-banks showed me that I had fallen into a trap exactly on the same model as that which the ant-lion sets for its prey. At each step the shifting sand poured down from above in tons and rattled on the drip-boards of the holes like small shot. A couple of ineffectual charges sent us both rolling down to the bottom, half choked with the torrents of sand; and I was constrained to turn my attention to the river-bank.

Here everything seemed easy enough. The sand-hills ran down to the river edge, it is true, but there were plenty of shoals and shallows across which I could gallop Pornic and find my way back to *terra firma* by turning sharply to the right or the left. As I led Pornic over the sands I was startled by the faint pop of a rifle across the river; and at the same moment a bullet dropped with a sharp "*whit*" close to Pornic's head.

There was no mistaking the nature of the missile—a regulation Martini-Henry "picket." About five hundred yards away a country-boat was anchored in midstream; and a jet of smoke drifting away from its bows in the still morning air showed me whence the delicate attention had come. Was ever a respectable gentleman in such an *impasse*? The treacherous sand slope allowed no escape from a spot which I had visited most involuntarily, and a promenade on the river frontage was the signal for a bombardment from some insane native in a boat. I'm afraid that I lost my temper very much indeed.

Another bullet reminded me that I had better save my breath to cool my porridge, and I retreated hastily up the sands and back to the horseshoe, where

I saw that the noise of the rifle had drawn sixty-five human beings from the badger-holes which I had up till that point supposed to be untenanted. I found myself in the midst of a crowd of spectators—about forty men, twenty women, and one child, who could not have been more than five years old. They were all scantily clothed in that salmon-coloured cloth which one associates with Hindu mendicants, and at first sight gave me the impression of a band of loathsome *fakirs*. The filth and repulsiveness of the assembly were beyond all description, and I shuddered to think what their life in the badger-holes must be.

Even in these days, when local self-government has destroyed the greater part of a native's respect for a Sahib, I have been accustomed to a certain amount of civility from my inferiors, and on approaching the crowd naturally expected that there would be some recognition of my presence. As a matter of fact, there was, but it was by no means what I had looked for.

The ragged crew actually laughed at me—such laughter I hope I may never hear again. They cackled, yelled, whistled, and howled as I walked into their midst, some of them literally throwing themselves down on the ground in convulsions of unholy mirth. In a moment I had let go Pornic's head, and irritated beyond expression at the morning's adventure, commenced cuffing those nearest to me with all the force I could. The wretches dropped under my blows like ninepins, and the laughter gave place to wails for mercy, while those yet untouched clasped me round the knees, imploring me in all sorts of uncouth tongues to spare them.

In the tumult, and just when I was feeling very much ashamed of myself for having thus easily given way to my temper, a thin, high voice murmured in English from behind my shoulder, "Sahib! Sahib! Do you not know me? Sahib, it is Gunga Dass, the telegraph-master."

I spun round quickly and faced the speaker.

Gunga Dass (I have, of course, no hesitation in mentioning the man's real name) I had known four years before as a Deccanee Brahmin lent by the Punjab government to one of the Khalsia States. He was in charge of a branch telegraph-office there, and when I had last met him was a jovial, full-stomached, portly government servant with a marvellous capacity for making bad puns in English—a peculiarity which made me remember him long after I had forgotten his services to me in his official capacity. It is seldom that a Hindu makes English puns.

Now, however, the man was changed beyond all recognition. Caste-mark, stomach, slate-coloured continuations, and unctuous speech were all gone. I looked at a withered skeleton, turbanless and almost naked, with long matted hair and deep-set codfish eyes. But for a crescent-shaped scar on the left cheek—the result of an accident for which I was responsible—I should never have known him. But it was indubitably Gunga Dass, and—for this I was thankful—an English-speaking native who might at least tell me the meaning of all that I had gone through that day.

The crowd retreated to some distance as I turned towards the miserable figure and ordered him to show me some method of escaping from the crater. He held a freshly plucked crow in his hand, and in reply to my question climbed slowly on a platform of sand which ran in front of the holes, and commenced lighting a fire there in silence. Dried bents, sand-poppies, and driftwood burn quickly, and I derived much consolation from the fact that he lit them with an ordinary sulphur match. When they were in a bright glow, and the crow was neatly spitted in front thereof, Gunga Dass began without a word of preamble: "There are only two kinds of men, sir. The alive and the dead. When you are dead you are dead, but when you are alive you live." (Here the crow demanded his attention for an instant as it twirled before the fire in danger of being burnt to a cinder.) "If you die at home and do not die when you come to the ghat to be burnt, you come here."

The nature of the reeking village was made plain now, and all that I had known or read of the grotesque and the horrible paled before the fact just communicated by the ex-Brahmin. Sixteen years ago, when I first landed in Bombay, I had been told by a wandering Armenian of the existence, somewhere in India, of a place to which such Hindus as had the misfortune to recover from trance or were conveyed and kept, and I recollect laughing heartily at what I was then pleased to consider a traveller's tale. Sitting at the bottom of the sand-trap, the memory of Watson's Hotel, with its winging punkahs, white-robed servants, and the sallow-faced Armenian, rose up in my mind as vividly as a photograph, and I burst into a loud fit of laughter. The contrast was too absurd!

Gunga Dass, as he bent over the unclean bird, watched me curiously. Hindus seldom laugh, and his surroundings were not such as to move him that way. He removed the crow solemnly from the wooden spit and as solemnly devoured it. Then he continued his story, which I give in his own words:

"In epidemics of the cholera you are carried to be burnt almost before you are dead. When you come to the riverside, the cold air perhaps makes you alive, and then, if you are only little alive, mud is put on your nose and mouth and you die conclusively. If you are rather more alive, more mud is put; but if you are too lively they let you go and take you away. I was too lively, and made protestation with anger against the indignities that they endeavoured to press upon me. In those days I was Brahmin and proud man. Now I am dead man and eat"—here he eyed the well-gnawed breast-bone with the first sign of emotion that I had seen in him since we met—"crows and—other things. They took me from my sheets when they saw that I was too lively and gave me medicines for one week, and I survived successfully. Then they sent me by rail from my place to Okara Station, with a man to take care of me; and at Okara Station we met two other men, and they conducted we three on camels, in the night, from Okara Station to this place, and they propelled me from the top to the bottom, and the other two succeeded, and I have been here ever since, two and a half years. Once I was Brahmin and proud man, and now I eat crows."

"There is no way of getting out?"

"None of what kind at all. When I first came I made experiments frequently, and all the others also, but we have always succumbed to the sand which is precipitated upon our heads."

"But surely," I broke in at this point, "the river-front is open, and it is worthwhile dodging the bullets; while at night—"

I had already matured a rough plan of escape which a natural instinct of selfishness forbade me sharing with Gunga Dass. He, however, divined my unspoken thought almost as soon as it was formed, and to my intense astonishment, gave vent to a long, low chuckle of derision—the laughter, be it understood, of a superior or at least of an equal.

"You will not"—he had dropped the "sir" after his first sentence—"make any escape that way. But you can try. I have tried. Once only."

The sensation of nameless terror which I had in vain attempted to strive against overmastered me completely. My long fast—it was now close upon ten o'clock, and I had eaten nothing since tiffin on the previous day—combined with the violent agitation of the ride had exhausted me, and I verily believe that for a few minutes I acted as one mad. I hurled myself against the sand-slope. I ran round the base of the crater blaspheming and praying by turns. I crawled out among the sedges of the river-front, only to be driven back each time in an agony of nervous dread by the rifle-bullets which cut up the sand round me—for I dared not face the death of a mad dog among that hideous crowd—and so fell, spent and raving, at the kerb of the well. No one had taken the slightest notice of an exhibition which makes me blush hotly even when I think of it now.

Two or three men trod on my panting body as they drew water, but they were evidently used to this sort of thing and had no time to waste upon me. Gunga Dass, indeed, when he had banked the embers of his fire with sand, was at some pains to throw half a cupful of fetid water over my head, an attention for which I could have fallen on my knees and thanked him, but he was laughing all the while in the same mirthless, wheezy key that greeted me on my first attempt to force the shoals. And so, in a half-fainting state, I lay till noon. Then, being only a man after all, I felt hungry, and said as much to Gunga Dass, whom I had begun to regard as my natural protector. Following the impulse of the outer world when dealing with natives, I put my hand into my pocket and drew out four annas. The absurdity of the gift struck me at once, and I was about to replace the money.

Gunga Dass, however, cried: "Give me the money, all you have, or I will get help, and we will kill you!"

A Briton's first impulse, I believe, is to guard the contents of his pockets, but a moment's thought showed me the folly of differing with the one man who had it in his power to make me comfortable, and with whose help it was possible that I might eventually escape from the crater. I gave him all the money in my possession, Rs.9–8–5—nine rupees, eight annas, and five pie—for I always keep small change as *bakshish* when I am in camp. Gunga Dass clutched the coins and hid them at once in his ragged loin-cloth, looking round to assure himself that no one had observed us.

"*Now* I will give you something to eat," said he.

What pleasure my money could have given him I am unable to say, but inasmuch as it did please him, I was not sorry that I had parted with it so readily, for I had no doubt that he would have had me killed if I had refused. One does not protest against the doings of a den of wild beasts, and my companions were lower than any beasts. While I ate what Gunga Dass had provided, a coarse *chapatti* and a cupful of the foul well-water, the people showed not the faintest sign of curiosity—that curiosity which is so rampant, as a rule, in an Indian village.

I could even fancy that they despised me. At all events, they treated me with the most chilling indifference, and Gunga Dass was nearly as bad. I plied him with questions about the terrible village, and received extremely unsatisfactory answers. So far as I could gather, it had been in existence from time immemorial—whence I concluded that it was at least a century old—and during that time no one had ever been known to escape from it. (I had to control myself here with both hands lest the blind terror should lay hold of me a second time and drive me raving round the crater.) Gunga Dass took a malicious pleasure in emphasizing this point and in watching me wince. Nothing that I could do would induce him to tell me who the mysterious "They" were.

"It is so ordered," he would reply, "and I do not yet know anyone who has disobeyed the orders."

"Only wait till my servant finds that I am missing," I retorted, "and I promise you that this place shall be cleared off the face of the earth, and I'll give you a lesson in civility too, my friend."

"Your servants would be torn in pieces before they came near this place; and besides, you are dead, my dear friend. It is not your fault, of course, but nonetheless you are dead *and* buried."

At irregular intervals supplies of food, I was told, were dropped down from the land side into the amphitheatre, and the inhabitants fought for them like wild beasts. When a man felt his death coming on he retreated to his lair and died there. The body was sometimes dragged out of the hole and thrown onto the sand, or allowed to rot where it lay.

The phrase "thrown onto the sand" caught my attention, and I asked Gunga Dass whether this sort of thing was not likely to breed a pestilence.

"That," said he with another of his wheezy chuckles, "you may see for yourself subsequently. You will have much time to make observations."

Whereat, to his great delight, I winced once more and hastily continued the conversation: "And how do you live here from day to day? What do you do?" The question elicited exactly the same answer as before, coupled with the information that "this place is like your European heaven; there is neither marrying nor giving in marriage."

Gunga Dass had been educated at a mission school, and as he himself admitted, had he only changed his religion "like a wise man," might have avoided the living grave which was now his portion. But as long as I was with him I fancy he was happy.

Here was a Sahib, a representative of the dominant race, helpless as a child and completely at the mercy of his native neighbours. In a deliberate, lazy way he set himself to torture me as a schoolboy would devote a rapturous half hour to watching the agonies of an impaled beetle, or as a ferret in a blind burrow might glue himself comfortably to the neck of a rabbit. The burden of his conversation was that there was no escape "of no kind whatever" and that I should stay here till I died and was "thrown onto the sand." If it were possible to forejudge the conversation of the damned on the advent of a new soul in their abode, I should say that they would speak as Gunga Dass did to me throughout that long afternoon. I was powerless to protest or answer, all my energies being devoted to a struggle against the inexplicable terror that threatened to overwhelm me again and again. I can compare the feeling to nothing except the struggles of a man against the overpowering nausea of the Channel passage—only my agony was of the spirit and infinitely more terrible.

As the day wore on, the inhabitants began to appear in full strength to catch the rays of the afternoon sun, which were now sloping in at the mouth of the crater. They assembled by little knots and talked among themselves without even throwing a glance in my direction. About four o'clock, so far as I could judge, Gunga Dass rose and dived into his lair for a moment, emerging with a live crow in his hands. The wretched bird was in a most draggled and deplorable condition, but seemed to be in no way afraid of its master. Advancing cautiously to the river-front, Gunga Dass stepped from tussock to tussock until he had reached a smooth patch of sand directly in the line of the boat's fire. The occupants of the boat took no notice. Here he stopped, and with a couple of dexterous turns of the wrist, pegged the bird on its back with outstretched wings. As was only natural, the crow began to shriek at once and beat the air with its claws. In a few seconds the clamour had attracted the attention of a bevy of wild crows on a shoal a few hundred yards away, where they were discussing something that looked like a corpse. Half a dozen crows flew over at once to see what was going on, and also, as it proved, to attack the pinioned bird. Gunga Dass, who had lain down on a tussock, motioned to me to be quiet, though I fancy this was a needless precaution. In a moment, and before I could see how it happened, a wild crow who had grappled with the shrieking and helpless bird was entangled in the latter's claws, swiftly disengaged by Gunga Dass, and pegged down beside its companion in adversity. Curiosity, it seemed, overpowered the rest of the Rock, and almost before Gunga Dass and I had time to withdraw to the tussock, two more captives were struggling in the upturned claws of the decoys. So the chase—if I can give it so dignified a name—continued until Gunga Dass had captured seven crows. Five of them he throttled at once, reserving two for further operations another day. I was a good deal impressed by this, to me, novel method of securing food, and complimented Gunga Dass on his skill.

"It is nothing to do," said he. "Tomorrow you must do it for me. You are stronger than I am."

This calm assumption of superiority upset me not a little, and I answered peremptorily, "Indeed, you old ruffian? What do you think I have given you money for?"

"Very well," was the unmoved reply. "Perhaps not tomorrow, nor the day after, nor subsequently; but in the end, and for many years, you will catch crows and eat crows, and you will thank your European God that you have crows to catch and eat."

I could have cheerfully strangled him for this, but judged it best under the circumstances to smother my resentment. An hour later I was eating one of the crows, and, as Gunga Dass had said, thanking my God that I had a crow to eat. Never as long as I live shall I forget that evening meal. The whole population were squatting on the hard sand platform opposite their dens, huddled over tiny fires of refuse and dried rushes. Death, having once laid his hand upon these men and forborne to strike, seemed to stand aloof from them now, for most of our company were old men, bent and worn and twisted with years, and women aged to all appearance as the Fates themselves. They sat together in knots and talked— God only knows what they found to discuss—in low equable tones, curiously in contrast to the strident babble with which natives are accustomed to make day hideous. Now and then an access of that sudden fury which had possessed me

in the morning would lay hold on a man or woman; and with yells and impreca-
tions the sufferer would attack the steep slope until, baffled and bleeding, he fell
back on the platform incapable of moving a limb. The others would never even
raise their eyes when this happened, as men too well aware of the futility of their
fellows' attempts and wearied with their useless repetition. I saw four such outbursts
in the course of that evening.

Gunga Dass took an eminently businesslike view of my situation, and while
we were dining—I can afford to laugh at the recollection now, but it was painful
enough at the time—propounded the terms on which he would consent to "do"
for me. My nine rupees, eight annas, he argued, at the rate of three annas a day,
would provide me with food for fifty-one days, or about seven weeks; that is to say,
he would be willing to cater for me for that length of time. At the end of it I was
to look after myself. For a further consideration—*videlicet* my boots—he would be
willing to allow me to occupy the den next to his own and would supply me with
as much dried grass for bedding as he could spare.

"Very well, Gunga Dass," I replied; "to the first terms I cheerfully agree, but
as there is nothing on earth to prevent my killing you as you sit here and taking
everything that you have" (I thought of the two invaluable crows at the time),
"I flatly refuse to give you my boots and shall take whichever den I please."

The stroke was a bold one, and I was glad when I saw that it had succeeded.
Gunga Dass changed his tone immediately and disavowed all intention of asking
for my boots. At the time it did not strike me as at all strange that I, a civil engineer,
a man of thirteen years' standing in the service, and, I trust, an average Englishman,
should thus calmly threaten murder and violence against the man who had, for a
consideration it is true, taken me under his wing. I had left the world, it seemed,
for centuries. I was as certain then as I am now of my own existence that in the
accursed settlement there was no law save that of the strongest, that the living dead
men had thrown behind them every canon of the world which had cast them out,
and that I had to depend for my own life on my strength and vigilance alone. The
crew of the ill-fated *Mignonette* are the only men who would understand my frame
of mind. "At present," I argued to myself, "I am strong and a match for six of
these wretches. It is imperatively necessary that I should, for my own sake, keep
both health and strength until the hour of my release comes—if it ever does."

Fortified with these resolutions, I ate and drank as much as I could and made Gunga Dass understand that I intended to be his master and that the least sign of insubordination on his part would be visited with the only punishment I had it in my power to inflict—sudden and violent death. Shortly after this I went to bed. That is to say, Gunga Dass gave me a double armful of dried bents, which I thrust down the mouth of the lair to the right of his, and followed myself, feet foremost, the hole running about nine feet into the sand with a slight downward inclination and being neatly shored with timbers. From my den which faced the river-front, I was able to watch the waters of the Sutlej flowing past under the light of a young moon and compose myself to sleep as best I might.

The horrors of that night I shall never forget. My den was nearly as narrow as a coffin, and the sides had been worn smooth and greasy by the contact of innumerable naked bodies, added to which it smelt abominably. Sleep was altogether out of the question to one in my excited frame of mind. As the night wore on, it seemed that the entire amphitheatre was filled with legions of unclean devils that, trooping up from the shoals below, mocked the unfortunates in their lairs.

Personally I am not of an imaginative temperament—very few engineers are—but on that occasion I was as completely prostrated with nervous terror as any woman. After half an hour or so, however, I was able once more to calmly review my chances of escape. Any exit by the steep sand walls was, of course, impracticable. I had been thoroughly convinced of this some time before. It was possible, that I might, in the uncertain moonlight, safely run the gauntlet of the rifle-shots. The place was so full of terror for me that I was prepared to undergo any risk in leaving it. Imagine, my delight, then, when after creeping stealthily to the river-front I found that the infernal boat was not there. My freedom lay before me in the next few steps!

By walking out to the first shallow pool that lay at the foot of the projecting left horn of the horseshoe, I could wade across, turn the flank of the crater, and make my way inland. Without a moment's hesitation I marched briskly past the tussocks where Gunga Dass had snared the crows, and out in the direction of the smooth white sand beyond. My first step from the tufts of dried grass showed me how utterly futile was any hope of escape, for as I put my foot down I felt an indescribable drawing, sucking motion of the sand below. Another moment, and my leg was swallowed up nearly to the knee. In the moonlight the whole surface of the sand seemed to be shaken with devilish delight at my disappointment. I struggled clear, sweating with terror and exertion, back to the tussocks behind me, and fell on my face.

My only means of escape from the semicircle was protected with a quicksand!

How long I lay I have not the faintest idea, but I was roused at the last by malevolent chuckle of Gunga Dass at my ear. "I would advise you, Protector of the Poor" (the ruffian was speaking English), "to return to your house. It is unhealthy to lie down here. Moreover, when the boat returns, you will most certainly be rifled at." He stood over me in the dim light of the dawn, chuckling and laughing to himself. Suppressing my first impulse to catch the man by the neck and throw him onto the quicksand, I rose sullenly and followed him to the platform below the burrows.

Suddenly, and futilely as I thought while I spoke, I asked, "Gunga Dass, what is the good of the boat if I can't get out *anyhow*?" I recollect that even in my deepest trouble I had been speculating vaguely on the waste of ammunition in guarding an already well-protected foreshore.

Gunga Dass laughed again and made answer, "They have the boat only in daytime. It is for the reason that *there is a way*. I hope we shall have the pleasure of your company for much longer time. It is a pleasant spot when you have been here some years and eaten roast crow long enough."

I staggered, numbed and helpless, towards the fetid burrow allotted to me and fell asleep. An hour or so later I was awakened by a piercing scream—the shrill, highpitched scream of a horse in pain. Those who have once heard that will never forget the sound. I found some little difficulty in scrambling out of the burrow. When I was in the open, I saw Pornic, my poor old Pornic, lying dead on the sandy soil. How they had killed him I cannot guess. Gunga Dass explained that horse was better than crow, and "greatest good of greatest number is political maxim. We are now republic, Mister Jukes, and you are entitled to a fair share of the beast. If you like, we will pass a vote of thanks. Shall I propose?"

Yes, we were a republic indeed! A republic of wild beasts penned at the bottom of a pit to eat and fight and sleep till we died. I attempted no protest of any kind, but sat down and stared at the hideous sight in front of me. In less time almost than it takes me to write this, Pornic's body was divided in some unclean way or other; the men and women had dragged the fragments onto the platform and were preparing their morning meal. Gunga Dass cooked mine. The almost irresistible impulse to fly at the sand walls until I was wearied, laid hold of me afresh, and I had to struggle against it with all my might. Gunga Dass was offensively jocular till I told him that if he addressed another remark of any kind whatever to me I should strangle him where he sat. This silenced him till silence became insupportable, and I bade him say something.

"You will live here till you die, like the other Feringhee," he said coolly, watching me over the fragment of gristle that he was gnawing.

"What other Sahib, you swine? Speak at once, and don't stop to tell me a lie."

"He is over there," answered Gunga Dass, pointing to a burrow-mouth about four doors to the left of my own. "You can see for yourself. He died in the burrow as you will die, and I will die, and as all these men and women and the one child will also die."

"For pity's sake tell me all you know about him. Who was he? When did he come, and when did he die?"

This appeal was a weak step on my part. Gunga Dass only leered and replied, "I will not—unless you give me something first."

Then I recollected where I was, and struck the man between the eyes, partially stunning him. He stepped down from the platform at once, and cringing and fawning and weeping and attempting to embrace my feet, led me round to the burrow which he had indicated.

"I know nothing whatever about the gentleman. Your God be my witness that I do not. He was as anxious to escape as you were, and he was shot from the boat, though we all did all things to prevent him from attempting. He was shot here." Gunga Dass laid his hand on his lean stomach and bowed to the earth.

"Well, and what then? Go on!"

"And then—and then, your Honour, we carried him into his house and gave him water, and put wet cloths on the wound, and he laid down in his house and gave up the ghost."

"In how long? In how long?"

"About half an hour after be received his wound. I call Vishnu to witness," yelled the wretched man, "that I did everything for him. Everything which was possible, that I did!"

He threw himself down on the ground and clasped my ankles. But I had my doubts about Gunga Dass's benevolence and kicked him off as he lay protesting.

"I believe you robbed him of everything he had. But I can find out in a minute or two. How long was the Sahib here?"

"Nearly a year and a half. I think he must have gone mad. But hear me swear, Protector of the Poor! Won't your Honour hear me swear that I never touched an article that belonged to him? What is your Worship going to do?"

I had taken Gunga Dass by the waist and had hauled him onto the platform opposite the deserted burrow. As I did so I thought of my wretched fellow prisoner's unspeakable misery among all these horrors for eighteen months and the final agony of dying like a rat in a hole, with a bullet-wound in the stomach. Gunga Dass fancied I was going to kill him and howled pitifully. The rest of the population, in the plethora that follows a full flesh meal, watched us without stirring.

"Go inside, Gunga Dass," said I, "and fetch it out."

I was feeling sick and faint with horror now. Gunga Dass nearly rolled off the platform and howled aloud.

"But I am Brahmin, Sahib—a high-caste Brahmin. By your soul, by your father's soul, do not make me do this thing!"

"Brahmin or no Brahmin, by my soul and my father's soul, in you go!" I said, and seizing him by the shoulders, I crammed his head into the mouth of the burrow, kicked the rest of him in, and sitting down, covered my face with my hands.

At the end of a few minutes I heard a rustle and a creak, then Gunga Dass in a sobbing, choking whisper speaking to himself, then a soft thud—and I uncovered my eyes.

The dry sand had turned the corpse entrusted to its keeping into a yellow-brown mummy. I told Gunga Dass to stand off while I examined it. The body—clad in an olive-green hunting-suit much stained and worn, with leather pads on the shoulders—was that of a man between thirty and forty, above middle height, with light, sandy hair, long moustache, and a rough, unkempt beard. The left canine of the upper jaw was missing, and a portion of the lobe of the right ear was gone. On the second finger of the left hand was a ring—a shield-shaped bloodstone set in gold, with a monogram that might have been either "B. K." or "B. L." On the third finger of the right hand was a silver ring in the shape of a coiled cobra, much worn and tarnished. Gunga Dass deposited a handful of trifles he had picked out of the burrow at my feet, and covering the face of the body with my handkerchief, I turned to examine these. I give the full list in the hope that it may lead to the identification of the unfortunate man:

1. Bowl of a brierwood pipe, serrated at the edge, much worn and blackened, bound with string of the screw.
2. Two patent-lever keys, wards of both broken.
3. Tortoiseshell-handled penknife, silver or nickel, name-plate marked with monogram "B. K."
4. Envelope, postmark undecipherable, bearing a Victorian stamp, addressed to "Miss Mon—" (rest illegible)—"ham'—'nt."
5. Imitation crocodile-skin notebook with pencil. First forty-five pages blank; four and a half illegible; fifteen others filled with private memoranda relating chiefly to three persons—a "Mrs. L. Singleton," abbreviated several times to "Lot Single," "Mrs. S. May," and "Garmison," referred to in places as "Jerry" or "Jack."
6. Handle of small-sized hunting-knife. Blade snapped short. Buck's horn, diamond-cut, with swivel and ring on the butt; fragment of cotton cord attached.

It must not be supposed that I inventoried all these things on the spot as fully as I have here written them down. The notebook first attracted my attention, and I put it in my pocket with a view to studying it later on. The rest of the articles I conveyed to my burrow for safety's sake, and there, being a methodical man, I inventoried them. I then returned to the corpse and ordered Gunga Dass to help me to carry it out to the river-front. While we were engaged in this, the exploded shell of an old brown cartridge dropped out of one of the pockets and rolled at my feet. Gunga Dass had not seen it; and I fell to thinking that a man does not carry exploded cartridge-cases, especially "browns," which will not bear loading twice, about with him when shooting. In other words, that cartridge-case had been fired inside the crater. Consequently there must be a gun somewhere. I was on the verge of asking Gunga Dass, but checked myself, knowing that he would lie. We laid the body down on the edge of the quicksand by the tussocks. It was my intention to push it out and let it be swallowed up—the only possible mode of burial that I could think of. I ordered Gunga Dass to go away.

Then I gingerly put the corpse out on the quicksand. In doing so—it was lying face downward—I tore the frail and rotten khaki shooting-coat open, disclosing a hideous cavity in the back. I have already told you that the dry sand had, as it were, mummified the body. A moment's glance showed that the gaping hole had been caused by a gunshot wound; the gun must have been fired with the muzzle almost touching the back. The shooting-coat, being intact, had been drawn over the body after death, which must have been instantaneous. The secret of the poor wretch's death was plain to me in a flash. Someone of the crater, presumably Gunga Dass, must have shot him with his own gun—the gun that fitted the brown cartridges. He had never attempted to escape in the face of the rifle-fire from the boat.

I pushed the corpse out hastily and saw it sink from sight literally in a few seconds. I shuddered as I watched. In a dazed, half-conscious way I turned to peruse the notebook. A stained and discoloured slip of paper had been inserted between the binding and the back, and dropped out as I opened the pages. This is what it contained: "*Four out from crow-clump; three left; nine out; two right; three back; two left; fourteen out; two left; seven out; one left; nine back; two right; six back; four right; seven back.*" The paper had been burnt and charred at the edges. What it meant I could not understand. I sat down on the dried bents, turning it over and over between my fingers, until I was aware of Gunga Dass standing immediately behind me with glowing eyes and outstretched hands.

"Have you got it?" he panted. "Will you not let me look at it also? I swear that I will return it."

"Got what? Return what?" I asked.

"That which you have in your hands. It will help us both." He stretched out his long, birdlike talons, trembling with eagerness.

"I could never find it," he continued. "He had secreted it about his person. Therefore I shot him, but nevertheless I was unable to obtain it."

Gunga Dass had quite forgotten his little fiction about the rifle-bullet. I heard him calmly. Morality is blunted by consorting with the dead who are alive.

"What on earth are you raving about? What is it you want me to give you?"

"The piece of paper in the notebook. It will help us both. Oh, you fool! You fool! Can you not see what it will do for us? We shall escape!"

His voice rose almost to a scream, and he danced with excitement before me. I own I was moved at the chance of getting away.

"Do you mean to say that this slip of paper will help us? What does it mean?"

"Read it aloud! Read it aloud! I beg and I pray to you to read it aloud."

I did so. Gunga Dass listened delightedly and drew an irregular line in the sand with his fingers.

"See now! It was the length of his gun-barrels without the stock. I have those barrels. Four gun-barrels out from the place where I caught crows. Straight out; do you mind me? Then three left. Ah! How well I remember how that man worked it out night after night. Then nine out, and so on. Out is always straight before you across the quicksand to the north. He told me so before I killed him."

"But if you knew all this, why didn't you get out before?"

"I did *not* know it. He told me that he was working it out a year and a half ago, and how he was working it out night after night when the boat had gone away, and he could get out near the quicksand safely. Then he said that we would get away together. But I was afraid that he would leave me behind one night when he had worked it all out, and so I shot him. Besides, it is not advisable that the men who once get in here should escape. Only I, and *I* am a Brahmin."

The hope of escape had brought Gunga Dass's caste back to him. He stood up, walked about, and gesticulated violently. Eventually I managed to make him talk soberly, and he told me how this Englishman had spent six months night after night in exploring inch by inch the passage across the quicksand, how he had declared it to be simplicity itself up to within about twenty yards of the river-bank after turning the flank of the left horn of the horseshoe. This much he had evidently not completed when Gunga Dass shot him with his own gun.

In my frenzy of delight at the possibilities of escape I recollect shaking hands wildly with Gunga Dass after we had decided that we were to make an attempt to get away that very night. It was weary work waiting throughout the afternoon.

About ten o'clock, as far as I could judge, when the moon had just risen above the lip of the crater, Gunga Dass made a move for his burrow to bring out the gun-barrels whereby to measure our path. All the other wretched inhabitants had retired to their lairs long ago. The guardian boat had drifted downstream some hours before, and we were utterly alone by the crow-clump. Gunga Dass, while carrying the gun-barrels, let slip the piece of paper which was to be our guide. I stooped down hastily to recover it, and as I did so, I was aware that the creature was aiming a violent blow at the back of my head with the gun-barrels. It was too late to turn round. I must have received the blow somewhere on the nape of my neck, for I fell senseless at the edge of the quicksand.

When I recovered consciousness, the moon was going down, and I was sensible of intolerable pain in the back of my head. Gunga Dass had disappeared, and my mouth was full of blood. I lay down again and prayed that I might die without more ado. Then the unreasoning fury which I have before mentioned laid hold upon me, and I staggered inland towards the walls of the crater. It seemed that someone was calling to me in a whisper—"Sahib! Sahib! Sahib!" exactly as my bearer used to call me in the mornings. I fancied that I was delirious until a hand-ful of sand fell at my feet. Then I looked up and saw a head peering down into the amphitheatre—the head of Dunnoo, my dog-boy, who attended to my collies. As soon as he had attracted my attention, he held up his hand and showed a rope. I motioned, staggering to and fro the while, that he should throw it down. It was a couple of leather punkah-ropes knotted together, with a loop at one end. I slipped the loop over my head and under my arms, heard Dunnoo urge something forward, was conscious that I was being dragged, face downward, up the steep sand-slope, and the next instant found myself choked and half-fainting on the sand-hills over-looking the crater. Dunnoo, with his face ashy grey in the moonlight, implored me not to stay, but to get back to my tent at once.

It seems that he had tracked Pornic's footprints fourteen miles across the sands of the crater, had returned and told my servants, who flatly refused to meddle with anyone, white or black, once fallen into the hideous Village of the Dead; where-upon Dunnoo had taken one of my ponies and a couple of punkah-ropes, returned to the crater, and hauled me out as I have described.

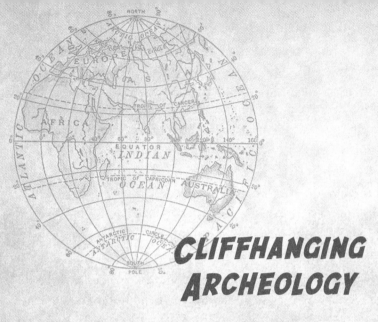

CLIFFHANGING ARCHEOLOGY

SIR HENRY RAWLINSON

(British soldier, diplomat, and archeologist)

The Behistun rock, or inscription, is similar to the Rosetta Stone, which contained one inscription in three different languages, enabling the first translation of Egyptian hieroglyphs. In the Behistun rock's case, the inscriptions were carved into parallel columns of limestone 500 feet up on a nearly inaccessible cliff-face in what is today western Iran. They turned out to be an edict from Darius the Great—who ruled the Persian Empire from 521 B.C. to 485 B.C.—carved in the three languages. The inscriptions—written in Old Persian, Babylonian, and Elamite—are in the wedge-shaped script known as cuneiform, which had baffled scholars for decades. From his transcriptions, starting in 1846 Colonel Rawlinson was able to decipher the Old Persian, which in turn revealed the Babylonian, and finally the more difficult Elamite. This was the key to understanding all of the cuneiform Asiatic languages.

This rock of Behistun is a very remarkable natural object on the high road between Ecbatana and Babylon. It was probably in the very earliest times invested with a holy character; for the Greek physician, Ctesias, who must have visited this spot in the fourth century before Christ, ascribes the most remarkable of the antiquities to be found there to the Assyrian queen Semiramis.

[…]The rock of Behistun doubtless preserved its holy character in the age of Darius, and it was on this account chosen by the monarch as a fit place for the commemoration of his war-like achievements.[…]

The rock or, as it is usually called by the Arab geographers, the mountain of Behistun, is not an isolated hill, as has been sometimes imagined. It is merely the terminal point of a long, narrow range which bounds the plain of Kermanshah to the eastward. This range is rocky and abrupt throughout, but at the extremity it rises in height, and becomes a sheer precipice. The altitude I found by careful triangulation to be 3,807 feet, and the height above the plain at which occur the tablets of Darius is perhaps 500 feet, or something more.

Notwithstanding that a French antiquarian commission in Persia described it a few years back to be impossible to copy the Behistun inscriptions, I certainly do not consider it any great feat in climbing to ascend to the spot where the inscriptions occur. When I was living at Kermanshah fifteen years ago, and was somewhat more active than I am at present, I used frequently to scale the rock three or four times a day without the aid of a rope or a ladder: without any assistance, in fact, whatever. During my late visits I have found it more convenient to ascend and descend by the help of ropes where the track lies up a precipitate cleft, and to throw a plank over these chasms where a false step in leaping across would probably be fatal. On reaching the recess which contains the Persian text of the record, ladders are indispensable in order to examine the upper portion of the tablet; and even with ladders there is considerable risk, for the foot-ledge is so narrow, about eighteen inches or at most two feet in breadth, that with a ladder long enough to reach the sculptures sufficient slope cannot be given to enable a person to ascend, and, if the ladder be shortened in order to increase the slope, the upper inscriptions can only be copied by standing on the topmost step of the ladder, with no other support than steadying the body against the rock with the left arm, while the left hand holds the notebook, and the right hand is employed

with the pencil. In this position I copied all the upper inscriptions, and the interest of the occupation entirely did away with any sense of danger.

To reach the recess which contains the Scythic [Elamite] translation of the record of Darius is a matter of greater difficulty. On the left-hand side of the recess alone is there any foot-ledge whatever; on the right hand, where the recess, which is thrown a few feet further back, joins the Persian tablet, the face of the rock presents a sheer precipice, and it is necessary therefore to bridge this intervening space between the left-hand Persian tablet and the foot-ledge on the left-hand of the recess. With ladders of sufficient length, a bridge of this sort can be constructed without difficulty; but my first attempt to cross the chasm was unfortunate, and might have been fatal, for, having previously shortened my only ladder in order to obtain a slope for copying the Persian upper legends, I found, when I came to lay it across to the recess in order to get at the Scythic translation, that it was not sufficiently long to lie flat on the foot-ledge beyond. One side of the ladder would alone reach the nearest point of the ledge, and, as it would of course have tilted over if a person had attempted to cross it in that position, I changed it from a horizontal to a vertical direction, the upper side resting firmly on the rock at its two ends, and the lower hanging over the precipice, and I prepared to cross, walking on the lower side, and holding to the upper side with my hands. If the ladder had been a compact article, this mode of crossing, although far from comfortable, would have been at any rate practicable; but the Persians merely fit in the bars of their ladders without pretending to clench them outside, and I had hardly accordingly begun to cross over when the vertical pressure forced the bars out of their sockets, and the lower and unsupported side of the ladder thus parted company from the upper, and went crashing down over the precipice. Hanging on to the upper side, which still remained firm in its place, and assisted by my friends, who were anxiously watching the trial, I regained the Persian recess, and did not again attempt to cross until I had made a bridge of comparative stability. Ultimately I took the cast of the Scythic writing by laying one long ladder, in the first instance, horizontally across the chasm, and by then placing another ladder, which rested on the bridge, perpendicularly against the rock.

> **"A most admirable servant of mine risked his life to reach a magnificent Bornean orchid, and tried to poison me an hour later when he thought I was going to take the plant away from him."**
> —zoologist WILLIAM BEEBE

The Babylonian transcript at Behistun is still more difficult to reach than either the Scythic or the Persian tablets. The writing can be copied by the aid of a good telescope from below, but I long despaired of obtaining a cast of the inscription; for I found it quite beyond my powers of climbing to reach the spot where it was engraved, and the cragsmen of the place, who were accustomed to track the mountain goats over the entire face of the mountain, declared the particular block inscribed with the Babylonian legend to be unapproachable. At length, however, a wild Kurdish boy, who had come from a distance, volunteered to make the attempt, and I promised him a considerable award if he succeeded. The mass of the rock in question is scarped, and it projects some feet over the Scythic recess, so that it cannot be approached by any of the ordinary means of climbing The boy's first move was to squeeze himself up a cleft in the rock a short distance to the left of the projecting mass. When he had ascended some distance above it, he drove a wooden peg firmly into the cleft, fastened a rope to this, and then endeavoured to swing himself across to another cleft at some distance on the other side; but in this he failed, owing to the projection of the rock. It then only remained for him to cross over to the cleft by hanging on with his toes and fingers to the slight inequalities on the bare face of the precipice, and in this he succeeded, passing over a distance of twenty feet of almost smooth perpendicular rock in a manner which to a looker-on appeared quite miraculous. When he had reached the second cleft the real difficulties were over. He had brought a rope with him attached to the first peg, and now, driving in a second, he was enabled to swing himself right over the projecting mass of rock. Here with a short ladder he formed a swinging seat, like a painter's cradle, and, fixed upon this seat, he took under my direction the paper cast of the Babylonian translation of the records of Darius which is now at the Royal Asiatic Society's rooms, and which is almost of equal value for the interpretation of the Assyrian inscriptions as was the Greek translation of the Rosetta Stone for the intelligence of the hieroglyphic texts of Egypt. I must add, too, that it is of the more importance that his invaluable Babylonian key should have been thus recovered, as the mass of rock on which the inscription is engraved bore every appearance, when I last visited the spot, of being doomed to a speedy destruction, water trickling from above having almost separated the overhanging mass from the rest of the rock, and its own enormous weight thus threatening very shortly to bring it thundering down into the plain, dashed into a thousand fragments.

EXCAVATION OF AN ASSYRIAN PALACE

Sir Austen Henry Layard

(British archeologist, ambassador, and politician)

From the summit of the pyramid my eye ranged, on one side, over a broad level, enclosed by the Tigris and the Zab; on the other, over a low undulating country bounded by the snow-capped mountains of Kurdistan; but it was no longer the dreary waste I had left a month before; the landscape was clothed in green, the black tents of the Arabs chequered the plain of Nimroud, and their numerous flocks pastured on the distant hills. The Jehesh and Shemutti Arabs had returned to their villages, and were now engaged in cultivating the soil. Even on the mound the plough opened its furrows, and corn was sown over the palaces of the Assyrian kings.

Security had been restored, and Nimroud offered a more convenient and more agreeable residence than Selamiyah. Hiring, therefore, from the owners three huts, which had been hastily built in the outskirts of the village, I removed to my new dwelling place. A few rude chairs, a table, and a wooden bedstead, formed the whole of my furniture. The servants constructed a rude kitchen, and the grooms shared the stalls with the horses. Mr. Hormuzd Rassam, the brother of the British Vice-Consul, came to reside with me, and undertook the daily payment of the workmen and the domestic arrangements.[...]

My labours had scarcely been resumed when I received information that the Cadi of Mosul was endeavouring to stir up the people against me, chiefly on the plea that I was carrying away treasure; and, what was worse, finding inscriptions which proved that the Franks once held the country and upon the evidence of which they intended immediately to resume possession of it, exterminating all true

> "[A.] Henry Layard, a headstrong youth, broke with his uncle and benefactor[...], and left London to make his fortune in Ceylon. On the way (he was traveling overland), he noticed some interesting lumps on the ground. They turned out to have Assyria beneath them."
>
> —THE NEW YORKER

believers. These stories, however absurd they may appear, rapidly gained ground in the town. A representation was ultimately made by the Ulema to Ismail Pasha; and as he expressed a wish to see me, I rode to Mosul. He was not, he said, influenced by the Cadi or the Mufti, nor did he believe the absurd tales, which they had spread abroad. I should shortly see how he intended to treat these troublesome fellows; but he thought it prudent at present to humour them, and made it a personal request that I would, for the time, suspend the excavations. I consented with regret; and once more returned to Nimroud without being able to gratify the ardent curiosity I felt to explore further the extraordinary building, the nature of which was still a mystery to me.

The Abou Salman Arabs, who encamp around Nimroud, are known for their thieving propensities, and might have caused me some annoyance. Thinking it prudent, therefore, to conciliate their chief, I rode over one morning to their principal encampment. Sheikh Abd-ur-rahman received me at the entrance of his capacious tent of black goat-hair, which was crowded with his relations, followers, and strangers, who were enjoying his hospitality. He was one of the handsomest Arabs I ever saw; tall, robust, and well-made, with a countenance in which intelligence was no less marked than courage and resolution. On his head he wore a turban of dark linen, from under which a many-coloured handkerchief fell over his shoulders; his dress was a simple white shirt, descending to the ankles, and an Arab cloak thrown loosely over it. Unlike Arabs in general, he had shaved his beard; and, although he could scarcely be much beyond forty, I observed that the little hair which could be distinguished from under his turban was grey. He received me with every demonstration of hospitality, and led me to the upper place, divided by a goat-hair curtain from the harem. The tent was capacious; half was appropriated for the women, the rest formed the place of reception, and was at the same time occupied by two favourite mares and a colt. A few camels were kneeling on the grass around and the horses of the strangers were tied by the halter to the tent-pins. From the carpets and cushions, which were spread for me, stretched on both sides a long line of men of the most motley appearance, seated on the bare ground. The Sheikh himself, as is the custom in some of the tribes, to show his respect for his guest, placed himself at the furthest end; and could only be prevailed upon, after many excuses and protestations, to share the carpet with me. In the centre of the group, near a small fire of camel's dung, crouched a half-naked Arab, engaged alternately in blowing up the expiring embers, and in pounding the roasted coffee in a copper mortar, ready to replenish the huge pots which stood near him.

After the customary compliments had been exchanged with all around, one of my attendants beckoned to the Sheikh, who left the tent to receive the presents I had brought to him,—a silk gown and a supply of coffee and sugar. He dressed himself in his new attire, and returned to the assembly. 'Inshallah,' said I, 'we are now friends, although scarcely a month ago you came over the Zab on purpose to appropriate the little property I am accustomed to carry about me.' 'Wallah, Bey,' he replied, 'you say true, we are friends; but listen: the Arabs either sit down and serve his Majesty the Sultan, or they eat from others, as others would eat from them. These lands were given [to my tribe] in return for the services we rendered the Turks in keeping back the Tai and the Shammar, who crossed the rivers to plunder the villages. All the great men of the Abou Salman perished in encounters with the Bedouin, and Injeh Bairakdar, Mohammed Pasha, upon whom God has had mercy, acknowledged our fidelity, and treated us with honour. When that blind dog, the son of the Cretan (May curses fall upon him!) came to Mosul, I waited upon him, as it is usual for the Sheikh; what did *he* do? Did he give me the cloak of honour? No; he put me, an Arab of the tribe of Zobeide, a tribe which had fought with the Prophet, into the public stocks. For forty days my heart melted away in a damp cell, and I was exposed to every variety of torture. Look at these hairs,' continued he, lifting up his turban, 'they turned white in that time, and I

"The Arabs marvelled at these strange figures. As each head was uncovered they showed their amazement by extravagant gestures, or exclamations of surprise. If it was a bearded man, they concluded at once that it was an idol or a jin, and cursed or spat upon it. If an eunuch, they declared that it was the likeness of a beautiful female, and kissed or patted the cheek. They soon felt as much interest as I did in the objects discovered, and worked with renewed ardour when their curiosity was excited by the appearance of a fresh sculpture. On such occasions they would strip themselves almost naked, throw the kerchief from their heads, and letting their matted hair stream in the wind, rush like madmen into the trenches, to carry off the baskets of earth, shouting, at the same time, the war cry of the tribe."

—*archeologist* SIR A. HENRY LAYARD

must now shave my beard, a shame amongst the Arabs. I was released at last; but how did I return to the tribe? —a beggar, unable to kill a sheep for my guests. He took my mares, my flocks, and my camels, as the price of my liberty. Now tell me, O Bey, in the name of God, if the Osmanlis have eaten from me and my guests, shall I not eat from them and theirs?'

The fate of Abd-ur-rahman had been such as he described it; and so had fared several chiefs of the desert and of the mountains. It was not surprising that these men, proud of their origin, and accustomed to the independence of a wandering life, had revenged themselves upon the unfortunate inhabitants of the villages, who had no less cause to complain than themselves.

It was nearly the middle of February before I thought it prudent to make fresh experiments among the ruins.[...]

As these ruins occurred on the edge of the mound, it was probable that they had been more exposed than the rest, and consequently had sustained more injury than other parts of the building. As there was a ravine running far into the mound, apparently formed by the winter rains, I determined to open a trench in the centre of it. In two days the workmen reached the top of a slab which appeared to be both well preserved, and to be still standing in its original position. On the south side I discovered, to my great satisfaction, two human figures, considerably above the natural size, sculptured in low relief, and still exhibiting all the freshness of a recent work. In a few hours the earth and rubbish were completely removed from the face of the slab, no part of which had been injured. The figures appeared to represent divinities, presiding over the seasons, or over particular religious ceremonies. The limbs were delineated with peculiar accuracy, and the muscles and bones faithfully, though somewhat too strongly, marked. An inscription ran across the sculpture.

To the west of this slab, and fitting to it, was a corner-stone ornamented with flowers and scroll-work, tastefully arranged, and resembling in detail those graven on the injured tablet, near entrance *d* of the south-west building. I recognised at once from whence many of the sculptures, employed in the construction of that edifice, had been brought; and, it was evident that I had at length discovered the earliest palace of Nimroud.

The corner stone led me to a figure of singular form. A human body clothed in robes similar to those of the winged men already described, was surmounted by the head of an eagle or of a vulture. The curved beak, of considerable length, was half open, and displayed a narrow pointed tongue, which was still coloured with red paint. On the shoulders fell the usual curled and bushy hair of the Assyrian images, and a comb of feathers rose on the top of the head. Two wings sprang from the back, and in either hand was the square vessel and fir-cone.

On all these figures paint could be faintly distinguished, particularly on the hair, beard, eyes, and sandals. The slabs on which they were sculptured had sustained no injury, and could be without difficulty packed and moved to any distance. There could no longer be any doubt that they formed part of a chamber, and that, to explore it completely, I had only to continue along the wall, now partly uncovered.

On the morning following these discoveries, I rode to the encampment of Sheikh Abd-ur-rahman, and was returning to the mound, when I saw two Arabs of his tribe urging their mares to the top of their speed. On approaching me they stopped. 'Hasten, O Bey,' exclaimed one of them—'hasten to the diggers, for they have found Nimrod himself. Wallah, it is wonderful, but it is true! we have seen him with our eyes. There is no God but God;' and both joining in this pious exclamation, they galloped off, without further words, in the direction of the tents.

On reaching the ruins I descended into the new trench, and found the workmen, who had already seen me as I approached, standing near a heap of baskets and

cloaks. Whilst Awad advanced and asked for a present to celebrate the occasion, the Arabs withdrew the screen they had hastily constructed, and disclosed an enormous human head sculptured in full out of the alabaster of the country. They had uncovered the upper part of a figure, the remainder of which was still buried in the earth. I saw at once that the head must belong to a winged lion or bull, similar to those of Khorsabad and Persepolis. It was in admirable preservation. The expression was calm, yet majestic, and the outline of the features showed a freedom and knowledge of art, scarcely to be looked for in the works of so remote a period. The cap had three horns, and, unlike that of the human-headed bulls hitherto found in Assyria, was rounded and without ornament at the top.

I was not surprised that the Arabs had been amazed and terrified at this apparition. This gigantic head, blanched with age, thus rising from the bowels of the earth, might well have belonged to one of those fearful beings which are pictured in the traditions of the country, as appearing to mortals, slowly ascending from the regions below. One of the workmen, on catching the first glimpse of the monster, had thrown down his basket and had run off towards Mosul as fast as his legs could carry him. I learnt this with regret, as I anticipated the consequences.

Whilst I was superintending the removal of the earth, which still clung to the sculpture, and giving directions for the continuation of the work, a noise of horsemen was heard, and presently Abd-ur-rahman, followed by half his tribe, appeared on the edge of the trench. When they beheld the head they all cried together, 'There is no God but God, and Mohammed is his Prophet!' It was some time before the Sheikh could he prevailed upon to descend into the pit, and convince himself that the image he saw was of stone. 'This is not the work of men's hands,' exclaimed he, 'but of those infidel giants of whom the Prophet—peace be with him!—has said that they were higher than the tallest date tree; this is one of the idols which Noah—peace be with him!—cursed before the flood.' In this opinion, the result of a careful examination, all the bystanders concurred.

I now ordered a trench to be dug due south from the head, in the expectation of finding a corresponding figure, and before night-fall reached the object of my search about twelve feet distant. Engaging two or three men to sleep near the sculptures, I returned to the village, and celebrated the day's discovery by a slaughter of sheep, of which all the Arabs near partook. As some wandering musicians chanced to be at Selamiyah, I sent for them, and dances were kept up during the greater part of the night. On the following morning Arabs from the other side of the Tigris, and the inhabitants of the surrounding villages, congregated on the mound. Even the women could not repress their curiosity, and came in crowds, with their children, from afar. My Cawass was stationed during the day in the trench, into which I would not allow the multitude to descend.

As I had expected, the report of the discovery of the gigantic head, carried by the terrified Arab to Mosul, had thrown the town into commotion. He had scarcely checked his speed before reaching the bridge. Entering breathless into the bazaars, he announced to everyone he met that Nimrod had appeared. The news soon got to the ears of the Cadi, who, anxious for a fresh opportunity to annoy me, called the Mufti and the Ulema together, to consult upon this unexpected occurrence. Their deliberations ended in a procession to the Governor, and a formal protest, on the part of the Mussulmans of the town, against proceedings so directly contrary to the laws of the Koran. The Cadi had no distinct idea whether the bones of the mighty hunter had been uncovered, or only his image; nor did Ismail Pasha very clearly remember whether Nimrod was a true-believing prophet, or an Infidel. I consequently received a somewhat unintelligible message from his Excellency, to the effect that the remains should be treated with respect and be by no means further disturbed; that he wished the excavation to be stopped at once, and desired to confer with me on the subject.

I called upon him accordingly, and had some difficulty in making him understand the nature of my discovery. As he requested me to discontinue my operations until the sensation in the town had somewhat subsided, I returned to Nimroud, and dismissed the workmen, retaining only two men to dig leisurely along the walls without giving cause for further interference.

* * *

The dry season had enabled me to carry on the excavations without interruption. I determined to send the sculptures to Busrah in the month of March or April, foreseeing that as soon as the Bedouins had moved northwards from Babylonia, and had commenced their plundering expeditions in the vicinity of Mosul, I should be compelled to leave Nimroud.

The Trustees of the British Museum had not contemplated the removal of either a winged bull or lion, and I had at first believed that, with the means at my disposal, it would have been useless to attempt it. They wisely determined that these sculptures should not be sawn into pieces, to be put together again in Europe, as the pair of bulls from Khorsabad. They were to remain, where discovered, until some favourable opportunity of moving them entire might

"The stone attracted my attention, and on observing it more closely, I perceived traces of sculpture. I summoned my men, and after a two hours' trial of patience and temper, I succeeded in raising from its bed of centuries another idol of massive proportions, but differing entirely from the others, and possessing an extraordinary and forbidding aspect. The lower half had been broken off, and could not be found; what remained was simply the bust and head. The latter was disproportionately great; the eyes were large, round, and staring; the ears broad and long; and from the widely-distended mouth, the lower jaw of which was forced down by the hands of the figure, projected a tongue which reached to the breast, giving to the whole an unnatural and horrible expression. As it stood in the pit, with its monstrous head rising above the ground, with its fixed stony gaze, it seemed like some gray monster just emerging from the depths of the earth, at the bidding of the wizard-priest of an unholy religion. My men stood back, and more than one crossed himself as he muttered to his neighbor, "Es el diablo!" "It is the devil!" I readily comprehended the awe with which it might be regarded by the devotees of the ancient religion, when the bloody priest daubed the lapping tongue with the yet palpitating hearts of his human victims."

—archeologist E. G. SQUIER

occur; and I was directed to heap earth over them, after the excavations had been brought to an end. Being loath, however, to leave all these fine specimens of Assyrian sculpture behind me, I resolved upon attempting the removal and embarkation of two of the smallest and best preserved. I had wished to secure the pair of lions forming the great entrance into the principal chamber of the north-west palace; the finest specimens of Assyrian sculpture discovered in the ruins. But after some deliberation I determined to leave them for the present; as, from their size, the expense attending their conveyance to the river would have been very considerable.

I formed various plans for lowering the smaller lion and bull, for dragging them to the river, and for placing them upon rafts. Each step had its difficulties, and a variety of original suggestions and ideas were supplied by my workmen, and by the good people of Mosul. At last I resolved upon constructing a cart sufficiently strong to bear any of the masses to be moved. As no wood but poplar could be procured in the town, a carpenter was sent to the mountains with directions to fell the largest mulberry tree, or any tree of equally compact grain, he could find; and to bring beams of it, and thick slices from the trunk, to Mosul.

By the month of March this wood was ready. I purchased from the dragoman of the French Consulate a pair of strong iron axles, formerly used by M. Botta in bringing sculptures from Khorsabad. Each wheel was formed of three solid pieces, nearly a foot thick, from the trunk of a mulberry tree, bound together by iron hoops. Across the axles were laid three beams, and above them several cross-beams, all of the same wood. A pole was fixed to one axle, to which were also attached iron rings for ropes, to enable men, as well as buffaloes, to draw the cart. The wheels were provided with moveable books for the same purpose.

Simple as this cart was, it became an object of wonder in the town. Crowds came to look at it, as it stood in the yard of the vice-consul's khan; as long as the cart was in Mosul, it was examined by every stranger who visited the town. But when the news spread that it was about to leave the gates, and to be drawn over the bridge, the business of the place was completely suspended. The secretaries and scribes from the palace left their divans; the guards their posts; the bazaars were deserted; and half the population assembled on the banks of the river to witness the manœuvres of the cart. A pair of buffaloes, with the assistance of a crowd of Chaldæans and shouting Arabs, forced the ponderous wheels over the rotten bridge of boats. The cart was the topic of general conversation in Mosul until the arrival, from Europe, of some children's toys—barking dogs and moving puppets—which gave rise to fresh excitement, and filled even the gravest of the clergy with wonder at the learning and wisdom of the Infidels.

To lessen the weight of the lion and bull, without in any way interfering with the sculpture, I reduced the thickness of the slabs, by cutting away as much as possible from the back. Their bulk was thus considerably diminished; and as the back of the slab was never meant to be seen, being placed against the wall of sun-dried bricks, no part of the sculpture was sacrificed. As, in order to move these figures at all, I had to choose between this plan and that of sawing them into several pieces, I did not hesitate to adopt it.

To enable me to move the bull from the ruins, and to place it on the cart in the plain below, a trench was cut nearly two hundred feet long, about fifteen feet

"[...] on examining the interior of the tunnel, I discovered a slab covered with cuneiform characters, which had fallen from a platform, and had been wedged in a crevice of the rock. With much difficulty I succeeded in ascertaining that an inscription was also cut on the back of the tablet. From the darkness of the place, I could scarcely copy even the few characters which had resisted the wear of centuries. Some days after, others who had casually heard of my visit, and conjectured that some Assyrian remains might have been found there, sent a party of workmen to the spot; who, finding the slab, broke it into pieces, in their attempt to displace it. This wanton destruction of the tablet is much to be regretted; as, from the fragment of the inscription copied, I can perceive that it contained an important, and, to me, new genealogical list of kings. I had intended to remove the stone carefully, and had hoped, by placing it in a proper light, to ascertain accurately the forms of the various characters upon it. This was not the only loss I had to complain of, from the jealousy and competition of rivals."

—*archeologist* Sɪʀ A. Hᴇɴʀʏ Lᴀʏᴀʀᴅ

wide, and, in some places, twenty feet deep. A road was thus constructed from the entrance, in which stood the bull, to the edge of the mound. About fifty Arabs and Nestorians were employed in the work.[...]

As the bull was to be lowered on its back, the unsculptured side the slab having to be placed on rollers, I removed the walls behind it. An open space was thus formed large enough to admit of the sculpture when prostrate, and leaving room for the workmen to pass on all sides of it. The principal difficulty was of course to lower the mass: when once on the ground, or on rollers, it could be dragged forwards by the united force of a number of men; but, during its descent, it could only be sustained by ropes. If they chanced to break, the sculpture would be precipitated to the ground, and would, probably, be broken in the fall. The few ropes I possessed had been expressly sent to me, across the desert, from Aleppo; but they were small. From Baghdad I had obtained a thick hawser, made of the fibres of the palm. In addition I had been furnished with two pairs of blocks, and a pair of jack-screws belonging to the steamers of the Euphrates expedition. These were all the means at my command for moving the bull and lion. The sculptures were wrapped in mats and felts, to preserve them, as far as possible, from injury in case of a fall; and to prevent the ropes chipping or rubbing the alabaster.[...]

My own people were reinforced by a large number of the Abou Salman. I had invited Sheikh Abd-ur-rahman to be present, and he came attended by a body of horsemen. The men being ready, and all my preparations complete, I stationed myself on the top of the high bank of earth over the second bull, and ordered the wedges to be struck out from under the sculpture to be moved. Still, however, it remained firmly in its place. A rope having been passed round it, six or seven men easily tilted it over. The thick, ill-made cable stretched with the strain, and almost buried itself in the earth round which it was coiled. The ropes held well. The mass descended gradually, the Chaldæans propping it up with the beams. It was a moment of great anxiety. The drums and shrill pipes of the Kurdish musicians increased the din and confusion caused by the war-cry of the Arabs, who were half frantic with excitement. They had thrown off nearly all their garments; their long hair floated in the wind; and they indulged in the wildest postures and gesticulations as they clung to the ropes. The women had congregated on the sides of the trenches, and by their incessant screams, and by the ear-piercing tahlehl, added to the enthusiasm of the men. The bull once in motion, it was no longer possible to obtain a hearing. The loudest cries I could produce were lost in the crash of discordant sounds. Neither the hippopotamus-hide whips of the Cawasses, nor the bricks and clods of earth with which I endeavoured to draw attention from some of the most noisy of the group, were of any avail. Away went the bull, steady enough as long as supported by the props behind; but as it came nearer to the rollers, the beams could no longer be used. The cable and ropes stretched more, and more. Dry from the climate, as they felt the strain, they creaked and threw out dust. Water was thrown over them, but in vain, for they all broke together when the sculpture was within four or five feet of the rollers. The bull was precipitated to the ground. Those who held the ropes, thus suddenly released, followed its example, and were rolling, one over the other, in the dust. A sudden silence succeeded to the clamour. I rushed into the trenches, prepared to find the bull in many pieces. It would be difficult to describe my satisfaction, when I saw it lying precisely where I had wished to place it, and uninjured! The

Arabs no sooner got on their legs again, than, seeing the result of the accident, they darted out of the trenches, and, seizing by the hands the women who were looking on, formed a large circle, and, yelling their war-cry with redoubled energy, commenced a most mad dance. Even Abd-ur-rahman shared in the excitement, and, throwing his cloak to one of his attendants, insisted upon leading off the debkhé. It would have been useless to endeavour to put any check upon these proceedings. I preferred allowing the men to wear themselves out—a result which, considering the amount of exertion and energy displayed both by limbs and throat, was not long in taking place.[...]

I rode back with Abd-ur-rahman. The Arab Sheikh, his enthusiasm once cooled down, gave way to moral reflections. 'Wonderful! Wonderful! There is surely no God but God, and Mohammed is his Prophet,' exclaimed he, after a long pause. 'In the name of the Most High, tell me, O Bey, what you are going to do with those stones. So many thousands of purses spent upon such things! Can it be, as you say, that your people learn wisdom from them; or is it, as his reverence the Cadi declares, that they are to go to the palace of your Queen, who, with the rest of the unbelievers, worships these idols? As for wisdom, these figures will not teach you to make any better knives, or scissors, or chintzes; and it is in the making of those things that the English show their wisdom. But God is great! God is great! Here are stones which have been buried ever since the time of the holy Noah—peace be with him! Perhaps they were under ground before the deluge. I have lived on these lands for years. My father, and the father of my father, pitched their tents here before me; but they never heard of these figures. For twelve hundred years have the true believers (and, praise be to God! all true wisdom is with them alone) been settled in this country, and none of them ever heard of a palace under ground. Neither did they who went before them. But lo! here comes a Frank from many days' journey off, and he walks up to the very place, and he takes a stick [illustrating the description at the same time with the point of his spear], and makes a line here, and makes a line there. Here, says he, is the palace; there, says he, is the gate; and he shows us what has been all our lives beneath our feet, without our having known anything about it. Wonderful! Wonderful! Is it by books, is it by magic, is it by your prophets, that you have learnt these things? Speak, O Bey; tell me the secret of wisdom.'

The wonder of Abd-ur-rahman was certainly not without cause, and his reflections were natural enough. Whilst riding by his side I had been indulging in a reverie, not unlike his own, which he suddenly interrupted by these exclamations. A stranger laying open monuments buried for more than twenty centuries, and thus proving to those who dwelt around them, that much of the civilisation and knowledge of which we now boast, existed amongst their forefathers when our 'ancestors were yet unborn', was, in a manner, an acknowledgement of the debt which the West owes to the East.

Archeologist Albert von Le Coq explained how some ancient frescoes in Chinese Turkestan were damaged by local farmers, saying, "For the belief still exists that painted men and animals, unless their eyes and mouths at least had been destroyed, come to life at night, descend from their places, and do all sorts of mischief to men, beasts and harvests."

This night was, of course, looked upon as one of rejoicing. Sheep were as usual killed, and boiled or roasted whole; they formed the essence of all entertainments and public festivities. They had scarcely been devoured before dancing was commenced. There were fortunately relays of musicians; for no human lungs could have furnished the requisite amount of breath. When some were nearly falling from exhaustion, the ranks were recruited by others. And so the Arabs went on until dawn. It was useless to preach moderation, or to entreat for quiet. Advice and remonstrances were received with deafening shouts of the war-cry, and outrageous antics as proofs of gratitude for the entertainment, and of ability to resist fatigue.

After passing the night in this fashion, these extraordinary beings, still singing and capering, started for the mound. Everything had been prepared on the previous day for moving the bull, and the men had now only to haul on the ropes.[...]

The lion and bull were at length placed side by side on the banks of the Tigris, ready to proceed to Busrah, as soon as I could make the necessary arrangements for embarking them on rafts.[...]

Many slabs, and about thirty cases containing small objects discovered in the ruins, were placed on the rafts with the lion and bull.[...]

On the morning of the 22nd, all the sculptures having been embarked, I gave two sheep to the raftmen to be slain on the bank of the river, as a sacrifice to ensure the success of the undertaking. The carcases were distributed, as is proper on such occasions, amongst the poor. A third sheep was reserved for a propitiatory offering, to be immolated at the tomb of Sultan Abd-Allah. This saint still appears to interfere considerably with the navigation of the Tigris, and had closed the further ascent of the river against the infidel crew of the Frank steamer the 'Euphrates', because they had neglected to make the customary sacrifice. All ceremonies having been duly performed, Mullah Ali kissed my hand, placed himself on one of the rafts, and slowly floated, with the cargo under his charge, down the stream.

I watched the rafts until they disappeared behind a projecting bank of the river. I could not forbear musing upon the strange destiny of their burdens; which, after adorning the palaces of the Assyrian kings, had been buried unknown for centuries beneath a soil trodden by Persians under Cyrus, by Greeks under Alexander, and by Arabs under the first successors of their prophet. They were now to visit India, to cross the most distant seas of the southern hemisphere, and to be finally placed in a British Museum.[...]

After the departure of the Abou Salman, the plain of Nimroud was a complete desert. The visits of armed parties of Arabs became daily more frequent, and we often watched them from the mound, as they rode towards the hills in search of pillage, or returned from their expeditions driving the plundered flocks and cattle before them. We were still too strong to fear the Bedouins; but I was compelled to put my house into a complete state of defence, and to keep patrols round my premises during the night to avoid surprise. The Jebour were exposed to constant losses, in the way of donkeys or tent furniture, as the country was infested by petty thieves, who issued from their hiding-places, and wandered to and fro, like jackals, after dark. Nothing was too small or worthless to escape their notice. I was roused almost nightly by shoutings and the discharge of firearms, when the whole encampment was thrown into commotion at the disappearance of a copper pot or an old grain sack. I was fortunate enough to escape their depredations.

The fears of my Jebour increased with the number of the plundering parties, and at last, when a small Arab settlement, within sight of Nimroud, was attacked by a band of Aneyza horsemen, who murdered several of the inhabitants, and carried away all the sheep and cattle, the workmen protested in a body against any further residence in so dangerous a vicinity. I determined, therefore, to bring the excavations to an end.

I now commenced burying with earth those parts of the ruins which still remained exposed, according to the instructions I had received from the Trustees of the British Museum. Had the numerous sculptures been left, without any pre-caution being taken to preserve them, they would have suffered, not only from the effects of the atmosphere, but from the spears and clubs of the Arabs, who are always ready to knock out the eyes, and to otherwise disfigure, the idols of the unbelievers. The rubbish and earth removed on opening the building, was accordingly heaped over the slabs until the whole was again covered over.

But before leaving Nimroud and reburying its palaces, I would wish to lead the reader once more through the ruins of the principal edifice, as they appeared when fully explored. Let us imagine ourselves issuing from my tent near the village in the plain. We ascend the mound, but see no ruins, not a stone protruding from the soil. There is only a broad level platform before us, perhaps covered with a luxuri-ant crop of barley, or may be yellow and parched, without a blade of vegetation, except here and there a scanty tuft of camel-thorn. Low black heaps, surrounded by brushwood and dried grass, a thin column of smoke issuing from the midst of them, are scattered here and there. These are the tents of the Arabs; and a few miserable old women are groping about them, picking up camel's-dung or dry twigs. One or two girls, with firm step and erect carriage, are just reaching the top of the mound, with the water-jar on their shoulders, or a bundle of brush-wood on their heads. On all sides of us, apparently issuing from underground, are long lines of wild-looking beings, with dishevelled hair, their limbs only half concealed by a short loose shirt, some jumping and capering, and all hurrying to and fro shouting like madmen. Each one carries a basket, and as he reaches the edge of the mound, or some convenient spot near, empties its contents, raising at the same time a cloud of dust. He then returns at the top of his speed, dancing and yelling as before, and flourishing his basket over his head; again he suddenly disappears in the bowels of the earth, from whence he emerged. These are the workmen employed in removing the rubbish from the ruins.

We will descend into the principal trench, by a flight of steps rudely cut into the earth, near the western face of the mound. As we approach it, we find a party of Arabs bending on their knees, and intently gazing at something beneath them. Each holds his long spear, tufted with ostrich feathers, in one hand; and in the other the halter of his mare, which stands patiently behind him. The party consists of a Bedouin Sheikh from the desert, and his followers; who, having heard strange reports of the wonders of Nimroud, have made several days' journey to remove their doubts and satisfy their curiosity. He rises as he hears us approach, and if we wish to escape the embrace of a very dirty stranger, we had better at once hurry into the trenches.

We descend about twenty feet, and suddenly find ourselves between a pair of colossal lions, winged and human-headed, forming a portal. In the subterraneous labyrinth which we have reached, all is bustle and confusion. Arabs are running about in different directions; some bearing baskets filled with earth, others carrying the water-jars to their companions. The Chaldæans or Tiyari, in their striped dresses and curious conical caps, are digging with picks into the tenacious earth, raising a dense cloud of fine dust at every stroke. The wild strains of Kurdish music may be heard occasionally issuing from some distant part of the ruins.

We issue from between the winged lions, and enter the remains of the principal hall. On both sides of us are sculptured gigantic winged figures; some with the heads of eagles, others entirely human, and carrying mysterious symbols in their hands. To the left is another portal, also formed by winged lions. One of them has, however, fallen across the entrance, and there is just room to creep beneath it. Beyond this portal is a winged figure, and two slabs with bas-reliefs; but they have been so much injured that we can scarcely trace the subject upon them. Further on there are no traces of wall, although a deep trench has been opened. The opposite side of the hall has also disappeared, and we only see a high wall of earth. On examining it attentively, we can detect the marks of masonry; and we soon find that it is a solid structure built of bricks of unbaked clay, now of the same colour as the surrounding soil, and scarcely to be distinguished from it.

The slabs of alabaster, fallen from their original position, have, however, been raised; and we tread in the midst of a maze of small bas-reliefs, representing chariots, horsemen, battles, and sieges. Perhaps the workmen are about to raise a slab for the first time; and we watch, with eager curiosity, what new event of Assyrian history, or what unknown custom or religious ceremony, may be illustrated by the sculpture beneath.

Having walked about one hundred feet amongst these scattered monuments of ancient history and art, we reach another door-way, formed by gigantic winged bulls in yellow limestone. One is still entire; but its companion has fallen, and is broken into several pieces—the great human head is at our feet.

We pass on without turning into the part of the building to which this portal leads. Beyond it we see another winged figure, holding a graceful flower in its hand, and apparently presenting it as an offering to the winged bull. Adjoining this sculpture we find eight fine bas-reliefs. There is the king, hunting, and triumphing over, the lion and wild bull; and the siege of the castle, with the battering-ram. We have now reached the end of the hall, and find before us an elaborate and beautiful sculpture, representing two kings, standing beneath the emblem of the supreme deity, and attended by winged figures. Between them is the sacred tree. In front of this bas-relief is the great stone platform, upon which, in days of old, may have been placed the throne of the Assyrian monarch, when he received his captive enemies, or his courtiers.

To the left of us is a fourth outlet from the hall, formed by another pair of lions. We issue from between them, and find ourselves on the edge of a deep ravine, to the north of which rises, high above us, the lofty pyramid. Figures of captives bearing objects of tribute—earrings, bracelets, and monkeys—may be seen on walls near this ravine; and two enormous bulls, and two winged figures above fourteen feet high, are lying on its very edge.

As the ravine bounds the ruins on this side, we must return to the yellow bulls. Passing through the entrance formed by them, we enter a large chamber surrounded by eagle-headed figures: at one end of it is a doorway guarded by two priests or divinities, and in the centre another portal with winged bulls. Whichever way we turn, we find ourselves in the midst of a nest of rooms; and without an acquaintance with the intricacies of the place, we should soon lose ourselves in this labyrinth. The accumulated rubbish being generally left in the centre of the chambers, the whole excavation consists of a number of narrow passages, panelled on one side with slabs of alabaster; and shut in on the other by a high wall of earth, half buried, in which may here and there be seen a broken vase, or a brick painted with brilliant colours. We may wander through these galleries for an hour or two, examining the marvellous sculptures, or the numerous inscriptions that surround us. Here we meet long rows of kings, attended by their eunuchs and priests—there lines of winged figures, carrying fir-cones and religious emblems, and seemingly in adoration before the mystic tree. Other entrances, formed by winged lions and bulls, lead us into new chambers. In every one of them are fresh objects of curiosity and surprise. At length, wearied, we issue from the buried edifice by a trench on the opposite side to that by which we entered and find ourselves again upon the naked platform. We look around in vain for any traces of the wonderful remains we have just seen, and are half inclined to believe that we have dreamed a dream, or have been listening to some tale of Eastern romance.

Some, who may hereafter tread on the spot when the grass again grows over the ruins of the Assyrian palaces, may indeed suspect that I have been relating a vision.

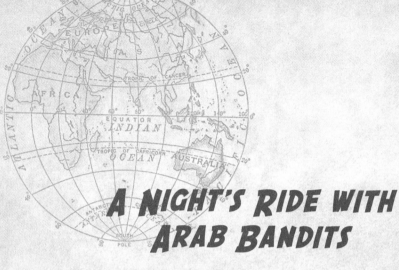

A NIGHT'S RIDE WITH ARAB BANDITS

CHARLES WELLINGTON FURLONG

(explorer, anthropologist, and journalist)

I suspected Muraiche, suspected him of an indefinite something, but the workings of his wily old Arab mind, its reasons and its purposes, were to me as mysterious as the great wastes of the Sahhra (Sahara) over which for days we had been crawling, and as elusive as the noxious sand-lizards which now and again scurried from beneath our horses' feet.

The long, hot caravan trail along which we had crawled during the day had led over the sun-scorched rocky wastes of the Djebel Nagaliza (Nagaliza Mountain), and at sundown emptied us into the little Arab town of Khoms. Here we parted with a small caravan forty camels strong bound for Misurata, with which we had travelled for the last three days. My two men, Mohammed and Ali, who were on foot, drove a large fast-walking pack-donkey; while Muraiche, like myself, rode an Arab stallion. His bent old figure, now ahead of me, now by my side, seemed lost in the folds of his barracan.

Some months previously, a viséed passport and other documents had landed me safely within the confines of the town of Tripoli, and later, after some difficulty, permission to travel into the desert had been granted by the Turkish Pasha who commanded the Turkish forces in that country. Many Arabs there were in the town who would gladly have risked the dangers of the desert as dragomen, but as my

object was to obtain information of desert life, a man who could act also as inter-preter was indispensable; and Muraiche proved to be the only available man. It is true that he had an unsavory record, and I was so warned by certain members of the little English colony there. But his broken English and lingua Franca were valuable assets; besides, forewarned was forearmed, so it came about that Muraiche picked the other men and became my dragoman.

Since sunrise, as we approached Khoms, a change had come over Muraiche; he no longer obeyed my orders with alacrity, and when several times it was neces-sary for me to repeat them sharply, he seemed to awaken with a start from deep meditation. This, at the time, I attributed to the fatigue of our journey mid antici-pated relaxation, for I had promised a rest at Khoms. Following the custom of the country, I reported to the Turkish governor on our arrival, and saw my men and animals comfortably fixed in a fonduk (caravansary), with orders to have everything in readiness to start at two the following afternoon, then spent the night at the house of Mr. Tate, the only Englishman in the place.

This night in mid-July and the following night, strangely different, stand out strongly in my memory—perhaps for the contrast with the dusty, monotonous, travelling of other days, and the sleeping in dirty, crowded fonduks; or, perhaps, in contrast with each other. If you would know the pleasure of bathing, of sleeping between the snow-white sheets of a bed, travel day after day on the burning, scorching, yellow-red sand of the Sahhra; fill your eyes, nose and ears, your very soul, with its fine-powdered dust; tie your handkerchief, after the manner of the Touaregs, across your mouth to prevent evaporation, that your throat may not parch too much. Travel early and late to make the most of the cool of the morning and evening. Sleep lightly if you are a lone stranger, and do not mind the uncomfortable lump of your pistol-holsters under your arm: they are better in your hands than in the other fellow's. So when, sunburnt, saddle-sore, and tired with long riding and little sleep, you find, what I did, a bath of delicious cold water, brought from an old Roman well still used by the Arabs in Khoms, and a snow-white bed, give praise to Allah. Then let the barbaric noises of a wild Sudanese dance in the distance and the musical chant of the Muezzin melt away with your thoughts into the quiet of the African night.

> "I well remember one day in mid-August; the mercury stood at 155 degrees in the sun. I do not know what it registered in the shade, for there was none save our own shadows. As the sun wore round behind us I shifted the broad band of my woollen cholera-belt to my back, and cast my own shadow to protect as far as possible the neck and head of my horse, for the poor beast was suffering terribly from the heat. All day we rode in this furnace, and the brave fellows trudged barefooted in the scorching sand."
> —CHARLES WELLINGTON FURLONG

Had it not been for a casual stroll through the Suk the next forenoon my men might now be recounting a different yarn over their smoking kief and coos-coos. I threaded my way among men, animals, shacks, scattered garden produce, grains and wares which covered the ground in interesting heaps, and as I pushed through a small crowd which had gathered about me, their curiosity and cupidity aroused by a gold filling in one of my teeth, I stopped for a moment. For there in the middle of an open space beside a Marabout (saint's tomb), Muraiche was engrossed in a low conversation with one of the irregular guards, an Arab in the Turkish employ. Disappearing unobserved to another part of the Suk, I should have thought no more of the matter, but for the fact that when later in the morning these two met in my presence, by the Governor's palace, they omitted the customary b'salaams and effusive greetings of Mohammedan acquaintances, and by no word or sign betrayed the least recognition.

Reminding Muraiche of my previous orders to have everything in readiness by two o'clock, I sauntered up to lunch at Mr. Tate's. The route to my next point of destination, the little town of Kussabat, was not only over a rough mountainous country, but it was considered by the Arabs dangerous on account of thieves. Being under the necessity of making the journey that day, I was anxious to arrive there by sundown. Consequently, when by half past two none of my outfit had put in an appearance, I despatched one of the house servants to learn the reason.

First by wily excuses, and then by open mutiny, my men delayed the departure until half past five, when by threats to appeal to the Turkish Pasha to have them thrown into prison and engage new men, we were finally ready to start.

"But a guard, Arbi (master)?" Twice Muraiche had asked the question and twice I answered him that I had notified the Turkish officials of my intention to depart at two o'clock. Had they intended to send a guard they would have done so. However, being desirous of conforming to custom, I sent Muraiche to the Governor's palace with instructions to report our departure, but not to ask for a guard, as personally I shared in the common opinion that often the traveller is safer without one.

I watched Muraiche after he rounded a corner and disappeared at a gallop down the narrow street to the palace, from which, immediately reappearing, he set off to a different quarter of the town. Questioned on his return, he replied that an officer had sent him to notify a guard who was to go with us.

"You'll see your way all right, for the full moon ought to be up in about two hours, but *ride last*," were Tate's parting words. It was good advice and had often been given me before. To travellers in North Africa, particularly those among the French colonists of Tunis and Algeria, the saying, "Never allow an Arab to ride behind you," has become an adage, and this night in the Gharian I proved its worth.

We rode to the top of the steep trail, down which the slanting afternoon sunbeams shot by in golden shafts. Back and beyond us these sun shafts sped, until striking the white walls of Khoms they broke, spilling over them a flood of orange gold, diffusing her surrounding olive groves and date-palms with a golden green, and through the shimmering, sifting gold mist above it all sparkled a scintillating sea of blue.

Our course now lay almost due south to the region of the Djebel Gharian, the region I had hoped to enter and pass through by day.

Resting on the site of ancient Lebda of the Romans, my golden city of Khoms lay nearly an hour's ride behind us, and as yet no guard, to my entire satisfaction. This was short-lived, however, for soon a yell, such as I had never yet heard loosed from the throat of a human being, caused us suddenly to draw rein. Down the steep, rocky incline, where an ordinary horseman could but carefully pick his way, out on to the sandy plateau upon which we had just ridden, riding wild and giving his wiry little animal free rein, dashed a guard, and when abreast of us drew up short out of a full run, after the manner of Arab horsemen.

"B'salaam" to Muraiche, and a nod of the head to me, which I slightly reciprocated; yes, very slightly, for before me was the one man out of all the Arabs I had ever seen that I would have chosen last for a companion that night. There in the glow of the late afternoon sunlight, the stock of his short carbine resting on his saddle, and the sweat making bright the high lights on his evil, brassy-bronze face, sat the worst cutthroat it was ever my fortune to look upon—Muraiche's friend, he of the market-place.

Although I had learned not to judge men too much by appearances. I resolved to watch him. After a short conversation with Muraiche, during which the guard's peculiar eyes scanned me from the rowels of my spurs to the top of my sun-helmet, I knew that the main objects of his searching glance were in my holsters, covered by my jacket; meantime, however, I lost no detail of his weapon, a hammerless magazine rifle of modern make. Then he addressed me in Arabic, but not speaking the language, I turned to Muraiche.

"He tells us to start," the latter replied.

This sudden assumption of leadership came most unexpectedly, his seeming intention being to bring up the rear. Now Arabs are daring though ignorant; but like all Orientals, fully respect only one thing, and that is a just and strong hand, which they must feel in order to appreciate. Consequently my course was plain.

"Tell the guard to head the caravan, and that if he goes with me, he goes as one of my men." As we got under way, the guard rode slowly ahead, meanwhile taking

"More than forty men of the caravan [traveling from Koko Nor to Lhasa] were abandoned still living, in the desert, without the slightest possibility of our aiding them. They were carried on horseback and on camelback so long as any hope remained, but when they could no longer eat, or speak, or hold themselves up, they were left on the way-side. The general body of the caravan could not stay to nurse them, in a barren desert, where there was hourly danger of wild beasts, of robbers, and, worse than all, of a deficiency of food. Yet, it was a fearful spectacle to see these dying men abandoned on the road! As a last token of sympathy, we placed beside each, a wooden cup and a small bag of barleymeal, and then the caravan mournfully proceeded on its way. As soon as the last straggler had passed on, the crows and vultures that incessantly hovered above the caravan, would pounce down upon the unhappy creatures who retained just enough of life to feel themselves torn and mangled by these birds of prey."

—*missionary* FATHER EVARISTE REGIS HUC

sidelong glances at me, out of the corners of his villainous gray-green eyes, filled with all the hatred of the Moslem for the Christian. I realized that never in my life had the assets and liabilities of my *status quo* received such careful auditing.

When the great red lantern of the sun disk had sunk beneath the earth-line, from without the deep mysterious valleys crept the blue-violet mist films of twilight shadows, absorbing and leavening into their dark tones the brighter crimson afterglow, against which moved the dark shapes of horses and men. Suddenly they bunched themselves and the guard dismounted, then Mohammed and Ali went on with the pack-donkey.

"The guard's saddle-girth is broken," Muraiche informed me. "But we will fix it, and you can ride on very slowly."

"I will wait," I replied, my hand instinctively resting on one of my pistols. "But *you* ride on, Muraiche." The girth was soon "fixed," which consisted in a vain effort to hitch it up another hole.

Steeper and more rugged grew the trail, and we entered the range of the Gharian. As daylight dimmed, an uncomfortable darkness hung over the mountains for a short space; then the moon-glow appeared in the East, and soon the

moon itself lifted its pale distorted
shape above the horizon, and suffused
everything with its pale blue-green
light, so cool and satisfying to the eye
and mind in contrast to the hot sun
glare that during the day reflected
through to the very brain.

But the dark shadow masses of
boulders, parched shrub patches, and
shaded slopes, what uncanny things
might they not contain? And those
gorges, too, which in the day reflected
heat like an oven from their hot, red
sides? Now they were cold, dank, and
foreboding, and a shudder passed
over me. For a moment a sense of
weakness, of fear, of almost helplessness, took possession of me; then
I reasoned with myself. I was tired,
unduly apprehensive, the conditions
of heat and long days in the saddle
had overtaxed my nerves. I fell to
watching the agile bodies of my Arabs
on foot, as, tiring of the pace, they
dropped back, until just in front of
me. Mohammed in particular; how

the lights and shadows played over his great, powerful, animal-like form, how
subtly his shoulder and calf muscles moved under the sleek, dark skin; how they
fascinated me! Willingly through the long journey they had served me, save at
Khoms. I started, my dreaming suddenly ended, and almost involuntarily my
spurs caused my horse to start ahead, The two men had so imperceptibly lessened
their pace that now they had dropped just back of me, one on either side of my
horse, and in Mohammed's hand was a wicked-looking knobbed club, which usu-

ally he had kept stuck in one of the packs. I knew that each carried a long Arab knife, so I ordered Muraiche to tell the men to keep alongside the donkey.

Down the other side of the moonlit valley I saw a caravan coming towards us heading for Khoms. Taking a small note-book from my pocket, I wrote, "Should any accident occur to me, thoroughly investigate, my men, including the guard," and signed it. Tearing the leaf from the book and folding it, I watched the great lumbering camels approach us, and dropped a little farther behind, intending to give it to the head man of the caravan for him to bear to the Pasha at Khoms. Then I decided that under the circumstances there was not sufficient evidence to thus prejudice the Turkish authorities against my men, so I chewed it up and spat it into a patch of sand-lilies.

From the distance came the faint report of a gun. Every one of my men heard it, I knew, but no comment was made, and we pushed deeper into the mountains. On our left, looking toward the moon, objects were indistinct in the half-tone and shadow, while seen from there we appeared in full moonlight. Now and again I sensed moving shadows from that direction, but it was some time before I was sure that, they were living forms following us, perhaps hyenas, jackals, or some sly chetah.

As we made sharp turns, at times in rounding the mountains, and their sides stood out in silhouette against the sky, I bent low on my horse's neck and watched intently. At one of these turns where the sky cut deep into the mountainside, leaving every irregularity in relief against it, I noticed that men were following us, parallel to our course and a little ahead of it. First, away up on the side, a fezzed head and the barrel of a long Arab flintlock bobbed against the sky for a second, as, dodging catlike among the rocks, their owner rounded the side. Then a second and a third appeared, and I knew we were followed by thieves. This was not comforting; but if we were attacked, the guard's rifle, Muraiche's old-fashioned five-shooter, and my two revolvers would be more than a match for them in point of armament.

One thing puzzled me, however, until later. The manner of these desert thieves being invariably to attack from the rear, I could not account for their seeming to forge ahead of us. Watching my men, I saw that they, too, were aware of the thieves; and Muraiche, who had been watching me closely when we occasionally rode abreast, remarked: "This is a bad country here; I think robbers are following us."

"Yes," I replied; "there *are* men off there,—I have seen three."

"Allah knows, everything is in the hand of Allah. 'There is neither might nor power save in Allah, the High, the Mighty.'[1] La! Arbi, you must not ride behind, it is dangerous; you had better ride first."

"Then I will ride last, Muraiche, for I have the best weapons, and I can shoot better than any of you."

After a sharp turn we wound, along a valley side. Just below us the dense foliage of an ancient olive

grove shut out every gleam of light from its black interior, the gnarled old branches reaching out as though to drag into their depths any who might come within their grasp, and the same weird sensations of awe passed over me which I had felt as a boy when I pored over [Gustave] Dorés illustrations of the wandering Dante and Virgil in that wonderful, gruesome nether world.

My sensation was complete when, as though it was the most natural thing in the world for a small caravan to leave the trail, dangerous at its best, my guard led and the men proceeded to follow him toward the dark wood, which it was manifestly their purpose to enter.

"Muraiche," I called, "why are the men leaving the trail?" Perhaps he did not hear, for the ground was rough, and the stones rattled down the steep bank. "Muraiche," I called loudly and peremptorily, as I rode up to him, "tell the men

[1]This saying is used by Moslems when anything alarming occurs.

to halt," at the same time drawing one of my pistols and resting it across my saddle. Then I repeated the question.

"The guard says it is shorter," Muraiche replied, still following the guard.

"Then let the guard take it if he chooses. Order the men on to the trail," and we scrambled our horses and donkey up the steep incline.

The guard turned in his saddle for a moment, made a low reply to Muraiche, then descended and disappeared in the darkness. Skirting the wood for half a mile, we passed beyond it, and my already well-aroused suspicions of intended treachery on the part of my men were confirmed, when in spite of the fact that the guard had by far the fastest-walking horse of our outfit and had taken a shorter route, there was no sign of him until we had passed a hundred yards beyond the grove and halted.

As he emerged I heard the faint click of his carbine as be pulled the bolt to a full-cock, upon which, half turning my horse, I awaited him; as he neared us I saw that he had been running his horse, which was breathing hard and sweating. Then the truth flashed upon me: my men were in league with the thieves, who, by a preconcerted arrangement, had gone ahead and hidden in the grove,—there to set upon me in the darkness, relying on my confidence in the guard to follow his lead. Failing in their end, the guard had stopped to parley with them and then made up time. Had their place of ambush not been so evidently dangerous to enter, they might have been successful. Nor would it have been the first time a guard and outfit had returned without the Arbi, telling a good story of how they were attacked by thieves and escaped while he was killed.

Now here in front of me that picturesque, venomous-looking devil sat, his rifle full-cocked across the pommel of his saddle, my other men at a little distance to my right, and I a good mark with my white sun-helmet, but my revolver resting on my saddle covered the guard.

"Muraiche, tell the guard to uncock his rifle. It might go off by accident." With a sullen look the guard obeyed.

"Now tell him to ride first to protect the goods. Let the men with the pack-donkey follow, then you behind them. I'll ride last. If any thieves approach within gun-shot, warn them away at once or I shall fire. You understand?"

"Yes, Arbi," and we strung out in single file. My purpose was to place the guard who possessed the most effective weapon where it was practically of no use against

me; for this gave me a screen of the men and animals. The danger from Mohammed and Ali depended entirely upon their ability to close in on me, so while in that position there was nothing to fear from them. As for Muraiche, he was under my direct surveillance with the advantage all my way, as I rode with drawn weapon.

But I knew the Arab well enough to know that so long as he is not excited or his fanaticism aroused he will not risk his own skin while strategy will serve his ends; and also knew that I had no one to depend upon but myself, and that my safety lay in maintaining, as far as possible a normal condition of thing's. So I watched; watched my men in front, and watched to the side and behind for signs of the thieves, of whom I caught glimpses now and again. My Arabs' conjunction with these men thwarted, it was but natural that they should communicate with each other to further their plans, and in various ways they sought to do this. While caravan men, when marching through a safe district and many strong, often chant to ease their dreary march or to pacify the camels, in our circumstances the less attention we could draw to ourselves the better. So when Mohammed started to chant in a loud voice by way of giving information, I ordered him to be quiet.

A SANDSTORM IN THE SAHARA

"For days we travelled over these hills of sand, sometimes wind-blown into all kinds of queer wave formations and shapes, sometimes over endless, level reaches; obliterated by the shifting sand, great sections of the gārfla [i.e. caravan] routes are mere directions, the only guides the sun and the stars.[...]

"Lightly blowing in the face of the south-bound gārflas, there springs from the southeast a gentle wind, the gibli, which playfully twirls little eddying whiffs of sand into miniature whirlwinds. In this manner it may blow for days, evaporating the water in the goatskin bags, and sometimes terminating in a terrible sand-storm. Then, when the jamal [which are a type of camel], craning their long necks, sniff high in the air and utter a peculiar cry, the gārfla men know well the ominous signs; far off on the horizon, creeping higher and higher, the sky of blue retreats before a sky of brass.

"To the hoarse cries and curses of the men as they try to hobble the fore legs of the excited camels are added uncanny guttural groanings of the jamal, the braying of the asses, and the pitiful bleating of goats and sheep. High in the air great flames of sand reach out, then the lurid sand-cloud, completely covering the sky, comes down upon the gārfla. In the confusion some of the water-bags are broken and the precious liquid disappears in the sand. Turning tail and driving down before

Again, as we rounded a sharp bend, Ali made a break for the brush, but he started a second too soon. I saw him, and called his name sharply; he halted and returned to the caravan.

When we passed within gun-shot of objects which might conceal a foe I rode abreast of Muraiche, using him to screen myself, knowing well that they would only attack from the side which from their position placed us in the full moonlight. And in the narrow ravines, though he growled, I often crowded him close, affording little or no opportunity to the Arabs to single me out for a shot without endangering Muraiche. So we travelled until a thong of one of Mohammed's sandals broke on the rocky ground, and he asked to be allowed to drop behind a little and fix it. Since we were entering a wide open stretch below a long slope of hill, I acceded; but as he fell behind some distance, I called to him to come, and when he approached us I turned my attention to the men ahead, feeling a sense of relief that we were in more open country.

the blast go some of the unhobbled camels, maybe carrying a driver with them, never to be heard of again.

"In the deep-yellow gloom the gārfla, back to the storm, lies huddled together; the men, wrapped up completely in their baracans on the leeward side of the camels, hug close to the goatskins of water. The whole air is surcharged with suffocating beat and fine powdered sand-dust, which finds its way even as far as Malta and Sicily. It penetrates everywhere, inflames the eyes, and cracks the skin of the already parched tongues and throats of the gārfla men. The torment at times is indescribable, and some poor devil, like the camels, will run maddened into the hurricane.

"The sand-storm lasts from a few hours to six or seven days, and during it the men lie thus, occasionally digging themselves to the surface as they become partially covered with sand. Frequently all the remaining water dries up. At such times camels are often sacrificed for the sake of the greenish water which may be obtained from the honeycomb cells of the reticulum, a mature camel yielding about five or six quarts; and, strange as it may seem, this water is cooler than that carried in goatskins. The storm over, a surviving gārfla of emaciated men and animals staggers on to the nearest oasis or town, over plains which before were sand-hills, and sand-hills which now are plains."

—*an anonymous travel writer*

The moon was slightly behind us, high in the heavens now, and cast our shadows diagonally to the right and ahead of us. I watched the shadows of my horse and myself squirm and undulate as they travelled over the ground. As I relaxed from the tension under which I had been for a moment gazing unthinkingly ahead, the movement of another shadow caught my eye, that of an upward-moving arm and knobbed club. There was no time to look first. Instinctively my right hand thrust my revolver under my reinarm, and I turned my head sharply to find, what I had expected, that my revolver was pointing full at the breast of the big fellow Mohammed, who, stealing up quietly behind me with sandals removed, had intended to strike.

"Boor-r-ro!" (go on), I said. Lowering his club, without a sign of embarrassment, he took his place in line, the others apparently having been oblivious to the whole affair.

After he left me, and the excitement of the moment had passed, cold chills chased one another up and down my spine. From then on I saw no sign of thieves.

> "You will find an occasional Arab who will tell you of a route heretofore unmentioned, a secret route known only to the Senusi[...]. Along this route never less than fifteen caravans cross the desert every year, which bring about ten thousand slaves alive to tell the tale, and they estimate that forty thousand victims fall on the march. Once on the secret route you cannot lose your way, for it is lined with human bones."
>
> —CHARLES WELLINGTON FURLONG

For five hours I had ridden with my finger on the trigger of my pistol covering my men. For five hours I had sensations which I trust I shall not experience again.

About one o'clock in the morning, high up on the hilltop we sighted the white walls of Kussabat, and, after some hard climbing, we came into full view of the silver city—glistening in a bath of silver as Khoms had shone in a flood of gold.

A few words with the town guard, and the great doors of its main gate, the Bab El Kussabat, creaked and groaned as they swung open, and we entered the city, clattered up the steep, narrow streets, where, from the low housetops on either side sleeping forms muffled in barracans awoke and peered over at us, and big white wolf-hounds craning their necks set pandemonium loose from one end of the town to the other, as they snarled and yelped in our very faces.

Soon we were in a small fonduk with doors heavily bolted. The other occupants were a selected stock of camels, goats, sheep, and fowls taken from the Arabs by the Turks in lieu of taxes; in fact, the fonduk had been converted into a sort of pound. On the roof were a dozen or so of Arabs and blacks asleep, and I preferred their company in the moonlight to that of my four men under the dark archways. To prevent scheming, I took with me Muraiche, the cause of all the trouble. Some of these blacks and Arabs raised up out of their sleep to see, probably for the first time, an apparition in khaki and a white helmet. Then we lay down, and, thanks to the previous night's rest, I managed to keep awake most of the night. When Muraiche rolled over in his sleep, or a neighboring black muttered in his savage dreams, I would start from my dozing.

True, I gave them no baksheesh at the journey's end. I might have had them thrown into the foul Turkish prison of the castle; but, after all, it was the life of these men of the desert,—they had only tried their little game and failed.

And the stakes? My revolvers and ammunition, the leather of my saddle and riding-leggings, and perhaps a gold filling in my teeth. They knew I had no money, for in the presence of Muraiche I had deposited it at Tripoli, and Muraiche himself carried only the necessary funds for the journey. But modern weapons are a prohibited import, save for the Turkish army, and are worth their weight in silver to the Arabs.

Why such a risk for such small stakes? Well, why will the desert thief risk his life for a barracan, or an Arab scavenger dig up the corpse of a plague victim for the miserable piece of sackcloth that girds his loins?

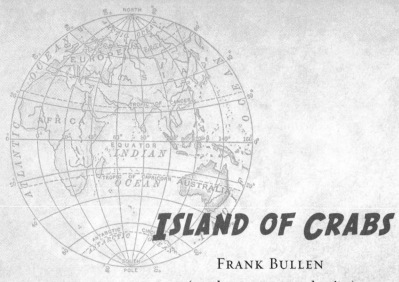

ISLAND OF CRABS

Frank Bullen

(merchant seaman and writer)

There is a tiny islet on the outskirts of the Solomon Archipelago that to all such casual wanderers as stray so far presents not a single feature of interest. Like scores of others in those latitudes, it has not yet attained to the dignity of a single coconut tree, although many derelict nuts have found a lodgment upon it, and begun to grow, only to be wiped out of existence at the next spring-tide. Viewed from a balloon it would look like a silly-season mushroom, but with a fringe of snowy foam around it marking the protecting barrier to which it owes its existence, to say nothing of its growth. Yet of all places in the world which I have been privileged to visit, this barren little mound of sand clings most tenaciously to my memory, for reasons which will presently appear.

One of those devastating cyclones that at long intervals sweep across the Pacific, leaving a long swath of destruction in their wake, had overtaken the pearling schooner of which I was mate. For twenty-four hours we fled before it, we knew not whither, not daring to heave-to. The only compass we possessed had been destroyed by the first sea that broke on board. Whether it was night or day we had no notion, except by watch, and even then we were doubtful, so appalling was the darkness. Hope was beginning to revive that, as the *Papalangi* had proved herself so staunch, she might yet "run it out," unless she hit something. But the tiny rag rigged forward to keep her before it suddenly flew into threads; the curl of the sea caught her under the counter and spun her up into the wind like a teetoture. The next vast comber took her broadside-on, rolled her over, and swallowed her up. We went "down quick into the pit."

Although always reckoned a powerful swimmer, even among such amphibia as the Kanakas, I don't remember making a stroke. But after a horrible, choking struggle in the black uproar I got my breath again, finding myself clinging, as a drowning man will, to something big and seaworthy. It was an ordinary ship's hencoop that the skipper had bought cheap from a passenger vessel in Auckland. As good a raft as one could wish, it bore me on over the mad sea, half dead as I was, until I felt it rise high as if climbing a cataract and descend amidst a furious boiling of surf into calm, smooth water. A few minutes later I touched a sandy beach. Utterly done up, I slept where I lay, at the water's edge, though the shrieking hurricane raged overhead as if it would tear the land up by the roots.

When I awoke it was fine weather, though to leeward the infernal reek of the departing meteor still disfigured a huge segment of the sky. I looked around, and my jaw dropped. Often I had wondered what a poor devil *would* do who happened to be cast away on such a spot as this. Apparently I was about to learn. A painful pinch at my bare foot startled me, and I saw an ugly beast of a crab going for me. He was nearly a foot across, his blue back covered with long spikes, and his wicked little eyes seemed to have an expression of diabolical malignity. I snatched at a handful of his legs and swung him around my head, dashing him against the side of my coop with such vigour that his armour flew to flinders around me. I never have liked crab, even when dressed, but I found the raw flesh of that one tasty enough—it quite smartened me up. Having eaten heartily, I took a saunter up the smooth knoll of sand, aimlessly, I suppose, for it was as bare as a plate, without a stone or a shell. From its highest point, about ten feet above high-water mark, I looked around, but my horizon was completely bounded by the ring of breakers aforesaid. I felt like the scorpion within the fiery circle, and almost as disposed to sting myself to death had I possessed the proper weapon. As I stood gazing vacantly at the foaming barrier and solemn enclosing dome of fleckless blue, I was again surprised by a vicious nip at my foot. There was another huge crab boldly attacking me—me, a vigorous man, and not a sodden corpse, as yet. I felt a grue of horror run all down my back, but I grabbed at the vile thing and hurled it from me half across the island. Then I became aware of others arriving, converging upon me from all around, and I was panic-stricken. For one mad moment I thought of plunging into the sea again; but reason reasserted itself in time, reminding me that, while I had certain advantages on my side where I was, in the water I should fall a helpless victim at once, if, as might naturally be expected, these ghouls were swarming there. Not a weapon of any kind could I see, neither stick nor stone. My feelings of disgust deepened into despair. But I got little time for thought. Such a multitude of the eerie things were about me that I was kept most actively employed seizing them and flinging them from me. They got bolder, feinting and dodging around me, but happily without any definite plan of campaign among them. Once I staggered forward, having trodden unaware upon a spiky back as I sprung aside, wounding my foot badly. I fell into a group of at least twenty, crushing some of them, but after a painful struggle among those needle-like spines regained my feet with several clinging to my body. A kind of frenzy seized me, and, regardless of pain, I clutched at them right and left, dashing them to fragments one against the other, until quite a pile of writhing, dismembered enemies lay around me, while my hands and arms were streaming from numberless wounds. Very soon I became exhausted by my violent exertions and the intense heat, but, to my unfathomable thankfulness, the heap of broken crabs afforded me a long respite, the sound ones finding congenial occupation in devouring them. While I watched the busy cannibals swarming over the yet writhing heap, I became violently ill, for imagination vividly depicted them rioting in my viscera. Vertigo seized me, I reeled and fell prone, oblivious to all things for a time.

When sense returned it was night. The broad moon was commencing her triumphal march among the stars, which glowed in the blue-black concave like globules of incandescent steel. My body was drenched with dew, a blessed relief, for my tongue was leathery and my lips were split with drouth. I tore off my shirt and sucked it eagerly, the moisture it held, though brackish, mitigating my tortures of thirst. Suddenly I bethought me of my foes, and looked fearfully around. There was not one to be seen, nothing near but the heap of clean-picked shells of those devoured. As the moon rose higher, I saw a cluster of white objects at a little distance, soon recognizable as boobies. They permitted me to snatch a couple of them easily, and wringing off their heads I got such a draught as put new life into me. Yet my position was almost as hopeless as one could imagine. Unless, as I much doubted, this was a known spot for *bêche de mer* or pearl-shell fishers, there was but the remotest chance of my rescue, while, without anything floatable but my poor little hencoop, passing that barrier of breakers was impossible. Fortunately I have always tried to avoid meeting trouble half-way, and with a thankful feeling of present wants supplied, I actually went to sleep again.

At daybreak I awoke again to a repetition of the agonies of the previous day. The numbers of my hideous assailants were more than doubled as far as I could judge. The whole patch of sand seemed alive with the voracious vermin. So much so that when I saw the approach of those horrible hosts my heart sank, my flesh shrank on my bones, and I clutched at my throat. But I could not strangle myself, though had I possessed a knife I should certainly have chosen a swift exit from the unutterable horror of my position, fiercely as I clung to life. To be devoured piecemeal, retaining every faculty till the last—I could not bear the thought. There was no time for reflection, however; the struggle began at once and continued with a pertinacity on the part of the crabs that promised a speedy end to it for me. How long it lasted I have no idea—to my tortured mind it was an eternity. At last, overborne, exhausted, surrounded by mounds of those I had destroyed, over which fresh legions poured in ever-increasing numbers, earth and sky whirled around me, and I fell backward. As I went, with many of the vile things already clinging to me, I heard a yell—a human voice that revived my dulling senses like a galvanic shock. With one last flash of vigour I sprang to my feet, seeing as I did so a canoe with four Kanakas in it, not fifty yards away, in the smooth water between the beach and the barrier. Bounding like a buck, heedless of the pain as my wounded feet clashed among the innumerable spiky carapaces of my enemies, I reached the water, and hurled myself headlong towards that ark of safety. How I reached it I do not know, nor anything further until I returned to life again on board the *Warrigal* of Sydney, as weak as a babe and feeling a century older.

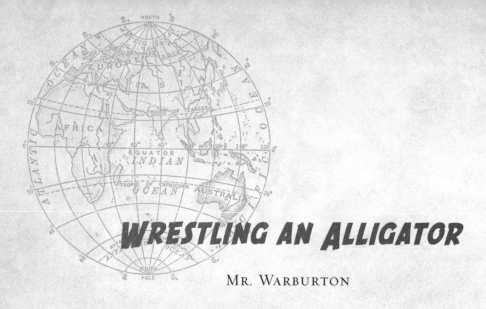

WRESTLING AN ALLIGATOR

MR. WARBURTON

❧

I was returning from the half-built sugarmill one day perhaps a month after my first arrival at the *hacienda*, at about four o'clock in the afternoon. I was riding homeward, then, thinking of many things—of the friends that I should perhaps never see again in the flesh; of—

"What was that? A cry of pain?" Yes, a cry, certainly of pain or terror—the shrill, appealing cry of a child's agonized voice; and I started, and wheeled my horse toward the quarter from which the sounds seemed to come. The cry was repeated, more feebly than before; and as I had now no doubt as to the direction whence the call for help proceeded, I dashed across a ravine, and, scrambling up the steep bank opposite, came in sight of the chain of lagoons, connected with the mighty Rio Plata by a small river, which skirted the plantations of rice and tobacco, and on the banks of which I had shot many a snipe and flamingo. Here, at the edge of a cane-bordered creek that ran up from the nearest lagoon into the broken ground, where the hillocks were gay with purple rhododendrons and the wild geraniums, I beheld a sight that chilled my blood with horror.

Close to the margin of the water, knee-deep in the flowers and the tall pampas grass, just where the white and yellow pond-lilies mingled with the rich-colored blossoms of the flowered prairie, was a child—little Charlie—Don Miguel's hope and heir—his one tie to life and its affections—I knew the bare little golden head at once. But the boy stood, rooted to the ground, transfixed by terror, crouching down, his blue eyes, dilated by mortal fear, fixed on something huge, shapeless, unclean, that drew nearer and nearer yet, a grim and monstrous thing, that had more the aspect of a large log, glistening with slimy mud, than of any thing else. What is the ugly thing that has crawled out from the creek, fringed with bushes of the laurel-rose, and that is clumsily climbing the bank with awkward hurry of its ungainly claw-tipped feet? An alligator, by Heaven! for I see the slanting sunlight glisten on its scaly back, and the formidable jaws open and display the curved row of gleaming white teeth, as, with its cruel red eye fixed upon its prey, it approached the spot where stood the fated child, frozen by a terror that denied him the power to flee.

"Run, Charlie, run! run toward me!" I called aloud, at the same time urging my horse down the bank. The little fellow turned his pale face toward me, and recognized me; but fear was still too potent with him, and he remained where he was, crying out to "Mirry Warburton" to save him. I dashed in the spurs rowel deep, and at one bound came crashing through the rhododendrons to within some three or four feet of the place where the child stood. The alligator wheeled angrily round, to confront the intruder who dared to come between him and his toothsome supper; and my horse, driven wild with terror at the sight and smell of the monstrous reptile, reared, swerved, and threw me, galloping off like a mad creature. I was on my feet in a moment, and kind just time to throw myself between the alligator and the boy, before the blood-thirsty jaws could close in the first fatal snap. The brute recoiled a little, for alligators are cowardly as well as fierce, and they have been known to watch for hour in their reedy ambush, allowing men to pass them uninjured, until they could pounce securely on a woman or a child. But the reptile's slow blood had been too much stirred, by the expectation of an easy triumph, to permit him to decline the fight, and he crawled in upon me, uttering the hoarse cry, half-roar, half-whimpering moan, that a cayman gives under the sting of pain or fury.

I had my sheath-knife out, a strong double-edged blade of Barcelona steel, with a cross-handle and buckthorn haft; but this seemed a poor weapon against such a foe. By a hasty impulse—one of those life-saving thoughts that come upon us at moments of extreme peril, as if they were the whisperings of inspiration—

I tore the blue woollen poncho from my shoulders—happily, I had adopted the New Spain style of dress—and, wrapping the mantle around the tough handle of whalebone riding-whip, I forced it between the alligator's jaws as he closed with me, while at the same time, bending forward, I struck hard with my two-edged knife at his white throat, which was comparatively unprotected. The first stab told, for the white streak was soon crimsoned with blood, but the second stroke failed, for the knife slipped, and rattled uselessly on the armor-plates of the creature's mailed back; and then began a struggle for death or life between my terrible antagonist and myself. My strength was nothing to that of the huge reptile, and I felt myself dragged to right and left as if I had been a rat in the gripe [*sic*] of a terrier, yet I held on fast to the whalebone handle of the whip, while the sharp teeth vainly gnashed and tore at the spongy wool that clogged them, and I retained my hold in sheer desperation, striking in with my knife whenever I got a chance, but usually baffled by the tenacious armor of my invulnerable adversary.

Charlie, a few feet distant, was sobbing piteously, at times crying aloud in appeal to Gauchos, whom he knew—"Sancho!" "Diego!" "El Negro!"—to help "Mirry Warburton" for the dear little fellow, delivered from his first agony of alarm, seemed now to think only of my peril. The idea was a good one, although the child's weak voice could not of course reach far. Exerting the full strength of my lungs, I twice shouted forth the well-known desert-cry when a jaguar is sighted: "*Mozos, a mi!—El tigre!—Mo-zos!*"—and I fancied, as I uttered the second call, that I heard a distant answer, like a faint echo. But now I had need of all my breath and all my muscles, for the infuriated animal with which I fought, tearing the cloth of the soft mantle to pulp, was gradually getting its grim jaws free. Twice, already, had my wrist and arm been grazed by its keen teeth—I bear the white scars to this day—and the horrible odor of the creature, and the remorseless glare of its small bloodshot eye, impressed me with the fantastic notion that my enemy was something evil beyond the mere furious greed of a wild beast. Yet I grasped the whalebone whip-handle, and I drove in the knife with all the force of an arm that was fast growing exhausted. Spent, breathless, giddy, I was dragged down, and, in a kneeling attitude, exerted the remains of my waning strength in a stab at the alligator's throat. The blade broke short off by the handle as it lodged among the stout scales of the neck!

Just then I heard a shout, and the tramp of a horse coming up at full and furious speed. On they came, the steed foam-flecked and gored by the spur, the rider brandishing high above his head the spiral coils of the lasso. I recognized the horseman in an instant. It was Juan, the boldest and most dexterous of all that Centaur brotherhood; and he knew me, and comprehended at a glance the state of affairs.

"Stand back, Englishman—stand back!" he cried aloud, "and I'll do the rest; *Mozos!—El tigre!—Mozos!*" And he whirled the lasso high, spurring his frightened horse near and nearer to the spot.

Events which it takes many words to describe, even inadequately, sometime occupy but a few second or minutes of actual time; and from the period of my hurrying up in response to young Charlie's scream for help, to that of Juan the Gaucho's arrival on the scene of action probably but a few moments had passed. But, to judge by my feelings, they might have been ages. I had rushed to the rescue just in time to save the tender limbs of Don Miguel's heir from the greedy jaws of the monster, and had made as good a fight as I could, nearly paying with my own life for the young life I had saved, when this new champion rode in hot haste to encounter common foe. Reeling, breathless, and dizzy of brain, I understood the Gaucho's meaning sufficiently to stand back letting go my hold of the tough whip-handle, which, with the tattered poncho wrapped around it, I had hitherto obstinately kept between the alligator's churning jaws. The infuriated brute followed me up with bitter hate, his hateful snout all but brushing my knee as I staggered back. But just at that instant, whir! crack! came the well-known sound of the heavy lasso whistling past, launched with unerring aim, and, as I gazed about me with haggard eyes, I saw that the noose was tightening round the reptile's neck; while Juan, with the end of the stout cord fastened to his saddle, had started off at a canter, towing along the alligator after him, as he had tugged along many a bull and many a wild steed.

For an instant it seemed as if the Gaucho's would be an easy triumph; but it was only the surprise of the shock that had mastered the alligator, a very large one, and the great weight and strength of which soon began to tell. I saw the horse brought, with a jerk, to a stop, and then, to my dismay, beheld steed and rider dragged by sheer force toward the lagoon, vainly striving to resist the superior power of the gigantic tyrant of the waters. Juan drove in his spurs, urging his panting and terrified horse by voice, hand, and knee, to put out its whole strength; but it soon seemed plain that, unless the saddle-girths gave way, dragged down into the pool he would be, horse and man, while there could be in such a case little doubt of the issue of the conflict. To cut the cord would have been the only mode of separating the combatants in this unequal duel; but I had let full my broken knife in the long pampas grass, and a Gaucho clings to his lasso with the same mechanical impulse that causes a seaman to hold fast to shroud or stay. "Let go the rope!" I called out to him as loudly as I could. "Loose the end from the saddle-ring, and let the brute go!" But Juan paid no heed to my advice, but spurred his struggling horse, uttering, at the full pitch of his voice, the "tiger-call" of the herdsman.

The child had crept close to me, and was holding on to my coat, weeping and calling on his absent father, and his presence embarrassed me; for, wearied and disarmed as I was, I felt eager to come to the aid of the bold lad who had saved me from the very jaws of death; but just at the moment that the mulatto girl, Charlie's nurse, came running down the hill with sobs and outcries in search of the truant charge who had strayed off while she was threading scarlet berries for a necklace, four of our mounted men came thundering down with cheery shouts and lassoes whirled aloft; and in a very short time the alligator, strong and savage as he was, noosed and entangled by the pliant cords, stabbed with knives, and beaten down by *bolas*, lay dead and harmless.

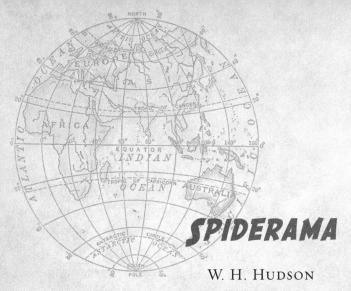

SPIDERAMA

W. H. HUDSON

(British-Argentinean naturalist)

Now, I have repeatedly remarked that all spiders, when the shrill humming of an insect caught in a web is heard near them, become agitated, like the *Pholcus*, and will, in the same way, quit their own webs and hurry to the point the sound proceeds from. This fact convinced me many years ago that spiders are attracted by the sound of musical instruments, such as violins, concertinas, guitars, etc., simply because the sound produces the same effect on them as the shrill buzzing of a captive fly. I have frequently seen spiders come down walls or from ceilings, attracted by the sound of a guitar, softly played; and by gently touching metal strings, stretched on a piece of wood, I have succeeded in attracting spiders on to the strings, within two or three inches of my fingers; and I always noticed that the spiders seemed to be eagerly searching for something which they evidently expected to find there, moving about in an excited manner and looking very hungry and fierce. I have no doubt that Pelisson's historical spider in the Bastille came down in a mood and with a manner just as ferocious when the prisoner called it with musical sounds to be fed.

The spiders I have spoken of up till now are timid, inoffensive creatures, chiefly of the Epeira family; but there are many others exceedingly high-spirited, and, like some of the most touchy hymenopteras, always prepared to "greatly quarrel" over matters of little moment. The *Mygales*, of which we have several species, are not to be treated with contempt. One is extremely abundant on the pampas [in Argentina], the *Mygale fusca*, a veritable monster, covered with dark brown hair, and called in the vernacular *aranea peluda*—hairy spider. In the hot month of December these spiders take to roaming about on the open plain, and are then everywhere seen travelling in a straight line with a slow even pace. They are very great in attitudes, and when one is approached it immediately throws itself back, like a pugilist preparing for an encounter, and stands up so erect on its four hind feet that the under surface of its body is displayed. Humble-bees are commonly supposed to carry the palm in attitudinizing; and it is wonderful to see the grotesque motions of these irascible insects when their nest is approached, elevating their abdomens and two or three legs at a time, so that they resemble a troupe of acrobats balancing themselves on their heads or hands, and kicking their legs about in the air. And to impress the intruder with the dangerous significance of this display they hum a shrill warning or challenge, and stab at the air with their naked stings, from which limpid drops of venom are seen to exude. These threatening gestures probably have an effect. In the case of the hairy spider, I do not think any creature, however stupid, could mistake its meaning when it stands up, a figure horribly grotesque; then, dropping down on all eights, charges violently forwards. Their long, shiny black, sickle-shaped falces are dangerous weapons. I knew a native woman who had been bitten on the leg, and who, after fourteen years, still suffered at intervals acute pains in the limbs.

The king of the spiders on the pampas is, however, not a *Mygale*, but a *Lycosa* of extraordinary size, light grey in color, with a black ring round its middle. It is active and swift, and irritable to such a degree that one can scarcely help thinking that in this species nature has overshot her mark. When a person passes near one—say, within three or four yards of its lurking-place—it starts up and gives chase, and will often follow for a distance of thirty or forty yards. I came once very nearly being bitten by one of these savage creatures. Riding at an easy trot over the dry grass, I suddenly observed a spider pursuing me, leaping swiftly along and keeping up with my beast. I aimed a blow with my whip, and the point of the lash struck the ground close to it, when it instantly leaped upon and ran up the lash, and was actually within three or four inches of my hand when I flung the whip from me.

*   *   *

ALGOT LANGE
(American ethnologist)

While convalescing from my first attack of swamp-fever, I had occasion to study a most remarkable species of spider which was a fellow lodger in the hut I then occupied. In size, the specimen was very respectable, being able to cover a circle of nearly six inches in diameter. This spider subsists on large insects and at times on the smaller varieties of birds, like finches, etc. Its scientific name is *Mygale avicularia.* The natives dread it for its poisonous bite and on account of its great size and hairy body. The first time I saw the one in my hut was when it was climbing the wall in close proximity to my hammock. I got up and tried to crush it with my fist, but the spider made a lightning-quick move and stopped about five or six inches from where I hit the wall.

Several times I repeated the attack without success, the spider always succeeding in moving before it could be touched. Somewhat out of temper, I procured a hammer of large size and continued the chase until I was exhausted. When my hand grew steady again, I took my automatic pistol, used for big game, and, taking a steady aim on the fat body of the spider, I fired. But with another of the remarkably quick movements the spider landed the usual safe distance from destruction. Then I gave it up. For all I know, that animal, I can scarcely call it an insect after using a big game pistol on it, is still occupying the hut. About nine months later I was telling Captain Barnett, of the R. M. S. *Napo* which picked me up on the Amazon on my way home, about my ill success in hunting the spider. "Lange," he asked, "why didn't you try for him with a frying-pan?"

AN EXPEDITION WITH HEADHUNTERS

F. W. UP DE GRAFF

(American electrical engineer and adventure seeker)

When the Amazon forests swallowed me up for the first time that morning my mind flew back to my High School days when I had gloated over the pages of Stanley, and longed to steer my own dugout through another Dark Continent. As the forest roof closed over my head, and we began slipping and splashing through interminable fields of black mud relieved only by mountain torrents which we forded waist-deep, little did I care for multitudes of discomforts which awaited me in the three thousand, five hundred mile journey before I could reach Pará [Brazil]. For all I knew or cared, I should be paddling through eternal rain, wading through eternal mud, living on what Fortune threw in my way, or starving in some trackless swamp. To Pará I was going, whether anybody had ever been that way before or not.

I had known the woods on the Pacific slopes of the Andes for a whole year, but here was something different. The same giant vegetation, the same seas of mud, the same monkeys and parrots chattering and screaming in the tree-tops, but here was the last jumping-off place before I should be buried in the Great Unknown. Only twenty-five miles ahead flowed the Napo, on whose further bank commenced the vast unexplored wilderness which stretched away toward the unchartered boundaries of Ecuador, Peru, Bolivia, and the Argentine. In that primeval maze of forest, swamp and river, peopled by men as wild and free as the animals which shared their gloomy home, untrodden by civilized man since the beginning of time, were locked a thousand secrets! Would that I could share them all!

With such thoughts in my mind I mushed ahead, pushing aside the dripping branches, soaked to the skin, tugging at my feet which stuck in the clinging slough at every step. I had started, and, equipped with the unconquerable spirit of youth, I knew nothing could stop me now.

After pushing on all day, we came across the regular halting-place, a shelter of palm-thatch with a raised floor on which to sleep clear of the mud and water. There we stayed the night. Next morning my bearers took up their packs at sun-rise, and we were off on the last stretch before the river would be reached again. Through the soaking tunnel we made our way all morning, till at last the foaming waters showed through the last few yards of forest as we emerged into the clearing where stood the town of Napo. It figures, in fairly large print on some maps, the draughtsmen of which have evidently paid a great deal of attention to detail. Actually the town had no inhabitants. It is composed of one house. The house had a good roof. It stands in the middle of the clearing into which I walked, and the clearing is as important to Napo as the house itself. For it lets in the blessed sun, and you can dry your sopping kit; more important still, had I but known it then, it keeps out ants.

I took possession of the house and sat down to await the coming of my first command, piloted by my newly hired crew. It would probably measure but twenty-five feet over all, but it was for me a matter of vast importance. If it turned out to be "unseaworthy" I should have to kick my heels in Napo for three or four weeks while a new one was being chopped out.

That afternoon I was overhauling my kit and having a look to see how much had been pilfered and whether the water had got in, greasing my rifle and revolver, and putting things in shape for the trip down-stream. The time for the evening meal was approaching, and the pot was on the fire. For my packers, whom I had induced to stay with me until the canoe turned up, I was preparing a huge pot of rice boiled up with molasses. I was in the act of taking it off the fire when

> "I remember those few days chiefly by having lost my pants, and run up against a tigre [puma], armed with an escopeta of the common 'trade' variety, a shot-gun which had once had two barrels. It then had half a barrel. The other one and a half had been blown off long ago; the half went on one memorable evening when I stalked a duck for dinner; I shot the duck, not only with the charge, but also twelve inches of barrel. (I believe that in the days of the Napoleonic wars, this would have been known as 'bar-shot'.) The whole barrel had been missing ever since the man who sold me the gun, Dr. Jones of Iquitos, tried to demonstrate the efficacy of smokeless powder, shortly after taking my money. He had a narrow escape, and I'm sorry. After watching half the gun fly over his left shoulder, he handed me back what was left, with the assurance that 'it was still a killing weapon.' I thanked him, and told him I fully realized that it was sure to kill something."
>
> —F. W. UP DE GRAFF

somebody stepped up to the house behind me, and a voice said with a good old Western drawl:

"I've heard you're pulling your freight down-stream."

"Good guess," I answered. "Bound for New York."

I was surprised, to say the least of it, to see a great, big raw-boned, typical prospector from the West standing at the edge of the raised floor on which I was doing my cooking. Barefoot, dressed only in a cotton undershirt and a pair of home-made pants of the same material, he stood surveying me calmly. There didn't seem to be any nonsense about those clear gray eyes, and that tough square jaw. The man was evidently one accustomed to a hard life in the open. He looked a rough and ready type, perhaps a Texas Ranger. (He told me afterwards that, as a matter of fact, the Rangers were the cause of his exile.) A bald spot surmounted his rugged face, and a rough grey beard, which looked as if it had been recently trimmed up with a machete, covered his chin. He wasn't very broadly built, but at the same time he gave the impression of having a great reserve of strength. He looked a man of forty-five.

Then I remembered the Governor of Archidona's words, which had never recurred to me till that moment.

"You must be Don Juan," I said.

"That's me," came the answer. "That's all the Spanish I know, but I guess that's what they call me. My name's really Jack Rouse."

"Well, come in and have something to eat, Mr. Rouse!"

"Cut out the titles," my guest put in.

"Dinner's just about ready," I went on, "the grub isn't much, but it's the best I can do."

Rouse took one look at the steaming pots of rice and beans, the open can of corned beef.

"Are you apologizing for stuff like this?" he said; "I've had nothing to eat for two months but bananas."[...]

[Back when he was in Nevada he] worked as messenger and driver on a stage-line. Finally he tired of risking his life for the poor pay he was getting, and got in the Company's bad books under suspicion of having turned over the mail-pouches to a pair of road-agents without putting up enough of a fight.

"Uncle Sam is looking for me," he ended up curtly.

For my part, I didn't care a hang who was looking for him. Here was a man of the right stamp for a trip through the country that lay ahead.[...]

We turned in that night on the floor of the shelter, each one of us pleased with the prospect of the journey we were to commence together on the morrow. My bearers slept at the other end of Napo, a dozen feet away. One thing struck me forcibly, and that was that the Indians swathed themselves from head to foot in the cotton blankets which each man carried as well as his food. I said something to Jack about "this bunch of mummies we've got with us," and he growled out a caustic remark on their "seeming to be afraid of the night air." And we left it at that.

We lay talking for some time, when suddenly I noticed that every now and then something would fly in at one end of the shelter, cross over our bodies, and disappear into the night at the other end. At times, as the night wore on, these spectres would pass over us so low that we could feel the air from their wings on our faces. "Owls" we decided, for they were the only things we knew of that fly so silently by night.

At last we fell off to sleep, and I did not wake up till dawn. When we got up, the first thing I noticed was a feeling of dizziness and lassitude which took me by surprise, for I had slept soundly enough. I turned to Jack to see how he felt, when I was dumbfounded to see a great ugly clot of blood hanging from the back of his head. Immediately I thought of the Indians, who were already up and about, busy with the fire. Jack confessed to feeling weak also, but as for wounds he had none. I spent the best part of a quarter of an hour searching in vain for any sign of a cut big enough to let flow so much blood. Then I noticed a dull red patch at the foot of my own blanket, but my feet seemed to be unstained. At last I called the Indians' attention to the state of affairs, at a loss for an explanation. And then it was that I saw that one of them had left a similar pool on the floor where he had slept. The porters laughed as if it was the most natural thing in the world, and said that "the night-birds had been feeding." They immediately pointed out to us our own wounds, which we had failed to find. Jack had been tapped on the forehead, and I on the big toe.

And that was my first experience of the Vampire Bat.

*   *   *

[After reaching the town of Iquitos in Peru, Up de Graff and Rouse joined forces with Edward Morse and William Game for an expedition up the Amazon in search of Inca gold. They were joined by some two hundred natives of the Aguaruna and Antipa headhunting tribes. While these two tribes were usually enemies, here they had overcome their differences and were going up the river to attack a mutual enemy—the Huambizas.]

On the 26th of October, no sign of the Huambizas had yet been seen. During the morning of that day we were paddling along in the usual formation, Indian file, when suddenly a commotion started among the leading canoes, followed by a "trombone concert." [These were arm movements the natives made to ward off the magic of their enemies.] Something which had been picked up out of the water was

> **"**We were now in the land of the bloodsucking bats, the vampire bats that suck the blood of living creatures [...] It is only here that fish no bigger than trout kill swimmers, and bats the size of the ordinary 'flittermice' of the northern hemisphere drain the life-blood of big beasts and of man himself.**"**
>
> —*President Theodore Roosevelt*

being handed round for inspection. On pushing up to the front of the column, we found that the centre of interest was indeed worthy of attention. It was no less than a piece of charred wood. So at last we were in touch with the enemy. After a lot of talk it was decided that we should push on and try and find the probable point from which it had drifted.

Paddling ahead for the remainder of the morning, we halted on a very long sand-bar for a mid-day rest. There was a feeling of war in the air. The Jívaro party[1] seemed to have settled down at last with a will to the prospect of attacking their long-standing enemies. There remained but one stepping-stone to be crossed before they would reach a state of white-hot zeal for the attack—the omens must be read.

The meal over, the Indians disappeared into the forest which came down to the edge of the sand. In a few moments they were back, each man carrying a branch from a tree which bears a small green berry. (I was never able to identify it.) Some of the berries they stripped from the twigs, and the branches themselves they planted in the sand in a long straight line parallel with the river. Tuhuimpui [a medicine man and chief of the Aguarunas] strolled up to me unconcernedly. "We are going to make it rain," he said simply. "I hope you will not bring down enough to drench us and our cargo," I said with mock solemnity. "Never fear," came his grave answer, "only a light shower. To-night it shall rain and thunder and blow, but before we summon the storm, we shall build you a house."

I was taken aback to say the least of it, for it seemed to me that he had very little hope of success, for all the effect a row of branches would have on a clear blue sky, the same sky which had smiled on us since we turned up the Santiago from the Marañon. In deference to his gravity, however, I said nothing more. On the contrary, I persuaded Jack and the rest to come along with me and take part in the show. So we cut our branches (we were not allowed to bring any but the right kind) and planted them.

The berries which they had pulled the Jívaros put into snails' shells, and threw into the river with a good deal of tom-foolery in the way of chanting and solemn gesture. (We used to call this kind of thing "monkey business.")

---

[1] The Aguarunas, Antipas, Huambizas and several other tribes are collectively referred to as Jívaros.

And then we simply embarked in the canoes and left the playa to itself.

Within half an hour, gentle rain fell. A light cloud had gathered I know not whence for the first time for three weeks. Now it may be said that it was a pure coincidence, but it was at the same time very strange that Tuhuimpui's efforts should so strikingly produce a result after so many perfect days had passed. It should be remembered that the rainy season does not set in, properly speaking, until the middle of January. Even down to the smallest detail the Aguaruna chief was right.

The gentlest of sun-showers fell that afternoon enough to freshen us all up, but only enough. Morse and I discussed the process of rain-making with the Indians. We discovered that Tuhuimpui had been making a test of his favour with the god *Yacu–Mámam*, the controller of Rivers and Rain, and that had he left the newly cut branches planted in the playa below to wither and die, our attack would never have been made. Without the River God's help, disaster would have over-taken us; but this gentle shower to refresh the tokens planted for his favour was his answering sign of approval and protection in their mooted ventures.

"You see the power I wield," grinned Tuhuimpui, finally. Suddenly his manner changed. Gravely he gave utterance to the sentiment which lies closest to the heart of every Jívaro. "Now indeed we shall return with many heads".... But in a moment he was boasting again. "This is nothing to what will fall to-night," he said mysteriously. "It will thunder, there will be lightning; a great wind will blow; a storm will rage; *Yacu–Mámam* will smile on me."

We began to think there might be something in what Tuhuimpui said after all, but the thought passed and we were soon joking about "those mighty strong houses we should have to build to keep the rain out."

By six o'clock that evening we had found what the Jívaros had been looking for since we picked up the piece of charcoal. We discovered the mouth of a stream which ran into the Santiago, covered so effectually with heavy undergrowth that it was invisible from the centre of the main river. Why, I do not know, but the Antipas and Aguarunas who guided our destiny decided at once that this was where the enemy was to be found. So a scouting party of four picked men was told off to take a canoe and spy out the land. They slid off noiselessly and disappeared in the gloom of the forest vault, moving with the catlike stealth of men who know that detection means death.

The chiefs signed to the rest of us to make for the bank of the Santiago opposite the mouth of the stream. Here we left the canoes, climbing ashore with great care on logs which had fallen over the bank, so as to leave no trail. Tuhuimpui was very particular that we should land in this way, himself supervising the operation. Next, a party of Jívaros collected all the canoes, moored them to the trees with *bejuco* strands, and half-filled them with mud dug from the water's edge. They sank from sight one by one, until of all that gallant array of craft there was no sign left. The *bejucos* appeared to be but vines which had lost their hold and fallen into the river—only a tiny detail of the vast network of tangled undergrowth which chokes the forest from end to end of the Amazon basin. The Antipas withdrew in the tracks of the main party which had moved into the forest, and anyone passing the spot in dugouts five minutes later could never have suspected the presence of a war-party.

Dusk was gathering by this time. Tuhuimpui, in solemn preparation for the storm which was due to rise, ordered the building of shelters for all his men and a specially well-built one for his white allies. In an hour the camp was pitched—one half for the Aguarunas, the other for the Antipas, our own shelter in the middle. Each of them was about thirty yards from us. We set to work to thin out the undergrowth all round our camp by way of precaution. There was no knowing what these friends of ours might be doing if rain fell a second time at their bidding! We felt cramped, too, and hedged in by darkness after the safety of the river and the open *playas*. I think as a matter of fact, that in their anxiety to be after the Huambizas, they had by this time forgotten us more or less, or at any rate relegated us to a place of secondary importance; we should come in handy after the Huambizas had been routed, perhaps.

Be that as it may, we detected no suspicion of foul play that night, though not one of us slept in the inky blackness of the forest. Anyone who has walked through a long railway tunnel can appreciate the blackness of the woods at night. This is the nearest comparison to anything in the world as we know it that I can get. Both tunnel and forest are clothed with that absolutely palpable gloom which seems to have its being, not in the surrounding space, but in the very retina of the eye itself.

We lit fires round our shelter, as the Jívaros themselves had done, and sat up for many an hour, spectators of the weirdest scene I have ever witnessed.

Tuhuimpui arrived at our shelter with a great gourd full of what looked for all the world like chutney sauce.

"We are going to paint," he announced. A short interrogation sufficed to satisfy myself that this was *huito*, a kind of giant walnut, of which the outer shell contains a stain or dye, in just the same way as a butternut or a black walnut. The thorny root of a palm is used as a grater to reduce the outer shell to pulp. With this the skin can be dyed jet-black, simply by rubbing it in the wet state. All the Jívaro tribes use it to paint themselves for battle, and are indeed loath to attack without doing so. It may be that they want a distinguishing sign so that in the excitement and confusion of the fight in close country a glance will suffice to tell friend from foe. I think, however, that this is a very unlikely explanation of the custom. It is more probably a part of the usual panoply of war in which all savage tribes indulge.[...]

We all readily agreed to paint up in preparation for the attack on the morrow. So we stripped, determined to do the thing thoroughly, and each saw to it that his companions did not overlook any odd corners. Even Jack's bald spot did not escape attention. The effect of the application of this dye is not immediately apparent. So it was not till morning that we noticed any change in our appearance. The rising sun, however, revealed to us the full possibilities of *huito.* Not only our skin, but even our hair and eyes seemed to have changed color overnight. We laughed till we were nearly sick. The Jívaros hearing the uproar, thought we were having a war-dance of our own. Tuhuimpui came over and inspected us, surveying with a face unmoved a scene the absurdity of which no white man could have resisted.

But to return to the night's vigil. A moment after Tuhuimpui left us, he returned to tell us of the safe arrival of the scouting party. The enemy had been located. The scouts had approached to within a few yards of a small settlement and had actually counted the warriors. With consummate skill they had withdrawn unseen. Had I not had so many personal experiences of these men's amazing skill in scouting, I should not have believed it possible for any living thing larger than a humming-bird to approach within earshot of a Jívaro in the forest.

Having painted themselves from head to foot, the Indians began to prepare themselves for the war-dance. Each camp built a huge fire, and supplies of fuel for the long night were stacked beside the shelters. At a given signal every man leapt to his feet, grabbed spear, and all joined in a great capering throng about the blazing fires; with raucous yells they danced and danced and danced, two bounding swaying circles careering round the blaze, spears shaken in grim emphasis of the threats they hurled at their unsuspecting enemies.

Now the whole crowd would be scampering round the flames, now a few tireless warriors who had outlasted their fellows; sometimes a solitary enthusiast would prance and yell to the delight of the squatting onlookers, uttering curses and vowing vengeance on the Huambizas who had stolen from him a wife.

Suddenly with a clap of thunder, the promised storm broke on the scene. Here was everything that Tuhuimpui had predicted—one of those summer storms of great intensity but short duration which occur in the tropics alone. Once more the necromancer's spell had worked. Even as he had said, the wind raged and the rain fell in sheets to the accompaniment of the thunder and the vivid lightning. So great was the fury of the elements that we had to post a sentry outside our shelter to warn us of falling limbs. All around the cave they came crashing down—any one of them enough to obliterate us and our puny cover.

In half an hour it had passed, and we were out again, uncovering the fire and restoring it to life while the dying wind swept the last drops of moisture from the forest roof. It had passed, but left behind in every Jívaro heart an undying faith in the prowess of their chief. Sure of their victory now, the savages bounded to the dance with redoubled energy, cavorting and pirouetting in a mad frenzy of hatred and battle-lust. All night long they kept it up, a pack of tireless demons. We on our part had no recourse but to sit with our rifles at hand and wait for dawn. Sleep had no charms for us while that waking delirium possessed the Indians, fanned to white-heat by the splendid augury of the storm.

It is useless for me to attempt an explanation of the prodigious success with which Tuhuimpui met that day. I cannot allow that it was merely a case of coincidence. The correctness *in detail* of his prognostications may suffice to confound that theory. No; either he knew by some sixth sense which many animals possess that there was rain somewhere near (a thing almost unbelievable, since there was apparently no difference in the barometric conditions of that day and the preceding days) or else he was able to detect the coming of the rain by a minute observation of the movements of certain animals, or even insects, signs which would mean nothing to any but the most highly trained child of the woods.

With the coming of dawn, groups of weary savages were to be seen lying about and preparing leisurely for the fight. Exhausted by the night's revelry, they seemed but poorly fitted for the trials of battle. But our ideas of battle differ very markedly from theirs. The long strain of a modern engagement is a thing undreamed of by these lovers of cunning and surprise. For us it may be a matter of days or weeks, for them it is one minute.

Here and there they strolled round the dying embers, busy with rouge-pots, feathers and loin-cloths, black from head to foot with the *huito* which had taken effect during the night hours, their black pointed teeth bared in a grin of anticipation—a band of veritable demons straight from Hell. But grouped round the fire which still burned before the central shelter of the camp was a company of creatures which fell not far behind them. Tousled, bewhiskered, stained the same ebony black, we sat and cooked our breakfast. Game, it was agreed, outstripped the rest of us in hideousness. With his mop of sandy hair, a three month's old ginger beard, blue eyes, great thick-set body half-clothed in ragged shirt and pants, every inch of skin as black as night, he was indeed a fearsome creature.[...]

Breakfast over—for the Jívaros a drink of *giamanchi*[2] sufficed—we all moved off to the water's edge. The moment had come for the attack. The savages with their new loin-cloths, rouged faces, tufts of *lumbiqui* feathers (red and yellow balls of fluff) in their ears, looked a formidable company. Quietly we raised the dugouts, and made across to a sand-spit which extended from the mouth of the stream, up which we were to go, to a point some two hundred yards down-stream, an excellent base for the day's operations. Here a party composed of old men and boys was told off to guard the canoes. Of the latter I have said nothing. A few lads of nine or ten years of age accompanied the party to learn the art of war from their fathers. It was manifest throughout the trip that they were happy and proud to have been called to an apprenticeship in the chief business of life.

Led up by the scouts who had come in the night before, in a long single file, we made our way into the forest, and moved up the left bank of the stream. According to plan the savages split up into two parties, the Antipas made off into

---

[2] This is an alcoholic drink made of chewed up arrowroot mixed with saliva that is fermented and then diluted with water. Up de Graff said it "looks and tastes like buttermilk."

the jungle on a detour, to take as their objective the further of the two settlements which had been selected for the raid, while the Aguarunas clung to the bank of the stream, moving on the nearer. We (black) white men brought up the rear of this latter column under the personal supervision of Tuhuimpui, who lived in fear and trembling of our clumsy movements. Game alone, had he come within a quarter of a mile of the enemy before the surprise had been sprung, would have queered the pitch. It was one of his whims never to go barefoot, with the result that he was forever the victim of his own shoes. They caught in the vine-roots, they were sucked off his feet by the mud, they slipped in the moss and they were ever half-full of dirt—an interminable nuisance which their owner could never be persuaded to abandon. Tuhuimpui protested in vain, while Game went crashing through the undergrowth with the delicacy of a tapir. At last it was too much for our chief. He stopped us. We were to wait till the attack had begun.

No sooner had we halted than there came to our ears the *whang-whang* of a machete on wood. So we were actually within earshot of a settlement at last.

It is at this point in my narrative that I must pause a moment to make a few comments on Jívaro methods of warfare. They are utterly distasteful to the white man—the *true* white man who is brought up to a code of fair play. The attackers display no bravery, the attacked have no chance to defend themselves. As a cat creeps up behind a bird which is digging up worms, so the Jívaro attacks his enemy. A square hand-to-hand fight he will not entertain. With all his paint and feathers he is, unlike the North American Indian, a coward at heart. I must have given the impression in the foregoing pages that our heart was in the business; but such was not the case. We used the war-party for our own ends—they were our only means of getting upriver with our kit, once Pitacunca[, an Antipas chief, and his men] had deserted us. To have left them to attack the Huambizas alone would have been to stamp ourselves in their eyes as cowards. To have turned them from their purpose would have been to place ourselves between two enemies, each waiting as anxiously as the other for our heads. So there was nothing for it but to indulge Tuhuimpui's caprice in the hope that the affair would prove to be but an incident in our onward movement.

So we sat and listened to that single distant clanging of steel on wood, the only sign of human life in all that vast forest into which a moment ago two hundred men had melted. *Whang-whang* came the sharp-cut noise of the blade falling on a paddle which was never to be finished.

With a hideous yell the van of the attackers leapt from cover, a bare ten yards from the nearest of their prey. We jumped to our feet at a word from Tuhuimpui, and in a moment were rushing to the scene of the slaughter. (The moment was a tragic one for Game, who left his shoes in the mud, only one of which he ever recovered.)

We never fired a shot, either in attack or defence that day. When we arrived at the scene of action, we found that the settlement, a mere handful of savages, male and female, had been rushed. The game was up.[...]

Those of the Huambizas, then, who had been fortunate enough to escape from the spears of the raiders had fled to the shelter of the largest of the little group of houses which had been attacked. There cannot have been more than ten or fifteen of them shut up within its walls, but the Aguarunas had not the spirit to attack them now that they were aroused. That is the Jívaro way.

The enemy having left their dead and dying behind them in their flight, the victors dashed forward to seize the most highly treasured of the spoils of battle— the heads of the enemy slain. With stone-axes and split bamboo knives, sharpened clam-shells (rubbed to a keen edge on sand-stone), and *chonta*-wood machetes, they went from corpse to corpse, gathering and stringing their gruesome emblems of victory.[...]

The party then set to work to loot the houses from which the occupants had been driven. Nothing escaped the raiders. I was there in one of the houses with them, and well remember the motley collection of things that we found. There were Peruvian coins, china cups and saucers, a butcher's knife, a number of red bandana handkerchiefs, all evidently looted from Barranca[, a town on the Peruvian coast], a Jívaro hand-loom with a half-finished piece of cloth on it, an iron spear-head, and a number of small Jívaro household objects which are to be found in any settlement. Nothing was too small to escape the Aguarunas' attention. They cleaned out the house from end to end, every man keeping for himself all he could lay hands on. Then they fired the roof, and in a moment the whole house was ablaze[...].

It will be remembered that a party of Antipas had separated from the main body, as agreed between the Indians before the attack, to storm another group of hutments further up the creek. It was at this moment, then, that we decided among ourselves to push on after them and see how they had fared. We had not gone more than a few yards when we were met by the same party returning, laden with dripping heads. No less than nine they brought; some tied in pairs by their own hair and slung round the neck of one of their conquerors, others slung with bark-ropes. This gruesome procession was led by a short, fat savage; laden with his share of the spoils, grinning in triumph, with his teeth stained black and filed to a point, his thick-set shoulders spattered with the blood of his victims, he was a diabolical-looking creature.[...]

The Jívaros never take adult male prisoners, but the women and children who are caught in the periodical raids are given the same standing in the victorious tribe as those who are born into it. Polygamy is forced on the Jívaro peoples by the constant drain on the male population caused by the incessant inter-tribal warfare. But for polygamy they would soon become extinct.

What the scalp is to the North American Indian, the battle-standard to the civilized warrior, the [shrunken] heads are to the Jívaro. But the comparison is only true up to a point. For whereas the glory of the battle-standard and the scalp is undying, that of the Jívaro heads endures only to the end of the great Festival of Rejoicing with which they are honoured on the return of the war-party to their homes.

During the absence of the warriors their women have made ready vast quantities of *giamanchi*. This preparation contains just enough alcohol to inebriate when taken in enormous quantities, as the savages do on these occasions. Unlike civilized intoxicants its only action is stupefying. The tom-toms are brought out, and men and women throw themselves into the business of dancing and drinking themselves to sleep. The rhythmic beats of the drums resound through the woods for many a long hour. Only the soporific effect of the liquor suffices to bring the orgy to an end.

Afterwards the heads are shorn of their hair, which is converted into permanent trophies in the form of belts to be worn round the loin-cloths of their distinguished owners in battle or at the feast. The possession of such a trophy singles a man out for special regard. But the heads themselves have now lost their value, as surely as pearls which have died. It is curious that the fanatical jealousy with which they are guarded up to the time of the festival should give place to that complete indifference which allows them to be thrown to the children as playthings and finally lost in river or swamp.

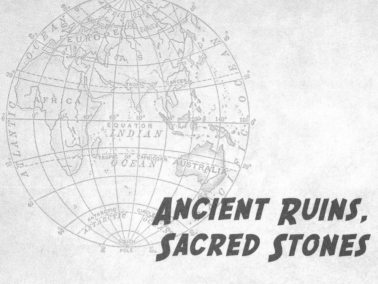

ANCIENT RUINS, SACRED STONES

JOHN LLOYD STEPHENS
(American diplomat, archeologist, and explorer)

Clouds gathered around the mountains, and for an hour we rode in the rain; when the sun broke through we saw the mountain tops still towering above us, and on our right, far below us, a deep valley. We descended, and found it narrower and more beautiful than any we had yet seen, bounded by ranges of mountains several thousand feet high, and having on its left a range of extraordinary beauty, with a red soil of sandstone, without any brush or underwood, and covered with gigantic pines. In front, rising above the miserable huts of the village, was the gigantic church of St. John the Hermit, reminding me of the Church of St. John in the wilderness of Judea, but the situation was even more beautiful. At two o'clock we crossed the stream and entered the village. Opposite the church the muleteer told us that the day's work was over, but, with all our toils, we had made only fifteen miles, and were unwilling to stop so soon. The exceeding beauty of the place might have tempted us, but the only good plastered hut was occupied by a band of ruffianly soldiers, and we rode on. The muleteer followed with curses, and vented his spite in lashing the mules. Again we crossed the stream, and, continuing up the valley along the dry bed, which bore marks of the flood that washed it in the rainy season, in an hour we crossed it half a dozen times. Heavy clouds rested on the mountains, and again we had rain. At four o'clock we saw on a high table on the left the village of Jocotan, with another gigantic church. According to the route agreed upon with the muleteer, this should have been the end of our first day's journey. We had been advised that the cura could give us much information about the ruins of Copan, and told him to cross over and stop there; but he refused, and, hurrying on the mules, added that we had refused to stop when he wished, and now he would not stop for us. I could not spur

my mule beyond her own gait, and, unable to overtake him, jumped off and ran after him on foot. Accidentally I put my hand on my pistols, to steady them in my belt, and he fell back and drew his machete. We came to a parley. He said that if we went there we could not reach Copan the next day; whereupon, willing to make a retreat, and wishing to leave him no excuse for failing, we continued.

At six o'clock we rose upon a beautiful table of land, on which stood another gigantic church. It was the seventh we had seen that day, and, coming upon them in a region of desolation, and by mountain paths which human hands had never attempted to improve, their colossal grandeur and costliness were startling, and gave evidence of a retrograding and expiring people. This stood in a more desolate place than any we had yet seen. The grass was green, the sod unbroken even by a mule path, not a human being was in sight, and even the gratings of the prison had no one looking through them. It was, in fact, a picture of a deserted village. We rode up to the cabildo, the door of which was fastened and the shed barricaded, probably to prevent the entrance of straggling cattle. We tore away the fastenings, broke open the door, and, unloading the mules, sent Augustin on a foraging expedition. In half an hour he returned with *one* egg, being all that he was able to procure; but he had waked up the village, and the alcalde [i.e. mayor], an Indian with a silver-headed cane, and several alguazils [i.e. policemen] with long thin rods or wands of office, came down to examine us. We showed them our passport, and told them where we were going, and which, with their characteristic indifference of manner, they expressed no surprise. They could not read the passport, but they examined the seal and returned it. We asked them for eggs, fowls, milk, &c., to all of which they answered, what afterward became but too familiar, "no hay," "there is none," and in a few minutes they retired and left us to ourselves.

The cabildo was about forty feet long and twenty broad, with plastered walls; its furniture consisted of a large table and two benches with high backs, and the alcalde sent us a jar of water. We abused the muleteer for stopping at a place where we could get nothing to eat, and made our dinner and supper upon bread and chocolate, taking care not to give him any. There were pins in the walls for swinging hammocks, and in the evening we prepared for sleep. Mr. [Frederick Catherwood, the illustrator] was in his hammock, and I was half undressed, when the door was suddenly burst open, and twenty-five men rushed in, the alcalde, alguazils, soldiers, Indians, and Mestitzoes, ragged and ferocious-looking fellows, armed with staves of office, swords, clubs, muskets, and machetes, and carrying blazing pine sticks. At the head of them was a young officer of about twenty-eight or thirty, with a glazed hat and sword, and a knowing and wicked expression, whom we afterward understood to be a captain of one of Carrera's[1] companies. The alcalde was evidently intoxicated, and said that he wished to see my passport again. I delivered it to him, and he handed it over to the young officer, who examined it, and said that it was not valid. In the mean time, Mr. Catherwood and I dressed ourselves. I was not very familiar with the Spanish language, and, through Augustin, explained my official character, and directed him particularly to the endorsements of Commandant Piñol and General Cascara. He paid no regard to my explanations; the alcalde said that he had seen a passport once before, and that it was printed on a small piece of paper not bigger than his

[1] Rafael Carrera was the leader of one side in the Guatemalan civil war.

hand; whereas mine was the one given by government on a quarto sheet. Besides this, they said that the seal of General Cascara was only that of the department of Chiquimula, and it ought to be that of the state of Guatimala. I did all in my power to show the insufficiency of these objections; but, after a warm altercation, the young man said that we should not proceed on our journey, but must remain at Comotan until information could be sent to Chiquimula, and orders received from that place. We had no disposition to remain in such hands; threatened them with the consequences of throwing any obstructions in our way; and I at length said that, rather than be detained there and lose time, I would abandon my journey to Copan altogether, and return by the road on which I came; but both the officer and the alcalde said peremptorily that we should not leave Comotan.

The young man then told me to give up my passport. I answered that the passport was given me by my own government; that it was the evidence of my official character, necessary for my personal security, and I would not give it up. Mr. Catherwood made a learned exposition of the law of nations, the right of an ambassador, and the danger of bringing down upon them the vengeance of the government del Norte, which I sustained with some warmth, but it was of no use. At length I told him again that I would not give up the passport, but offered to go with it myself, under a guard of soldiers, to Chiquimula or wherever else they chose to send it; he answered insultingly that we should not go to Chiquimula or anywhere else; neither forward nor backward; that we must stay where we were, and must give up the passport. Finding arguments and remonstrances of no use, I placed the paper inside my vest, buttoned my coat tight across my breast, and told him he must get it by force; and the officer, with a gleam of satisfaction cross-ing his villanous face, responded that he would. I added that, whatever might be the immediate result, it would ultimately be fatal to them; to which he answered, with a sneer, that they would run the risk. During the whole time, the band of cowardly ruffians stood with their hands on their swords and machetes, and two assassin-looking scoundrels sat on a bench with muskets against their shoulders, and the muzzles pointed within three feet of my breast. If we had been longer in the country we should have been more alarmed; but as yet we did not know the sanguinary character of the people and the whole proceeding was so outrageous and insulting that it roused our indignation more than our fears. Augustin, who, from having had a cut across the head with a machete, which did not kill him, was always bellicose, begged me in French to give the order to fire, and said that one round would scatter them all. We had eleven charges, all sure; we were excited, and, if the young man himself had laid his hands upon me, I think I should have knocked him down at least; but, most fortunately, before he had time to give his order to fall upon us, a man, who entered after the rest, of a better class, wearing a glazed hat and round-about jacket, stepped forward and asked to see the passport. I was determined not to trust it out of my hands, and held it up before a blazing pine stick while he read it, and, at Mr. Catherwood's request, aloud.

I have since doubted whether even the officer had read it, or, if so, whether he had communicated its contents, for it produced an effect upon the alcalde and his alguazils; and, after some moments of anxious suspense to us, they forbore to execute their threat, but said that we must remain in custody. I demanded a courier to carry a letter immediately to General Cascara, which they refused; but, on my offering to pay the expense of the courier, the alcalde promised to send it. Knowing General Cascara to be an Italian, and afraid to trust my Spanish, I wrote a note, which Mr. C. translated into Italian, informing him of our arrest and imprisonment; that we had exhibited to the alcalde and soldiers who arrested us my special passport from my own government, with the endorsements of Commandant Piñol and himself, certifying my official character, which were not deemed sufficient; demanding to be set at liberty immediately, and allowed to proceed on our journey without farther molestation; and adding that we should, of course, represent to the government at Guatimala, and also to my own, the manner in which we had been treated. Not to mince matters, Mr. Catherwood signed the note as Secretary; and, having no official seal with me, we sealed it, unobserved by anybody, with a new American half dollar, and gave it to the alcalde. The eagle spread his wings, and the stars glittered in the torchlight. All gathered round to examine it, and retired, locking us up in the cabildo, stationing twelve men at the door with swords, muskets, and machetes; and, at parting, the officer told the alcalde that, if we escaped during the night, his head should answer for it.

The excitement over, Mr. C. and I were exhausted. We had made a beautiful beginning of our travels; but a month from home, and in the hands of men who would have been turned out of any decent state prison lest they should contaminate the boarders. A peep at our beautiful keepers did not reassure us. They were sitting under the shed, directly before the door, around a fire, their arms in reach, and smoking cigars. Their whole stock of wearing apparel was not worth a pair of old boots; and with their rags, their arms, their dark faces reddened by the firelight, their appearance was ferocious; and, doubtless, if we had attempted to escape, they would have been glad of the excuse for murder. We opened a basket of wine with which Col. M'Donald had provided us, and drank his health. We were relieved from immediate apprehensions, but our prospects were not pleasant; and, fastening the door as well as we could inside, we again betook ourselves to our hammocks.

During the night the door was again burst open, and the whole ruffianly band entered, as before, with swords, muskets, machetes, and blazing pine sticks. In an instant we were on our feet, and my hurried impression was, that they had come to take the passport; but, to our surprise, the alcalde handed me back the letter with the big seal, said there was no use in sending it, and that we were at liberty to proceed on our journey when we chose.

We were too well pleased to ask any questions, and to this day do not know why we were arrested. My belief is, that if we had quailed at all, and had not kept up a high, threatening tone to the last, we should not have been set free; and I have no doubt that the big seal did much in our behalf. Our indignation, however, was not the less strong that we considered ourselves safe in pouring it out. We insisted that the matter should not end here, and that the letter should go to General Cascara. The alcalde objected; but we told him that, if not sent, it would be the worse for him; and, after some delay, he thrust it into the hands of an Indian, and beat him out of doors with his staff; and in a few minutes the guard was withdrawn, and they all left us.

It was now nearly daylight, and we did not know what to do; to continue was to expose ourselves to a repetition of the same treatment, and perhaps, as we advanced farther into the interior, with a worse result. Undetermined, for the third time we turned into our hammocks. At broad daylight we were again roused by the alcalde and his alguazils, but this time they came to pay us a visit of ceremony. The soldiers, who had accidentally passed through the village, and had made all the disturbance, had left. After some deliberation we determined to continue;

and, charging the alcalde again about the letter to General Cascara, turned our backs upon him and his alguazils. In a few minutes they all withdrew. We took a cup of chocolate, loaded our mules, and, when we left, the place was as desolate as when we entered. Not a person had been there to welcome us, and there was not one to bid us farewell.[...]

At two o'clock we reached the village of Copan, which consisted of half a dozen miserable huts thatched with corn. Our appearance created a great sensation. All the men and women gathered around us to gaze. We inquired immediately for the ruins, but none of the villagers could direct us to them, and all advised us to go to the hacienda of Don Gregorio. We had no wish to stop at a village, and told the muleteer to go on, but he refused, and said that his engagement was to conduct us to Copan. After a long wrangle we prevailed, and, riding through a piece of woods, forded once more the Copan River, came out upon a clearing, on one side of which was a hacienda, with a tile roof, and having cosina and other outbuildings, evidently the residence of a rich proprietor. We were greeted by a pack of barking dogs, and all the doorways were filled with women and children, who seemed in no small degree surprised at our appearance. There was not a man in sight; but the women received us kindly, and told us that Don Gregorio would return soon, and would conduct us to the ruins. Immediately the fire was rekindled in the cosina, the sound of the patting of hands gave notice of the making of tortillas, and in half an hour dinner was ready. It was served up on a massive silver plate, with water in a silver tankard, but without knife, fork, or spoon; soup or *caldo* was served in cups to be drunk. Nevertheless, we congratulated ourselves upon having fallen into such good quarters.

In a short time a young man arrived on horseback, gayly dressed, with an embroidered shirt, and accompanied by several men driving a herd of cattle. An ox was selected, a rope thrown around its horns, and the animal was drawn up to the side of the house, and, by an other rope around its legs, thrown down. Its feet were tied together, its head drawn back by a rope tied from its horns to its tail, and with one thrust of the machete the artery of life was severed. The pack of hungry dogs stood ready, and, with a horrible clicking, lapped up the blood with their tongues. All the women were looking on, and a young girl took a puppy dog and rubbed its nose in the crimson stream, to give it early a taste for blood. The ox was skinned, the meat separated from the bones, and, to the entire destruction of steaks, sirloins, and roasting-pieces, in an hour the whole animal was hanging in long strings on a line before the door.

During this operation Don Gregorio arrived. He was about fifty, had large black whiskers, and a beard of several days' growth, and, from the behavior of all around, it was easy to see that he was a domestic tyrant. The glance which he threw at us before dismounting seemed to say, "Who are *you*?" but, without a word, he entered the house. We waited until he had finished his dinner, when, supposing that to be the favourable moment, I entered the house. In my intercourse with the world I have more than once found my overtures to an acquaintance received coldly, but I never experienced anything quite so cool as the don's reception of me. I told him that we had come into that neighbourhood to visit the ruins of Copan, and his manner said, What's that to me? but he answered that they were on the other side of the river. I asked him whether we could procure a guide, and again he said that the only man who knew anything about them lived on the other side of the river. As yet we did not make sufficient allowance for the distracted state of the country, nor the circumstance that a man might incur danger to himself by giving shelter to suspected persons; but, relying on the reputation of the country for hospitality, and the proof of it which we had already met with, I was rather slow in coming to the disagreeable conclusion that we were not welcome. The don was not pleased with our looks. I ordered the muleteer to saddle the mules; but the rascal enjoyed our confusion, and absolutely refused to saddle his beasts again that day. We applied to Don Gregorio himself, offering to pay him; and, as Augustin said, in the hope of getting rid of us, he lent us two, on which to ride back to the village. Unfortunately, the guide we sought was away; a brisk cockfight was then pending, and we received no encouragement, either from the appearance of the people or from invitation, to bring back our luggage to the place. And we learned, what was very provoking, that Don Gregorio was the great man of Copan; the richest man, and the petty tyrant; and it would be most unfortunate to have a rupture with him, or even to let it be known at the village that we were not well received at his house. Reluctantly, but in the hope of making a more favourable impression, we returned to the hacienda. Mr. C. dismounted on the steps, and took a seat on the piazza. I happened to dismount outside; and, before moving, took a survey of the party. The don sat on a chair, with our detestable muleteer by his side, and a half concealed smile of derision on his face, talking of "idols," and looking at me. By this time eight or ten men, sons, servants, and labourers, had come in from their day's work, but not one offered to take my mule, or made any of these demonstrations of civility which are always shown to a welcome guest. The women turned away their heads, as if they had been reproved for receiving us; and all the men, taking their cue from the don, looked so insulting, that I told Mr. Catherwood we would tumble our luggage into the road, and curse him for an inhospitable churl; but Mr. Catherwood warned me against it, urging that, if we had an open quarrel with him, after all our trouble we would be prevented seeing the ruins. The don probably suspected something of what passed; and, fearing that he might push things too far, and bring a stain upon his name, pointed to a chair, and asked me to take a seat. With a great effort, I resolved to smother my indignation until I could pour it out with safety. Augustin was very indignant at the treatment we received; on the road he had sometimes swelled his own importance by telling of the flags hoisted and cannon fired when we left Balize; and here he hoisted more flags and fired more guns than usual, beginning with forty guns, and afterward going on to a cannonade; but it would not do. The don did not like us, and probably was willing to hoist flags and fire cannons too, as at Balize, when we should go away.

Toward evening the skin of an ox was spread upon the piazza, corn in ears thrown upon it, and all the men, with the don at their head, sat down to shell it. The cobs were carried to the kitchen to burn, the corn taken up in baskets, and three pet hogs, which had been grunting outside in expectation of the feast, were let in to pick up the scattered grains. During the evening no notice was taken of us, except that the wife of the don sent a message by Augustin that supper was preparing; and our wounded pride was relieved, and our discontent somewhat removed, by an additional message that they had an oven and flour, and would bake us some bread if we wished to buy it.

After supper all prepared for sleep. The don's house had two sides, an inside and an out. The don and his family occupied the former, and we the latter; but we had not even this to ourselves. All along the wall were frames made of sticks about an inch thick, tied together with bark strings, over which the workmen spread an untanned oxhide for a bed. There were three hammocks besides ours, and I had so little room for mine that my body described an inverted parabola, with my heels as high as my head. It was vexatious and ridiculous; or, in the words of the English tourist in Fra Diavolo, it was "shocking! positively shocking!"

In the morning Don Gregorio was in the same humour. We took no notice of him and made our toilet under the shed with as much respect as possible to the presence of the female members of the family, who were constantly passing. We had made up our minds to hold on and see the ruins; and fortunately, early in the morning, one of the crusty don's sons, a civil young man, brought over from the village Jose, the guide of whom we stood in need.

By reason of many vexatious delays, growing out of difficulties between Jose and the muleteer, we did not get away until nine o'clock. Very soon we left the path or road, and entered a large field, partially cultivated with corn. Riding some distance through this, we reached a hut, thatched with corn-leaves, on the edge of the woods, at which some workmen were preparing their breakfast. Here we dismounted, and, tying our mules to trees near by, entered the woods, Jose clearing a path before us with a machete; soon we came to the bank of a river, and saw directly opposite a stone wall, perhaps a hundred feet high, with furze growing out of the top, running north and south along the river, in some places fallen, but in others entire. It had more the character of a structure than any we had ever seen; ascribed to the aborigines of America, and formed part of the wall of Copan, an ancient city, on whose history books throw but little light.[...]

> "It is impossible to describe the interest with which I explored these ruins. The ground was entirely new; there were no guide-books or guides; the whole was a virgin soil. We could not see ten yards before us, and never knew what we should stumble upon next."
>
> —JOHN LLOYD STEPHENS

The wall was of cut stone, well laid, and in a good state of preservation. We ascended by large stone steps, in some places perfect, and in others thrown down by trees which had grown up between the crevices, and reached a terrace, the form of which it was impossible to make out, from the density of the forest in which it was enveloped. Our guide cleared a way with his machete, and we passed, as it lay half buried in the earth, a large fragment of stone elaborately sculptured, and came to the angle of a structure with steps on the sides, in form and appearance, so far as the trees would enable us to make it out, like the sides of a pyramid. Diverging from the base, and working our way through the thick woods, we came upon a square stone column, about fourteen feet high and three feet on each side, sculptured in very bold relief, and on all four of the sides, from the base to the top. The front was the figure of a man curiously and richly dressed, and the face, evidently a portrait, solemn, stern, and well fitted to excite terror. The back was of a different design, unlike anything we had ever seen before, and the sides were covered with hieroglyphics. This our guide called an "Idol;" and before it, at a distance of three feet, was a large block of stone, also sculptured with figures and emblematical devices, which he called an altar. The sight of this unexpected monument put at rest at once and forever, in our minds, all uncertainty in regard to the character of American antiquities, and gave us the assurance that the objects we were in search of were interesting, not only as the remains of an unknown people, but as works of art, proving, like newly-discovered historical records, that the people who once occupied the Continent of America were not savages. With an interest perhaps stronger than we had ever felt in wandering among the ruins of Egypt, we followed our guide, who, sometimes missing his way, with a constant and vigorous use of his machete, conducted us through the thick forest, among half-buried fragments, to fourteen monuments of the same character and appearance, some with more elegant designs, and some in workmanship equal to the finest monuments of the Egyptians; one displaced from its pedestal by enormous roots; another locked in the close embrace of branches of trees, and almost lifted out of the earth; another hurled to the ground, and bound down by huge vines and creepers; and one standing, with its altar before it, in a grove of trees which grew around it, seemingly to shade and shroud it as a sacred thing; in the solemn stillness of the woods, it seemed a divinity mourning over a fallen people. The only sounds that disturbed the quiet of this buried city were the noise of monkeys moving among the tops of the trees, and the cracking of dry branches broken by their weight. They moved over our heads in long and swift processions, forty or fifty at a time, some with little ones wound in their long arms, walking out to the end of boughs, and holding on with their hind feet or a curl of the tail, sprang to a branch of the next tree, and, with a noise like a current of wind, passed on into the depths of the forest. It was the first time we had seen these mockeries of humanity, and, with the strange monuments around us, they seemed like wandering spirits of the departed race guarding the ruins of their former habitations.

We returned to the base of the pyramidal structure, and ascended by regular stone steps, in some places forced apart by bushes and saplings, and in others thrown down by the growth of large trees, while some remained entire. In parts they were ornamented with sculptured figures and rows of death's heads. Climbing over the ruined top, we reached a

F. Catherwood.   S. H. Gunther.

terrace overgrown with trees and descended by stone steps into an area so covered with trees that at first we could not make out its form, but which, on clearing the way with the machete, we ascertained to be a square with steps on all the sides almost as perfect as those of the Roman amphitheatre. The steps were ornamented with sculpture, and on the south side, about half way up, forced out of its place by roots, was a colossal head, evidently a portrait. We ascended these steps, and reached a broad terrace a hundred feet high, overlooking the river, and support-ed by the wall which we had seen from the opposite bank. The whole terrace was covered with trees, and even at this height from the ground were two gigantic Ceibas, or wild cotton-trees of India, above twenty feet in circumference, extending

"The top of the Sacrificatorio is broken and ruined, but there is no doubt that it once supported an altar for those sacrifices of human victims which struck even the Spaniards with horror. It was barely large enough for the altar and officiating priests, and the idol to whom the sacrifice was offered. The whole was in full view of the people at the foot.

"The barbarous ministers carried up the victim entirely naked, pointed out the idol to which the sacrifice was made, that the people might pay their adorations, and then extended him upon the altar. This had a convex surface, and the body of the victim lay arched, with the trunk elevated and the head and feet depressed. Four priests held the legs and arms, and another kept his head firm with a wooden instrument made in the form of a coiled serpent, so that he was prevented from making the least movement. The head priest then approached, and with a knife made of flint cut an aperture in the breast, and tore out the heart, which, yet palpitating, he offered to the sun, and then threw it at the feet of the idol. If the idol was gigantic and hollow, it was usual to introduce the heart of the victim into its mouth with a golden spoon. If the victim was a prisoner of war, as soon as he was sacrificed they cut off the head to preserve the skull, and threw the body down the steps, when it was taken up by the officer or soldier to whom the prisoner had belonged, and carried to his house to be dressed and served up as an entertainment for his friends."

—*explorer* JOHN LLOYD STEPHENS

their half-naked roots fifty or a hundred feet around, binding down the ruins, and shading them with their wide-spreading branches. We sat down on the very edge of the wall, and strove in vain to penetrate the mystery by which we were surrounded. Who were the people that built this city? In the ruined cities of Egypt, even in the long-lost Petra, the stranger knows the story of the people whose vestiges are around him. America, say historians, was peopled by savages; but savages never reared these structures, savages never carved these stones. We asked the Indians who made them, and their dull answer was "Quen sabe?" "who knows?"

There were no associations connected with the place; none of those stirring recollections which hallow Rome, Athens, and "The world's great mistress on the Egyptian plain;" but architecture, sculpture, and painting, all the arts which embellish life, had flourished in this overgrown forest; orators, warriors, and statesmen, beauty, ambition, and glory, had lived and passed away, and none knew that such things had been, or could tell of their past existence. Books, the records of knowledge, are silent on this theme. The city was desolate. No remnant of this race hangs round the ruins, with traditions handed down from father to son, and from generation to generation. It lay before us like a shattered bark in the midst of the ocean, her masts gone, her name effaced, her crew perished, and none to tell whence she came, to whom she belonged, how long on her voyage, or what caused her destruction; her lost people to be traced only by some fancied resemblance in the construction of the vessel, and, perhaps, never to be known at all. The place where we sat, was it a citadel from which an unknown people had sounded the trumpet of war? or a temple for the worship of the God of peace? or did the inhabitants worship the idols made with their own hands, and offer sacrifices on the stones before them? All was mystery, dark, impenetrable mystery, and every circumstance increased it. In Egypt the colossal skeletons of gigantic temples stand in the unwatered sands in all the nakedness of desolation; here an immense forest shrouded the ruins, hiding them from sight, heightening the impression and moral effect, and giving an intensity and almost wildness to the interest.

*   *   *

The long street by which we entered [the Indian village of Tecpan, Guatemala] was paved with stones from the ruins of the old city, and filled with drunken Indians. At the head of this street was a fine plaza, with a large cabildo, and twenty or thirty Indian alguazils under the corridor, with wands of office in their hands, silent, in full suits of blue cloth, the trousers open at the knees, and cloak with a hood like the Arab burnouse. Adjoining this was the large courtyard of the church, paved with stone, and the church itself was one of the most magnificent in the country. It was the second built after the conquest. The facade was two hundred feet, very lofty, with turrets and spires gorgeously ornamented with stuccoed figures, and a high platform, on which were Indians, the first we had seen in picturesque costume; and with the widely-extended view of the country around, it was a scene of wild magnificence in nature and in art. We stopped involuntarily; and while the Indians, in mute astonishment, gazed at us, we were lost in surprise and admiration.

As usual, Don Saturnino was the pioneer, and we rode up to the house of the padre, where we were shown into a small room, with the window closed and a ray of light admitted from the door, in which the padre was dozing in a large chair. Before he had fairly opened his eyes, Don Saturnino told him that we had come to visit the ruins of the old city, and wanted a guide, and thrust into his hands Carrera's passport and the letter of the provesor.

The padre was old, fat, rich, and infirm, had been thirty-five years cure of Tecpan Guatimala, and was not used to doing things in a hurry; but our friend, knowing the particular objects of our visit, with great earnestness and haste told the padre that the minister of New York had heard in his country of a remarkable stone, and the provesor and Carrera were anxious for him to see it. The padre said that it was in the church, and lay on the top of the grand altar; the cup of the sacrament stood upon it; it was covered up, and very sacred; he had never seen it, and he was evidently unwilling to let us see it, but said he would endeavour to do so when we returned from the ruins. He sent for a guide, and we went out to the courtyard of the church; and while Mr. Catherwood was attempting a sketch, I walked up the steps. The interior was lofty, spacious, richly ornamented with stuccoed figures and paintings, dark and solemn, and in the distance was the grand altar, with long wax candles burning upon it, and Indians kneeling before it. At the door a man stopped me, and said that I must not enter with sword and spurs, and even that I must take off my boots. I would have done so, but saw that the Indians did not like a stranger going into *their* church. They were evidently entirely unaccustomed to the sight of strangers, and Mr. Catherwood was so annoyed by their gathering round him that he gave up his drawing. Fearing it would be worse on our return, I told Don Saturnino that we must make an effort to see the stone now.

We went back in a body to the padre, and Don Saturnino told him that we were anxious to see the stone now, to prevent delay on our return. The good padre's heavy body was troubled. He asked for the provesor's letter again, read it over, went out on the corridor and consulted with a brother about as old and round as himself, and at length told us to wait in that room and he would bring it. As he went out he ordered all the Indians in the courtyard, about forty or fifty, to go to the cabildo and tell the alcalde to send the guide. In a few minutes he returned, and opening with some trepidation the folds of his large gown, produced the stone.

The stone was sewed up in a piece of cotton cloth, which looked certainly as old as the thirty-five years it had been under the cure's charge. One or two stitches were cut in the middle, and this was perhaps all we should have seen; but Don Saturnino whipped out his penknife, and the good old padre, heavy with agitation and his own weight, sunk into his chair, still holding on with both hands. Don Saturnino ripped till he almost cut the good old man's fingers, slipped out the sacred tablet, and left the sack in the padre's hands. The padre sat a picture of self-abandonment, helplessness, distress, and self-reproach. We moved toward the light. Don Saturnino, with a twinkle of his eyes, consummated the padre's fear and horror by scratching the sacred stone with his knife. This oracular slab is a piece of common slate, fourteen inches by ten, and about as thick as those used by boys at school, without characters of any kind upon it. Don Saturnino handed it back to the padre, and told him that he had better sew it up and put it back; and probably it is now in its place on the top of the grand altar, with the sacramental cup upon it, an object of veneration to the fanatic Indians.

The agitation of the padre destroyed what was comic in the scene. He told us not to go back through the town; that there was a road direct to the old city. Concealing the tablet under his gown, he walked out with a firm step, and in a strong, unbroken voice, rapidly called to the Indians to bring up our horses. He feared that the Indians might discover our sacrilegious act; and we were well satisfied to get away before any such discovery was made.

*   *   *

In two hours we reached the River Micol, and in half an hour more that of Otula. Fording this, soon we saw masses of stones, and then a round sculptured stone. We spurred up a sharp ascent of fragments, so steep that the mules could barely climb it, to a terrace so covered with trees, that it was impossible to make out the form. Continuing on this terrace, we stopped at the foot of a second, when our Indians cried out "el Palacio," and through openings in the trees we saw the front of a large building richly ornamented with stuccoed figures on the pilasters, curious and elegant; trees growing close against it, and their branches entering the doors. We tied our mules to the trees, ascended a flight of stone steps and entered the palace, ranged for a few moments along the corridor and into the courtyard, and after the first gaze of eager curiosity was over, went back to the entrance, and, standing in the doorway, fired a feu-de-joie of four rounds each, the last charge of our firearms. It was intended for effect upon the Indians, who regarded our weapons as instruments which spit lightning, and who, we knew, would make such a report in the village as would keep any of their friends from paying us a visit at night.

For the first time we were in a building standing before the Europeans knew of the existence of this continent, and we prepared to take up our abode under its roof. We selected the front corridor as our dwelling, turned turkey and fowls loose in the courtyard, which was so overgrown with trees that we could barely see across it. As there was no pasture for the mules except the leaves of the trees, and we could not turn them loose into the woods, we brought them up the steps through the palace, and turned them into the courtyard also. At one end of the corridor Juan built a kitchen, which operation consisted in laying three stones anglewise, so as to have room for a fire between them. Our luggage was stowed away or hung on poles reaching across the corridor. Pawling mounted a stone about four feet long on stone legs for a table, and with the Indians cut a number

Casa No. 1.

of poles, which they fastened together with bark strings, and laid them on stones at the head and foot for beds.

The tablecloth was two broad leaves, each about two feet long, plucked from a tree on the terrace before the door. Our saltcellar stood like a pyramid, being a case made of husks of corn put together lengthwise, and holding four or five pounds, in lumps from the size of a pea to that of a hen's egg. All went merry as a marriage-bell, when the sky became overcast, and a sharp thunder-clap heralded the afternoon's storm. The palace commanded a view of the top of the forest, and we could see the trees bent down by the force of the wind; very soon a fierce blast swept through the open doors, which was followed instantaneously by heavy rain. The table was cleared by the wind, and, before we could make our escape, was drenched by the rain.

The rain continued, with heavy thunder and lightning, all the afternoon. At night we could not light a candle, but the darkness of the palace was lighted up by fireflies of extraordinary size and brilliancy, shooting through the corridors and stationary on the walls, forming a beautiful and striking spectacle. Known by the name shining beetles, they are more than half an inch long, and have a sharp movable horn on the head; when laid on the back they cannot turn over except by pressing this horn against a membrane upon the front. Behind the eyes are two round transparent substances full of luminous matter, about as large as the head of a pin, and underneath is a larger membrane containing the same luminous substance. Four of them together threw a brilliant light for several yards around, and by the light of a single one we read distinctly the finely-printed pages of an American newspaper. It was one of a packet, full of debates in Congress, which I had as yet barely glanced over, and it seemed stranger than any incident of my journey to be reading by the light of beetles, in the ruined palace of Palenque, the sayings and doings of great men at home.

In the morning, bedclothes, wearing apparel, and hammocks were wet through, and there was not a dry place to stand. A good breakfast would have done much to restore our equanimity; but, unhappily, we found that the tortillas which we had brought out the day before, probably made of half-mouldy corn, were matted together, sour, and spoiled. We went through our beans, eggs, and chocolate without any substitute for bread, and, as often before in time of trouble, composed ourselves with a cigar. Blessed be the man who invented smoking, the soother of a troubled spirit, allayer of angry passions, a comfort under the loss of breakfast.

We expected to live upon game, but were disappointed. A wild turkey we could shoot at any time from the door of the palace; but after trying one, we did not venture to trifle with our teeth upon another. Besides these, there was nothing but parrots, monkeys, and lizards, all very good eating. But the density of the forest and the heavy rains made sporting impracticable.[...]

Referring to the huge cockroaches in Chinese Turkestan, German archeologist Albert von Le Coq wrote, "It was enough to make a man uncontrollably sick to wake in the morning with such a creature sitting on his nose, its big eyes staring down at him and its long feelers trying to attack its victim's eyes. We used to seize the insect in terror and crush it, when it gave off an extremely disagreeable smell."

The whole country for miles around is covered by a dense forest of gigantic trees, with a growth of brush and underwood impenetrable in any direction except by cutting a way with a machete. What lies buried in that forest it is impossible to say; without a guide, we might have gone within a hundred feet of all the buildings without discovering one of them.[...]

We had distributed our beds along the corridors, under cover of the outer wall, and were better protected, but suffered terribly from moschetoes, the noise and stings of which drove away sleep. In the middle of the night I took up my mat to escape from these murderers of rest. The rain had ceased, and the moon, breaking through the heavy clouds, lighted up the ruined corridor. I climbed over a mound of stones at one end, where the wall had fallen, and, stumbling alone outside the palace, entered a building near the foot of the tower, groped in the dark along a low damp passage, and spread my mat before a low doorway at the extreme end. Bats were flying and whizzing through the passage, noisy and sinister; but the ugly creatures drove away moschetoes. The dampness of the passage was cooling and refreshing; and, with some twinging apprehensions of the snakes and reptiles, lizards and scorpions, which infest the ruins, I fell asleep.

PIRANHA

THEODORE ROOSEVELT
(American president and explorer)

For three days, as we steamed northward toward the Tropic of Capricorn, and then passed it, we were within the Republic of Paraguay.[...]

Late on the evening of the second day of our trip, just before midnight, we reached Concepcion. On this day, when we stopped for wood or to get provisions—at picturesque places, where the women from rough mud and thatched cabins were washing clothes in the river, or where ragged horsemen stood gazing at us from the bank, or where dark, well-dressed ranchmen stood in front of red-roofed houses—we caught many fish. They belonged to one of the most formidable genera of fish in the world, the piranha or cannibal fish, the fish that eats men when it can get the chance. Farther north there are species of small piranha that go in schools. At this point on the Paraguay the piranha do not seem to go in regular schools, but they swarm in all the waters and attain a length of eighteen inches or over. They are the most ferocious fish in the world. Even the most formidable fish, the sharks or the barracudas, usually attack things smaller than themselves. But the piranhas habitually attack things much larger than themselves. They will snap a finger off a hand incautiously trailed in the water; they mutilate swimmers—in every river town in Paraguay there are men who have been thus mutilated; they will rend and devour alive any wounded man or beast;

One day we came to a place where the river had cut a new channel and left the still warm water in a loop of the old bed. Here we had a chance of making some highly interesting experiments with that freak of nature, the electric eel.[...] They are so heavily charged with electricity that a man cannot possibly retain his hold of a metal instrument if it comes in contact with their skins, or even with a metal pail in which one is swimming. Of course I was carrying with me no electrical instruments with which to test their voltage, so could only measure the force of the shock they can give by touching the fish myself. With my machete I attempted to cut the head off one which had been speared and landed. I might just as well have tried to cut a trolley-wire with uninsulated pliers. The machete flew out of my hands and my arm was temporarily paralysed.

—F. W. Up de Graff

for blood in the water excites them to madness. They will tear wounded wild fowl to pieces; and bite off the tails of big fish as they grow exhausted when fighting after being hooked. [Naturalist Leo] Miller, before I reached Asuncion, had been badly bitten by one. Those that we caught sometimes bit through the hooks, or the double strands of copper wire that served as leaders, and got away. Those that we hauled on deck lived for many minutes. Most predatory fish are long and slim, like the alligator-gar and pickerel. But the piranha is a short, deep-bodied fish, with a blunt face and a heavily undershot or projecting lower jaw which gapes widely. The razor-edged teeth are wedge-shaped like a shark's, and the jaw muscles possess great power. The rabid, furious snaps drive the teeth through flesh and bone. The head with its short muzzle, staring malignant eyes, and gaping, cruelly armed jaws, is the embodiment of evil ferocity; and the actions of the fish exactly match its looks. I never witnessed an exhibition of such impotent, savage fury as was shown by the piranhas as they flapped on deck. When fresh from the water and thrown on the boards they uttered an extraordinary squealing sound. As they flapped about they bit with vicious eagerness at whatever presented itself. One of them flapped into a cloth and seized it with a bulldog grip. Another grasped one of its fellows; another snapped at a piece of wood, and left the teeth-marks deep therein. They are the pests of the waters, and it is necessary to be exceedingly cautious about either swimming or wading where they are found. If cattle are driven into, or of their own accord enter, the water, they are commonly not molested; but if by chance some unusually big or ferocious specimen of these fearsome fishes does bite an animal—taking off part of an ear, or perhaps of a teat from the udder of a cow—the blood brings up every member of the ravenous throng which is anywhere near, and unless the attacked animal can immediately make its escape from the water it is devoured alive. Here on the Paraguay the

"[. . .]I learned that certain Indian tribes leave their dead in the river for the piranhas to strip the flesh from the bones. It is then customary to take the remaining skeleton and let it dry in the sun, after which it is rubbed with the juice of the *urucu* plant (the *Bixa orellana*), which produces a bright scarlet color. Then it is hung up in the hut and the Indians consider that a token of great reverence has been thus bestowed on the deceased."
—*ethnologist* ALGOT LANGE

natives hold them in much respect, whereas the caymans are not feared at all. The only redeeming feature about them is that they are themselves fairly good to eat, although with too many bones.[. . .]

The steamers halted; Colonel Rondon [of the Brazilian Army] and several of his officers, spick and span in their white uniforms, came aboard; and in the afternoon I visited him on his steamer to talk over our plans. When these had been fully discussed and agreed on we took tea. I happened to mention that one of our naturalists, Miller, had been bitten by a piranha, and the man-eating fish at once became the subject of conversation. Curiously enough, one of the Brazilian taxidermists had also just been severely bitten by a piranha. My new companions had story after story to tell of them. Only three weeks previously a twelve-year-old boy who had gone in swimming near Corumbá was attacked, and literally devoured alive by them. Colonel Rondon during his exploring trips had met with more than one unpleasant experience in connection with them. He had lost one of his toes by the bite of a piranha. He was about to bathe and had chosen a shallow pool at the edge of the river, which he carefully inspected until he was satisfied that none of the man-eating fish were in it; yet as soon as he put his foot into the water one of them attacked him and bit off a toe. On another occasion while wading across a narrow stream one of his party was attacked; the fish bit him on the thighs and buttocks, and when he put down his hands tore them also; he was near the bank and by a rush reached it and swung himself out of the water by means of an overhanging limb of a tree; but he was terribly injured, and it took him six months before wounds healed and he recovered. An extraordinary incident occurred on another trip. The party were without food and very hungry. On reaching a stream they dynamited it, and waded in to seize the stunned fish as they floated on the surface. One man, Lieutenant Pyrineus, having his hands full, tried to hold one fish by putting its head into his mouth; it was a piranha and seemingly stunned, but in a moment it recovered and bit a big section out of his tongue. Such a hemorrhage followed that his life was saved with the utmost difficulty. On another occasion a member of the party was off by himself on a mule. The mule came into camp alone. Following his track back they came to a ford, where in the water they found the skeleton of the dead man, his clothes uninjured but every particle of flesh stripped from his bones. Whether he had drowned, and the fishes had then eaten his body, or whether they had killed him it was impossible to say. They had not hurt the clothes, getting in under them, which made it seem likely that there had been no struggle. These man-eating fish are a veritable scourge in the waters they frequent.[...]

"In the historical documents on the war between Brazil and Paraguay, there are several references to tragic cases of soldiers who, wounded and obliged by the enemy to ford the creeks or rivers of that region, were quickly killed by piranhas, leaving only their white skeletons on the bottom of the transparent waters of the streams."
—*Brazilian writer* Couto de Magalhães

Miller had made a special study of the piranhas, which swarmed at one of the camps he and [naturalist George] Cherrie had made in the Chaco. So numerous were they that the members of the party had to be exceedingly careful in dipping up water. Miller did not find that they were cannibals toward their own kind; they were "cannibals" only in the sense of eating the flesh of men. When dead piranhas, and even when mortally injured piranhas, with the blood flowing, were thrown among the ravenous living, they were left unmolested.

Moreover, it was Miller's experience, the direct contrary of
which we had been told, that
splashing and a commotion in
the water attracted the piranhas,
whereas they rarely attacked
anything that was motionless
unless it was bloody. Dead birds
and mammals, thrown whole
and unskinned into the water
were permitted to float off unmo-

lested, whereas the skinned carcass of a good-sized monkey was at once seized,
pulled under the water, and completely devoured by the blood-crazy fish. A man
who had dropped something of value waded in after it to above the knees, but
went very slowly and quietly, avoiding every possibility of disturbance, and not
venturing to put his hands into the water. But nobody could bathe, and even the
slightest disturbance in the water, such as that made by scrubbing the hands vigorously with soap, immediately attracted the attention of the savage little creatures,
who darted to the place, evidently hoping to find some animal in difficulties. Once,
while Miller and some Indians were, attempting to launch a boat, and were making
a great commotion in the water, a piranha attacked a naked Indian who belonged
to the party and mutilated him as he struggled and splashed, waist-deep in the
stream. Men not making a splashing and struggling are rarely attacked; but if one
is attacked by any chance, the blood in the water maddens the piranhas, and they
assail the man with frightful ferocity.

*   *   *

This same day others of our party had an interesting experience with the creatures
in another pond. One of them was Commander da Cunha (of the Brazilian Navy),
a capital sportsman and delightful companion. They found a deepish pond a hundred yards or so long and thirty or forty across. It was tenanted by the small caymans
and by capybaras—the largest known rodent, a huge aquatic guinea-pig, the size of
a small sheep. It also swarmed with piranhas, the ravenous fish of which I have so

often spoken. Undoubtedly the caymans were subsisting largely on these piranhas. But the tables were readily turned if any caymans were injured. When a capybara was shot and sank in the water, the piranhas at once attacked it, and had eaten half the carcass ten minutes later. But much more extraordinary was the fact that when a cayman about five feet long was wounded the piranhas attacked and tore it, and actually drove it out on the bank to face its human foes. The fish first attacked the wound; then, as the blood maddened them, they attacked all the soft parts, their terrible teeth cutting out chunks of tough hide and flesh. Evidently they did not molest either cayman or capybara while it was unwounded; but blood excited them to frenzy. Their habits are in some ways inexplicable. We saw men frequently bathing unmolested; but there are places where this is never safe, and in any place if a school of the fish appear swimmers are in danger; and a wounded man or beast is in deadly peril if piranhas are in the neighborhood. Ordinarily it appears that an unwounded man is attacked only by accident. Such accidents are rare; but they happen with sufficient frequency to justify much caution in entering water where piranhas abound.

*　　*　　*

The huge catfish which the men had caught was over three feet and a half long, with the usual enormous head, out of all proportions to the body, and the enormous mouth, out of all proportion to the head. Such fish, although their teeth are small, swallow very large prey. This one contained the nearly digested remains of a monkey. Probably the monkey had been seized while drinking from the end of a branch; and once engulfed in that yawning cavern there was no escape. We Americans were astounded at the idea of a catfish making prey of a monkey; but our Brazilian friends told us that in the lower Madeira and the part of the Amazon near its mouth there is a still more gigantic catfish which in similar fashion occasionally makes prey of man. This is a grayish-white fish over nine feet long, with the usual disproportionately large head and gaping mouth, with a circle of small teeth; for the engulfing mouth itself is the danger, not the teeth. It is called the piraiba— pronounced in four syllables. While stationed at the small city of Itacoatiara, on the Amazon, at the mouth of the Madeira, the doctor had seen one of these monsters which had been killed by the two men it had attacked. They were fishing in a canoe when it rose from the bottom—for it is a ground fish—and raising itself half out of the water lunged over the edge of the canoe at them, with open mouth. They killed it with their *falcóns*, as machetes are called in Brazil. It was taken round the city in triumph in an ox-cart; the doctor saw it, and said it was three metres long. He said that swimmers feared it even more than the big cayman, because they could see the latter, whereas the former lay hid at the bottom of the water.

"Perhaps the most dangerous inhabitant of Paraguayan waters is the *piraña*, which I suspect of causing more loss of life to man and beast than alligators, *surubìs*, or *mangarulùs*, and such like aquatic monsters. The *piraña* is a scaled fish, similar in shape to our European perch, only the head is of more aggressive appearance, the mouth being armed with a most formidable set of teeth, more like those of a wild animal than a fish. With these, and aided by his powerful jaws, there is literally nothing that he will not bite through. I have put a lead pencil into the mouth of one, and seen it bitten clean off, and I have also seen him bite off the edge of a keenly tempered knife. His ferocity is equally developed, and one has to be very careful in handling these demons when caught, and when getting the hooks out of their mouths. When taken out of the water they make a barking noise.

"A friend of mine, a police inspector, while bathing, was attacked by a shoal of them, which mutilated him in such a manner that he at once swam back to the bank to the spot where his clothes were, picked up his revolver, and blew out his brains."

—*English diplomat CECIL GOSLING*

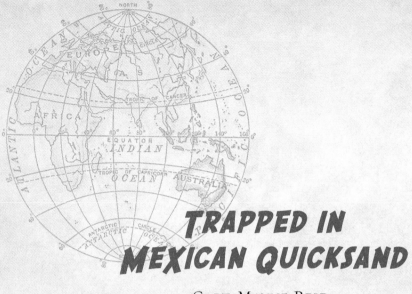

TRAPPED IN MEXICAN QUICKSAND

CAPT. MAYNE REID
(novelist)

A small party of traders—myself among the number—had pushed forward ahead of the caravan. Our object was to arrive at Santa Fe a day or two before the wagons, in order to have everything arranged with the governor for their entrance into the capital. We took the route by the Cimmaron.

Our road, for a hundred miles or so, lay through the barren desert, without game, and almost without water. The buffalo had all disappeared, and deer were equally scarce. We had to content ourselves on dried meat which we had bought from the settlements. We were in the desert of the Artemisa. Now and then we could see a stray antelope bounding away before us, but keeping far out of range. They, too, seemed to be unusually shy.

On the third day after leaving the caravan, as we were riding near the Cimmaron, I thought I saw a pronged head disappearing behind a swell in the prairie. My companions were skeptical, and none of them would go with me; so, wheeling out of the trail, I started alone. One of them—for Gode was behind—kept charge of my dog, as I did not choose to take him with me, lest he might alarm the antelopes. My horse was fresh and willing, and whether successful or not, I knew I could easily overtake the party by camping time.

I struck directly toward the spot where I had seen the object. It appeared to be only half a mile or so from the trail, but proved more distant—a common illusion in the crystal atmosphere of these upland regions.

A curiously formed ridge traversed the plain from east to west. A thicket of cactus covered part of its summit. Toward the thicket I directed myself.

I dismounted at the bottom of the slope, and leading my horse silently up among the cactus, tied him to one of its branches. I then cautiously crept through the thorny leaves toward the point where I fancied I had seen the game. To my joy, not one antelope, but a brace of those beautiful animals, was quietly grazing beyond; but alas! too far off for the carry of my rifle. They were fully three hundred yards distant, upon a smooth grassy slope. There was not even a sage bush to cover me, should I attempt to approach them. What was to be done?

I lay for several minutes thinking over the different tricks, known in hunter craft, for taking the antelope. Should I imitate their call? Should I hoist my handkerchief and try to lure them up? I saw that they were too shy for, at short intervals, they threw up their graceful heads, and looked inquiringly around them. I remembered the red blanket on my saddle. I could display this upon the cactus-bushes, perhaps it would attract them.

I had no alternative, and was turning to go back for the blanket when, all at once, my eye rested upon a clay-colored line, running across the prairie, beyond where the animals were feeding. It was a break in the plain, a buffalo road, or the channel of an *arroyo*, in either case the very cover I wanted for the animals were not a hundred yards from it, and were getting still nearer to it as they fed.

Creeping back out of the thicket, I ran along the side of the slope toward a point where I had noticed that the ridge was depressed to the prairie level. Here to my surprise, I found myself on the banks of a broad *arroyo*, whose water, clear and shallow, ran slowly over a bed of sand and gypsum.

The banks were low, not over three feet above the surface of the water except where the ridge impinged upon the stream. Here there was a high bluff, and hurrying around its base, I entered the channel and commenced wading upward.

As I had anticipated, I soon came to a bend where the stream, after running parallel to the ridge, swept around and canyoned through it. At this place I stopped, and looked cautiously over the bank. The antelopes had approached within less than rifle range of the *arroyo*, but they were yet far above my position. They were still quietly feeding, and unconscious of danger. I again bent down and waded on.

It was a difficult task proceeding in this way. The bed of the creek was soft and yielding, and I was compelled to tread slowly and silently, lest I should alarm the game, but I was cheered in my exertions by the prospect of fresh venison for my supper.

After a weary drag of several hundred yards, I came opposite a small clump of wormwood bushes, growing out of the bank. "It may be high enough," thought I; "these will serve for cover." I raised my body gradually, until I could see through the leaves. I was in the right spot. I brought my rifle to a level, sighted for the heart of the buck, and fired. The animal leaped from the ground and fell back lifeless.

I was about to rush forward, and secure my prize, when I observed the doe, instead of running off as I expected, go up to her fallen partner, and press her tapering nose to his body. She was not more than twenty yards from me, and I could plainly ace that her look was one of inquiry and bewilderment. All at once she seemed to comprehend the fatal truth, and, throwing back her head, commenced uttering the most piteous cries, at the same time running in circles around the body.

I stood wavering between two minds. My first impulse had been to reload, and kill the doe, but her plaintive voice entered my heart, disarming me of all hostile intentions. Had I dreamed of witnessing this painful spectacle I should not have left the trail. But the mischief was now done. "I have worse than killed her," I thought, "It will be better to dispatch her at once."

Actuated by these principles of common, but to her fatal, humanity, I rested the butt of my rifle, and reloaded. With a faltering hand I again leveled the piece and fired.

My nerves were steady enough to do the work. When the smoke floated aside, I could see the little creature bleeding on the grass—her head resting upon the body of her murdered mate.

I shouldered my rifle, and was about to move forward, when, to my astonishment, I found that I was caught by the feet. I was held firmly as if my legs had been placed in a vise!

I made an effort to extricate myself, another more violent and equally unsuccessful, and with a third, I lost my balance and fell back upon the water. Half suffocated I gained my upright position, but only to find that I was held as fast as ever. Again I struggled to free my limbs, I could neither move backward nor forward—to the right nor the left, and I became aware that I was gradually going down. Then the fearful truth flashed upon me—I was sinking in quicksand! A feeling of horror came over me. I renewed my efforts with the energy of desperation. I leaned to one side, then to the other, almost wrenching my knees from their sockets. My feet remained as fast as ever. I could not move them an inch.

The soft, clingy sand already overtopped my horse-skin boots, wedging them around my ankles, so that I was unable to draw them off; and I could feel that I was sinking slowly but surely, as though some subterranean monster was leisurely dragging me down. The very thought gave me a fresh thrill of horror, and I called aloud for help. To whom? There was no one within miles of me—no living thing. Yes! the neigh of my horse answered me from the hill, mocking me in my despair.

I bent forward as well as my constrained position would permit, and with frenzied fingers commenced tearing up the sand. I could barely reach the surface, and the little hollow I was able to make filled up almost as soon as it had been formed. A thought occurred to me. My rifle might support me, placed horizontally. I looked for it. It was not to be seen. It had sunk beneath the sand. Could I throw my body flat and prevent my sinking deeper? No! The water was two feet in depth. I should drown at once. This last hope left me as soon as formed. I could think of no plan to save myself. I could make no further effort. A strange stupor seized upon me. My very thoughts became paralyzed. I knew that I was going mad. For a moment I was mad.

After an interval, my senses returned. I made an effort to arouse my mind from its paralysis in order that I might meet death which I now believed to be certain, as a man should. I stood erect. My eyes had sunk to the prairie level, and rested upon the still bleeding victims of my cruelty. My heart smote me at the sight. Was I suffering a retribution of God? With humbled and penitent thoughts, I turned my face to heaven, almost dreading that some sign of omnipotent anger would scowl upon me from above. But no! The sun was shining as brightly as ever, and the blue canopy of the world was without a cloud. I gazed upward with earnestness known only to the hearts of men in positions of peril like mine.

As I continued to look up, an object attracted my attention. Against the sky I distinguished the outlines of a large bird. I knew it to be the obscene bird of the plains, the buzzard-vulture. Whence had it come? Who knows? Far beyond the reach of human eye, it had seen or scented the slaughter of the antelopes and on broad, silent wing was now descending to the feast of death. Presently another, and another, and many others, mottled the blue field of the heavens, curving and wheeling silently earthward. Then the foremost swooped down upon the bank, and after gazing around for a moment, flapped off towards its prey. In a few seconds, the prairie was black with the filthy birds. They clambered over the dead antelopes, and beat their wings against each other while they tore out the eyes of the quarry with their fetid beaks. And now came gaunt wolves, sneaking and hungry, stealing out of the cactus thicket, and loping, coward-like, over the green swells of the prairie. These, after a battle, drove away the vultures and tore up the prey, all the while growling and snapping vengefully at each other. "Thank heaven! I shall at least be saved from this."

I was soon relieved from the sight. My eyes had sunk below the level of the bank. I had looked my last on the fair, green earth. I could now see only the clayey wall that contained the stream, and the water that ran unheeding past me. Once more I fixed my gaze upon the sky, and with prayerful heart, endeavored to resign myself to my fate. In spite of my endeavors to be calm, the memories of earthly pleasures, and friends, and home, came over me, causing me, at intervals, to break into wild paroxysms, and fresh though fruitless struggles.

Then I was attracted by the neighing of my horse. A thought entered my mind filling me with fresh hope. "Perhaps my horse…" I lost not a moment. I raised my voice to the highest pitch, and called the animal by name. I knew that he would come at my call. I had tied him loosely. The cactus limbs would snap off. I called again, repeating words that were well known to him. I listened with a bounding heart. For a moment there was silence. Then I heard the quick sounds of his hoof, as though the animal were rearing and struggling to free himself; then I could distinguish the stroke of his heels, in a measured and regular gallop. Nearer came the sounds, nearer and clearer, until the gallant brute bounded out on the bank above me. There he halted, and, flinging back his tossed mane, uttered a shrill neigh. He was bewildered and looked upon every side snorting loudly.

I knew that having once seen me he would not stop until he had pressed his nose against my cheek, for this was his usual custom. Holding out my hands I uttered the magic words. Now looking downward he perceived me, and stretching himself sprang out into the channel. The next moment I held him by the bridle. There was no time to be lost. I was still going down, and my armpits were fast nearing the surface of the quicksand. I caught the lariat, and passing it under the saddle-girths, fastened it in a tight, firm knot. Then I looped the trailing end, making it secure around my body. I had left enough of the rope between the bit-ring and girth to enable me to check and guide the animal, in case the drag upon my body would be too painful.

All this while the dumb brute seemed to comprehend what I was about. He knew, too, the nature of the ground on which he stood, for during the operation, he kept lifting his feet alternately to prevent himself from sinking. My arrangements were at length completed, and, with a feeling of terrible anxiety, I gave my horse a signal to move forward. Instead of going off with a start, the intelligent animal stepped away slowly, as through he understood my situation. The lariat tightened, I felt my body moving, and at that moment experienced a wild delight; a feeling I cannot describe, as I found myself dragged out of the sand. I sprang to my feet with a shout of joy. I rushed up to my steed, and throwing my arms around his neck, kissed him with as much delight as I would have kissed a beautiful girl. He answered my embrace with a low whimper that told me he understood.

I looked for my rifle. Fortunately it had not sunk deeply and I soon found it. My boots were behind me, but I did not stay to look for them, being smitten with a wholesome dread of the place where I had left them. I was not long in retreating from the *arroyo* and, mounting, I galloped back to the trail. It was sundown before I reached the camp, where I was met by the inquiries of my companions. I answered all their questions by relating my adventures, and for that night, I was the hero of the campfire.

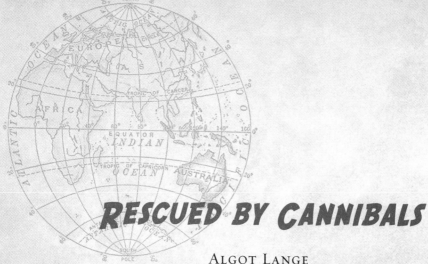

RESCUED BY CANNIBALS

ALGOT LANGE

(American ethnologist)

In 1910 at the age of 26, Algot Lange launched his first expedition into the unexplored jungle of the upper Amazon. It was an amazing and extremely dangerous journey that Lange ultimately just barely survived. An explorer friend commented, "[Lange] started in fine spirits: buoyant, strong, vigorous. When I saw him again in New York, on his return, he was an emaciated fever-wreck, placing one foot before the other only with much exertion and indeed barely able to hold himself erect." But this did not stop Lange, for in spite of his physical ailments, he quickly returned to the Amazon for another expedition. What follows is his account of that first deadly expedition.

Thus I lived among these kind and hospitable people [who were workers on a rubber plantation far up the Amazon] for five months until one day my lust for further excitement broke out again, induced by a seemingly commonplace notice posted outside the door of the storeroom. It read: "The men—Marques, Freitas, Anisette, Magellaes, Jerome, and Brabo—are to make themselves ready to hunt caoutchouc in the eastern virgin forest." Puzzled as to the meaning of this, I consulted the Chief and was informed that Coronel da Silva was about to equip and send out a small expedition into the forests, far beyond the explored territory, to locate new caoutchouc trees, which were to be cut and the rubber or caoutchouc collected, whereupon the expedition was to return to headquarters with these samples and a report on the number of trees observed. This greatly interested me, and I asked the Chief, Marques, whose wife I had operated upon previously [amputating her arm which saved her life from gangrene], if I could accompany him on this trip. He consented unwillingly, saying that it was very dangerous and that the same number of men that went out never came back. However, this was too rare a chance to let pass, and I made my preparations to accompany the expedition on this journey into regions where even the native *caucheros* had never before been.

On a Monday morning we all assembled at the Floresta headquarters, where Coronel da Silva bade us good-bye, and at the same time once more warned me against venturing on this trip, but I was determined and could not be persuaded to give it up.

The expedition consisted of the six men, above mentioned, all, except the Chief, Marques, unmarried. After leaving the main building we went down to the store-room where we chose the necessary articles of food—enough to last us for three or four weeks. Our staples were to be dried *pirarucu*, the largest fish of the Amazon, some dried or "jerked" beef, and a large quantity of the farinha, the eternal woody and unpalatable meal that figures on every Brazilian's table. Besides these, we carried sugar, coffee, rice, and several bottles of "Painkiller" from Fulton Street, N. Y. Hammocks and cooking utensils completed our outfit. I took with me a large plate camera, photographic plates and paper, chemicals, scales and weights; also a magnifying glass, a primitive surgical outfit, and a hypodermic needle with several dozen prepared "ampules." My men were armed with the usual .44 Winchesters, and some ancient muzzle-loaders, while I had my 9mm automatic Luger pistol. When we were fully packed, each man carried a load weighing eighty-five pounds, strapped by means of bark strips to the shoulders, with his rifle in his left hand and a machete to clear the path in his right.

Thus equipped, we left headquarters, not knowing how or when we would see it again, while the natives fired a farewell salute, wishing us God-speed.

After a few hours by canoe, up the Itecoahy, we left the river and turned our faces inland. Our way now led through dense forest, but for four hours we travelled in a region familiar to the rubber-workers, and we were able to follow pathways used by them in their daily work.

Let no one think that a jungle trail is broad and easy. As I stumbled along the tortuous, uneven path, in the sweltering mid-day heat, pestered by legions of *piums* or sand-flies and the omnipresent mosquitoes, climbing fallen trees that impeded us at every turn, I thought that I had reached the climax of discomfort. Little could I know that during the time to come I was to look back upon this day as one of easy, delightful promenading.

The four hours' march brought us to an open place, apparently a clearing, where the *estrada* suddenly seemed to stop. Exhausted, I threw myself on the moist ground while the Chief explained our position. He said that we were now at the end of the cut *estrada* and that beyond this we would have no path to follow, though he had somewhat explored the region farther on the year previous, during a similar expedition. We found that the undergrowth had been renewed to such an extent that his old track was indistinguishable, and we had to hew our every step.

"In order to clear the path, the natives have cut down the young trees to about eighty centimetres to one metre from the ground, and this leaves a forest of stakes on which one might be impaled at any moment. As in the course of one's passage one brushes against the trees and creepers, they let fall bits of dead wood, ants' nests stuck in the branches, dry leaves and rotten boughs, all in a blinding shower. One can count oneself lucky not to be injured or maimed by some great lump of old wood suspended twenty metres or more above one's head, which could be dislodged at a touch."
—*French explorer* Louis-Gustave Binger

When we resumed the march I received a more thorough understanding of what the word *jungle* really means. Ahead of us was one solid and apparently impenetrable wall of vegetation, but my men attacked it systematically with their heavy machetes. Slowly we advanced, but I wondered that we made any progress at all. The skill of these sons of the forest in cutting a pathway with their long knives became a constant wonder to me. Where an inexperienced person would have lost himself, looking for a round-about easy course, these men moved straight ahead, hewing and hacking right and left, the play of the swift blades seemingly dissolving all obstacles in their path. Some idea of the density of the growth can be gathered from the fact that if a man moved off he became instantly invisible although he might be only a yard or two away.

Late in the afternoon we reached a small hut or *tambo* built on the former trip by the Chief. It was nothing but a roof on poles, but it was a welcome sight to us as it meant rest and food. We were tired and hungry and were glad to find a small creek close by where we could refresh ourselves, taking care to keep out of the reach of the alligators and water-snakes swimming close to the weeds by the shore. For our supper we gave the dried *pirarucu* flesh a boil and soaked some farinha in water, eating this tasteless repast with as much gusto as we would if it had been roast beef. Let me here recommend this diet for any gourmet whose appetite has been impaired, and he will soon be able to enjoy a stew of shoe-leather. One of the men, a good-natured athlete, Jerome by name, was sent out after fresh meat, and brought back a weird little animal resembling a fox (*cuti*). We decided to test it as a stew, but, lacking salt, we found the dried *pirarucu* preferable.

The excitement of the night was furnished by ants, which had built a nest in the *tambo* where we had swung our hammocks. The visitors swarmed up poles and down ropes and would not be denied entrance. Wads of cotton smeared with vaseline and bandaged around the fastenings of the hammock proved no obstacle. It was impossible to sleep; mosquitoes came to the assistance of the ants and managed to find their way through the mosquito-net. To complete the general "cheerfulness," the tree-tops were full of little spider-monkeys whispering mournfully throughout the dark and showery night.

The second day's march took us through the region which the Chief had explored the year before, and we spent the night in another *tambo* built on that occasion. Our progress, however, was made with increasing difficulty, as the land had become more hilly and broken and the forest, if possible, more dense and wild. We were now at a considerable distance from the river-front and in a region where the yearly inundation could never reach. This stage of the journey remains among the few pleasant memories of that terrible expedition, through what I may call the gastronomic revel with which it ended. Jerome had succeeded in bringing down with his muzzle-loader a *mutum*, a bird which in flavour and appearance reminds one of a turkey, while I was so lucky as to bag a nice fat deer (marsh-deer). This happened at *tambo* No. 2. We called each successive hut by its respective number. Here we had a great culinary feast, so great that during the following days I thought of this time with a sad "*ils sont passés, ces jours de fête.*"

Now, guided by the position of the sun, we held a course due west, our ultimate destination being a far-off region where the Chief expected to find large areas covered with fine caoutellouc trees. The ground was hilly and interspersed with deeply cut creeks where we could see the ugly heads of the *jararaca* snakes pop up as if they were waiting for us. There was only one way of crossing these creeks; this was by felling a young tree across the stream for a bridge. A long slender stick was then cut and one end placed at the bottom of the creek, when each man seizing this in his right hand steadied himself over the tree to the other side of the deep treacherous water. It required steady nerve to walk this trunk, such as I did not possess, therefore I found it safer to hang from the levelled bole by my hands and travel across in that manner. *Tambo* No. 3 we constructed ourselves, as we did every other for the rest of the journey. We always selected a site near a creek that we were following, and cleared away the underbrush so as to leave an open area of about twenty-five feet square, always allowing one tree to remain for a corner. A framework of saplings tied together with strips of *matamata* bark was raised for a roof, and across this were laid gigantic leaves of the *murumurū*, twenty-five to thirty feet long. The hammocks were then strung beneath, and we managed to keep comparatively sheltered from the nightly rain that always occurs in these deep forests. After the frugal meal of *pirarucu* and dried farinha, or of some game we had picked up during the march, we would creep into our hammocks and smoke, while the men told hunting stories, or sang their monotonous, unmelodious tribal songs.

It must have been about two o'clock in the morning when I was awakened by a terrific roaring which fairly made the forest tremble. Sitting up and staring

"From time to time a tapir, sportively inclined, or perhaps chased by a *tigre* [puma], comes crashing through the undergrowth and dives into the water in a blind rush which heeds no obstacle, be it man or canoe. By some strange freak of nature these huge, ungainly, 600 lb. beasts are endowed with the power to make but one noise, which might be the chirp of a wren!"

—F. W. UP DE GRAFF

fearfully into the darkness, I heard the crashing of underbrush and trees close upon us. My first thought was of a hurricane, but in the confusion of my senses, stunned by the impact of sound, I had few clear impressions. My companions were calling one another. The noise grew louder, more terrifying. Suddenly the little world around me went to smash in one mad upheaval. The roof of the *tambo* collapsed and fell upon us. At the same instant I felt some huge body brush past me, hurling me sprawling to the ground. The noise was deafening, mingled with the shrieks and excited yellings of my men, but the object passed swiftly in the direction of the creek.

Some one now thought of striking a light to discover the extent of the damage. The *tambo* was a wreck; the hammocks were one tangled mass. Jerome, who had jumped from his hammock when he first heard the noise, followed the "hurricane" to the creek and soon solved the mystery of the storm that swept our little camp. He told us it was a jaguar, which had sprung upon the back of a large tapir while the animal was feeding in the woods behind our *tambo*. The tapir started for the creek in the hope of knocking the jaguar off its back by rushing through the underbrush; not succeeding in this, its next hope was the water in the creek. It had chosen a straight course through our *tambo*.

The next day we were successful in killing two howling monkeys; these were greeted with loud yells of joy, as we had not been able to locate any game during the last twenty-four hours' march. This is easy to understand. We were much absorbed in cutting our way through the bushes and the game was scared away long before we could sight it.

After the ninth day of wearisome journeying, the Chief found signs of numerous caoutchouc trees, indicating a rich district, and it was accordingly decided that *tambo* No. 9 should be our last. We were now fully 150 miles from the Floresta headquarters and some 120 miles back in the absolutely unknown. That night the temperature went down to 41° Fahrenheit, a remarkable drop so close to the equator and on such low ground, but it was undoubtedly due to the fact that the sun never penetrates the dark foliage of the surrounding dense forests where the swamps between the hills give off their damp exhalations.

Up to this point I had not feared the jungle more than I would have feared any other forest, but soon a dread commenced to take hold of me, now that I could see how a great danger crept closer and closer—danger of starvation and sickness. Our supplies were growing scant when we reached *tambo* No. 9, and yet we lingered, forgetful of the precarious position into which we had thrust ourselves, and the violated wilderness was preparing to take its revenge.

I suppose our carelessness in remaining was due in part to the exhausted state to which we had been reduced, and which made us all rejoice in the comfort of effortless days rather than face new exertions.

We were three weeks at *tambo* No. 9 before the sharp tooth of necessity began to rouse us to the precarious situation. Occasionally a lucky shot would bring down a *mutum* or a couple of monkeys and, on one occasion, a female tapir. Thus feasting to repletion, we failed to notice that the lucky strikes came at longer intervals; that the animals were deserting our part of the forest. During these three weeks we were not wholly idle. The Chief had the men out every day making excursions in the neighbourhood to locate the caoutchouc trees. As soon as a tree was found, they set to work bleeding the base of it to let the milky sap ooze out on the ground where it would collect in a small pool. Then they would fell the tree and cut rings in the bark at regular intervals so that the milk could flow out. In a few days when the milk had coagulated, forming large patches of caoutchouc, they would return for it. The pieces were washed in the creek and then tied into large bundles ready for transporting.

In all they located more than 800 caoutchouc trees. At this time too I made my remarkable discovery of gold deposits in the creek. It seems to me now like the plot of some old morality play, for while we were searching eagerly for the thing that we considered the ultimate goal of human desires—wealth, the final master, Death was closing his net upon us day by day. Our food supply was nearly gone.

While strolling along the shores of the creek in search of game, I noticed irregular clumps or nodules of clay which had accumulated in large quantities in the bed of the stream, especially where branches and logs had caused whirlpools and eddies to form. They had the appearance of pebbles or stones, and were so heavy in proportion to their size that my curiosity was aroused, and throwing one of them on the bank I split it open with my machete. My weakened heart then commenced to beat violently, for what I saw looked like gold.

I took the two pieces to my working table near our *tambo*, and examining the dirty-yellow heart with my magnifying glass, I found the following: A central mass about one cubic inch in size, containing a quantity of yellowish grains measuring, say, one thirty-second of an inch in diameter, slightly adhering to each other, but separating upon pressure of the finger, and around this a thick layer of hard clay or mud of somewhat irregular shape. It immediately struck me that the yellow substance might be gold, though I could not account for the presence of it in the centre of the clay-balls.

I carefully scraped the granules out of the clay, and washing them clean, placed them on a sheet of paper to dry in the sun. By this time the attention of the other men had been attracted to what I was doing, and it seemed to amuse the brave fellows immensely to watch my painstaking efforts with the yellow stuff. I produced some fine scales I had for weighing chemicals for my photographic work, and suspended these above a gourd filled with water. Then I went down to the creek and collected more of the clay-balls and scraped the mud of one away from the solid centre of what I took to be grains of gold. A fine thread I next wound around the gold ball and this was tied to one end of the balance. After an equilibrium had been established, I found that the weight of the gold was 660 grains. Next I raised the gourd until the water reached the suspended ball, causing the opposite pan of the scales to go down. To again establish equilibrium, I had to add 35 grains. With this figure I divided the actual weight of the gold, which gave me 18.9, and this I remembered was close to the specific gravity of pure gold.

Still a little in doubt, I broke the bulb of one of my clinical thermometers and, placing the small quantity of mercury thus obtained in the bottom of a tray, I threw a few of the grains into it, and found that they immediately united, forming a dirty-grey amalgam. I was now sure the substance was gold and in less than five hours I collected enough to fill five photographic 5 × 7 plate-boxes, the only empty receptacles I could lay my hands on. I could have filled a barrel, for the creek was thick with the clay-balls as far as I could see; but I had a continuous fever and this, with the exhaustion from semi-starvation, caused me to be indifferent to this great wealth. In fact, I would have gladly, given all the gold in the creek for ONE square meal. If the difficulties in reaching this infernal region were not so great, I have no doubt that a few men could soon make themselves millionaires.

The deadly fever came among us after a few days. It struck a young man called Brabo first; the next day I fell sick with another serious attack of swamp-fever, and we both took to our hammocks. For five days and nights I was delirious most of the time, listening to the mysterious noises of the forest and seeing in my dreams visions of juicy steaks, great loaves of bread, and cups of creamy coffee. In those five days the only food in the camp was howling monkey, the jerked beef and the dried farinha having given out much to my satisfaction, as I became so heartily disgusted with this unpalatable food that I preferred to starve rather than eat it again. At first I felt the lack of food keenly, but later the pain of hunger was dulled, and only a warm, drugged sensation pervaded my system. Starvation has its small mercies.

I became almost childishly interested in small things. There was a peculiar sound that came from the deep forest in the damp nights; I used to call it the "voice of the forest." To close one's eyes and listen was almost to imagine oneself near the murmuring crowd of a large city. It was the song of numerous frogs which inhabited a creek near our *tambo*. Then I would hear four musical notes uttered in a major key from the tree-tops close by, soon answered by another four in a similar pitch, and this musical and cheerful(!) conversation was continued all night long. The men told me that this was the note of a species of frog that lived in the trees.

One day the jungle took the first toll from us. Young Brabo was very low; I managed to stagger out of my hammock to give him a hypodermic injection, but he was too far gone for it to do him any good. He died in the early afternoon. We dug a grave with our machetes right behind our *tambo*. No stone marks this place; only a small wooden cross tied together with bark-strips shows where our comrade lies—a son of the forest whom the forest claimed again.

The arrival of Death in our camp showed us all how far we were in the grasp of actual, threatening danger. We stood about the grave in silence. These men, these Indians of the Amazon, were very human; somehow, I always considered them equals and not of an inferior race. We had worked together, eaten and slept and laughed together, and now together we faced the mystery of Death. The tie between us became closer; the fraternity of common flesh and blood bound us.

The next day I arose and was able to walk around, having injected my left arm with copious doses of quinine and arsenical acid. Borrowing thus false strength from drugs, I was able to some extent, to roam around with my camera and secure photographs that I wanted to take home with me to the States.

I had constructed a table of stalks of the *murumurū* palm-leaves, and I had made a sun-dial by the aid of a compass and a stick, much to the delight of the men, who were now able to tell the hour of the day with precision. The next day I had another attack of fever and bled my arm freely with the bistoury, relieving myself of about sixteen ounces of blood. Shortly after nine o'clock in the morning I heard a shot which I recognised as being that of Jerome's muzzle-loader; soon afterward he made his appearance with a splendid specimen of a jet-black jaguar, killed by a shot behind the ear. He skinned it after first asking me if I wanted to get up and take a photograph of it, but I was too weak to do it and had to decline.

The Chief one day brought into camp a fine deer and a *mutum* bird, which relieved our hunger for a while. As we were preparing a luxurious meal, Jerome returned with two red howling monkeys, but we had all the meat we could take care of, and these monkeys were rejected and thrown away.

By this time the Chief informed us that enough caoutchouc trees had been located to justify our return to the Floresta headquarters with a satisfactory report—of course, excepting the death of poor Brabo. Furthermore it was decided that owing to the lack of provisions we should separate. He directed that the men Freitas, Magellaes, and Anisette should take a course at a right angle to the Itecoahy, so as to reach this river in a short time, where they were to procure a canoe and secure assistance for the rest of us. This, of course, was a chance, but under the circumstances every step was a chance. The Chief himself, Jerome, and I would retrace the route which we had lately travelled and reach Floresta that way. The evening before our departure I did not think myself strong enough to carry my load a single step, but the hypodermic needle, with quinine, which had now become my constant stand-by, lent me an artificial strength, and when the packing was done the next morning, I stood up with the rest and strapped the load on my shoulders.

We parted with the other three men before sunrise, with clasps of the hand that were never to be repeated, and so turned our faces toward the outer world. My only hope was to retain sufficient strength in my emaciated, fever-racked body to drag myself back to Floresta, and from there, in the course of time, get canoe or launch connection to the frontier down the river, and then wait for the steamer that would take me back to "God's Country," where I could eat proper food, and rest—rest.

The jungle no longer seemed beautiful or wonderful to me, but horrible—a place of terror and death.

In my drug-dazed sleep on that back-track, I started up in my hammock, bathed in a sweat of fear from a dream; I saw myself and my companions engulfed in a sea of poisonous green, caught by living creepers that dragged us down and held us in a deadly octopus embrace. The forest was something from which I fled; it was hideous, a trap, with its impenetrable wall of vegetation, its dark shadows, and moist, treacherous ground.

I longed for the open; struggled for it, as the swimmer struggles up for air to escape from the insidious sucking of the undertow.

Starving, weak from fever, oppressed by the thought of death, but lashed on by stimulants and the tenacity of life, I headed with my two comrades out of the world of the unknown, toward the world of men—to LIFE.

On the second day of the return trip, we had a remarkable experience. Probably not more than two hundred yards from the *tambo* where we had spent the night, we heard the noise, as we thought, of a tapir, but nothing could surpass our astonishment when we saw a human being. Who could it be that dared alone to disturb the solitude of the virgin forest, and who went along in these dreary woods humming a melody?

It was a young Indian who approached us cautiously when Jerome spoke in a tongue I did not understand, and evidently told him that we were friends on the way back to our homes by the river. He was an unusually fine specimen of a savage, well built, beautifully proportioned, and with a flawless skin like polished bronze. His clothing was limited to a bark girdle, and a feather head-dress, not unlike that worn by some North American Indians.

He was armed with bow and arrows and a blow-gun; and he had a small rubber pouch filled with a brownish substance, the remarkable wourahli poison. He explained to Jerome that his tribe lived in their *maloca*, or tribal house, about 24 hours' march from this place, and that he had been chasing a tapir all day, but had lost its track, and was now returning to his home. He pointed in a north-western direction with his blow-gun, signifying thereby the general route he was going to follow in order to reach his destination. We sat down on the ground and looked at each other for quite a while, and thus I had my first chance of studying a blow-gun and the poisoned arrows, outside a museum, and in a place where it was part of a man's life. At the time I did not know that I was to have a little later a more thorough opportunity of examining this weapon. I asked the Indian, Jerome acting as interpreter, to demonstrate the use of the gun, to which he consented with a grin. We soon heard the chattering of monkeys in the tree-tops, and deftly inserting one of the thin poisoned arrows in the ten-foot tube he pointed the weapon at a swiftly moving body among the branches, and filling his lungs with air, let go. With a slight noise, hardly perceptible, the arrow flew out and pierced the left thigh of a little monkey. Quick as lightning he inserted another arrow and caught one of the other monkeys, as it was taking a tremendous leap through the air to a lower branch. The arrow struck this one in the shoulder, but it was a glancing shot and the shaft dropped to the ground. In the meantime the Indian ran after the first monkey and carried it up to me. It seemed fast asleep, suffering no agony whatever; and after five or six minutes its heart ceased beating. The other monkey landed on the branch it was aiming for in its leap, but after a short while it seemed uneasy and sniffed at everything. Finally, its hold on the branch relaxed, it dropped to the ground and was dead in a few minutes. It was a marvellous thing to behold these animals wounded but slightly, the last one only scratched, and yet dying after a few minutes as if they were falling asleep. It was then explained to me that the meat was still good to eat and that the presence of poison would not affect the consumer's stomach in the least; in fact, most of the game these Indians get is procured in this manner. I was lucky enough to secure a snap-shot of this man in the act of using his blow-gun. It proved to be the last photograph I took in the Brazilian jungles. Accidents and sickness subsequently set in, and the fight for life became too hard and all-absorbing even to think of photographing. He left us after an hour's conversation, and we resumed our journey homewards.

We had a slight advantage in retracing our former path. Although the reedy undergrowth had already choked it, we were travelling over ground that we knew, and it was also no longer necessary to delay for the building of *tambos*; we used the old ones again.

Jerome had complained for some time of a numbness in his fingers and toes, and also of an increasing weakness of the heart that made every step a torment. The Chief and I tried our best to cheer him up, although I felt certain that the brave fellow himself knew what dreadful disease had laid its spell upon him. However, we kept on walking without any words that might tend to lower our already depressed spirits.

But our march was no longer the animated travel it had been on the way out; we talked like automatons rather than like human, thinking beings. Suffering, hunger, and drugs had dulled our senses. Only the will to escape somehow, the instinct of self-preservation, was fully awake in us. A sweep of the machete to cut a barrier bushrope or climber, one foot placed before the other, meant that much nearer to home and safety. Such was now the simple operation of our stupefied and tired brains, brains that could not hold one complex thought to its end; too tired—tired!

At nightfall we stumbled into our old *tambo* No. 7. There was no thought of securing food, no possibility of getting any; we had been too tired to even attempt to shoot game during the day. The two monkeys which the Indian had killed with his blow-gun were the only food we had and these we now broiled over the camp-fire and devoured fiercely. After this meal, none too good, we slung our hammocks with difficulty and dropped in. Jerome's numbness increased during the night. We were up and on the trail again with the dawn.

In the afternoon we descended a hill to find ourselves confronted by a swamp of unusual extent. The Chief was in the lead as we crossed the swamp and we lost him from our sight for a few minutes. While crossing this wide, slimy-bottomed place, I noticed a peculiar movement in the water near me, and soon made out the slender bodies of swamp-snakes as they whipped past among the branches and reeds. These snakes are called by the Brazilians *jararacas* and are very poisonous; however, I had no fear for myself as I wore heavy buffalo-hide boots, but the men walked barefooted, and were in great danger. I cried out a warning to Jerome, who took care to thrash about him. We supposed that we had passed this snake-hole without mishap when we rejoined the Chief on "terra firma." He was leaning over, as we approached him, and be turned a face to us that was stricken with fear. He pointed to the instep of his right foot and there on the skin were two tiny spots, marked by the fangs of the snake. Without a word we sank to the ground beside him in despair. The unfortunate man, with dilated eyes fixed upon the ground, crouched waiting for the coming of the pain that would indicate that the poison was working its deadly course, and that the end was near if something was not done immediately.

Losing no more time, I cried to Jerome to pour out some gunpowder while I sucked the wound. While doing this I fumbled in the spacious pockets of my khaki hunting-coat and secured the bistoury with which I made a deep incision in the flesh over the wound, causing the blood to flow freely. In the meantime, Jerome had filled a measure with black powder and this was now emptied into the bleeding wound and a burning match applied at once. The object of this was to cauterise the wound, a method that has been used with success in the outskirts of the world where poisonous reptiles abound and where proper antidotes cannot be had.

> "The poison of venomous serpents is not in the least uniform in its quality.[...] The bite of a cobra or other colubrine poisonous snake is more painful in its immediate effects than is the bite of one of the big vipers. The victim suffers more. There is a greater effect on the nerve-centers, but less swelling of the wound itself, and, whereas the blood of the rattlesnake's victim coagulates, the blood of the victim of an elapine snake—that is, of one of the only poisonous American colubrines—becomes watery and incapable of coagulation."
>
> —*President Theodore Roosevelt*

The Chief stood the ordeal without a murmur, never flinching even at the explosion of the gunpowder. Jerome and I made him as comfortable as possible, and sat sadly by his side watching him suffer and die by inches.

It is no easy thing to see a man meet death, but under these circumstances it was particularly distressing. The Chief had been a man of a strong constitution particularly adapted to the health-racking work of a rubber-hunter. He it was who with his forest-wisdom had planned all our moves, and had mapped our course through the blind forest, where a man could be lost as easily as on the open sea. He had proved himself a good leader, save for the fatal mistake in delaying our return, over-anxious as he was to render his employer, Coronel da Silva, full and faithful service. He was extremely capable, kind, and human, and a good friend to us all.

We had looked to him for advice in all our needs. He knew the language of the wild beasts of the forest, he knew a way out of everything, and at home he was a most devoted father. Now, this splendid fellow, the sole reliance, in this vast and intricate maze, of Jerome and myself, succumbed before our eyes to one of the dangers of the merciless wilderness. He was beyond all hope. Nothing in our power could to any extent add to the prolongation of his life which slowly ebbed away. About four o'clock in the afternoon his respirations grew difficult, and a few moments later he drew his last painful breath. He died three hours after being bitten by the *jararaca*. For the second time during that ill-fated journey I went to work digging a grave with my machete, Jerome lending me whatever assistance he could in his enfeebled state. My own condition was such that I had to rest and recover my breath with every few stabs of the machete.

We completed that day's journey late in the afternoon, arriving at *tambo* No. 6 after taking almost an hour for the last half mile. Jerome could now scarcely stand without my assistance. There was no longer any attempt to disguise the nature of his sickness. He had *beri-beri*, and that meant in our situation not the slightest chance of recovery. Even with the best of care and nursing his case would be hopeless, for in these regions the disease is absolutely fatal.

We built a fire and managed to get our hammocks fastened in some fashion, but there was not a scrap of food to be had. The heart-leaves from a young palm were chewed in a mood of hopeless desperation.

The next morning it was a task of several minutes for me to get out of the hammock and on my feet. Jerome made several painful efforts and, finally, solved his problem by dropping to the ground. He could not rise until I came to his assistance. Then we two tottering wrecks attempted to carry our heavy loads, but Jerome could not make it; he cast from him everything he owned, even the smallest personal belongings so dear to his simple, pure soul. It was heartrending to see this young man, who in health would have been able to handle three or four of his own size, now reduced to such a pitiful state.

And in my own case, the fever which I had fought off by constant use of the hypodermic needle, now swept over me with renewed violence. The drug did not have the same effect as when I was new to the ravages of the fever.

At this point my recollections became almost inextricably confused. I know that at times I raved wildly as I staggered on, for occasionally I came to myself with strange phrases on my lips addressed to no one in particular. When these lucid moments brought coherent thought, it was the jungle, the endless, all-embracing, fearful jungle, that overwhelmed my mind. No shipwrecked mariner driven to madness by long tossing on a raft at sea ever conceived such hatred and horror of his surroundings as that which now came upon me for the fresh, perpetual, monotonous green of the interminable forest.

About noon the weight on my back became unbearable and I resolved to sacrifice my precious cargo. I threw away my camera, my unexposed plates, all utensils, and four of the boxes of gold dust. This left me with one box of gold, a few boxes of exposed plates (which I eventually succeeded in carrying all the way back to New York), and fifty-six bullets, the automatic revolver, and the machete. Last, but not least, I kept the hypodermic needle and a few more ampules.

We had walked scarcely a quarter of a mile when Jerome collapsed. The poor fellow declared that he was beaten; it was no use to fight any more; he begged me to hurry the inevitable and send a bullet through his brain. The prospect of another visitation of Death aroused me from my stupor. I got him to a dry spot and found some dry leaves and branches with which I started a fire. Jerome was beyond recognising me. He lay by the fire, drawing long, wheezing breaths, and his face was horribly distorted, like that of a man in a violent fit. He babbled incessantly to himself and occasionally stared at me and broke out into shrill, dreadful laughter, that made my flesh creep.

All this overwhelmed me and sapped the little energy I had left. I threw myself on the ground some little distance from the fire, not caring if I ever rose again.

How long it was before a penetrating, weird cry aroused me from this stupor, I do not know, but when I raised my head I saw that the forest was growing dark and the fire burning low. I saw too that Jerome was trying to get on his feet, his eyes bulging from their sockets, his face crimson in colour. He was on one knee, when the thread of life snapped, and he fell headlong into the fire. I saw this as through a hazy veil and almost instantly my senses left me again.

I have no clear knowledge of what happened after this. Throughout the rest of the night, my madness mercifully left me insensible to the full appreciation of the situation and my future prospects. It was night again before I was able to arouse myself from my collapse. The fire was out, the forest dark and still, except for the weird cry of the owl, the uncanny "Mother of the Moon." Poor Jerome lay quiet among the embers. I did not have the courage, even if I had had the strength, to pull the body away, for there could be nothing left of his face by now. I looked at him once more, shuddering, and because I could not walk, I crept on all fours through the brush, without any object in mind,—just kept moving—just crept on like a sick, worthless dog.

One definite incident of the night I remember quite distinctly. It occurred during one of those moments when my senses returned for a while; when I could realise where I was and how I got there. I was crawling through the thicket making small, miserable progress, my insensible face and hands torn and scratched by spines and thorns which I did not heed, when something bumped against my thigh; I clutched at it and my hand closed around the butt of my automatic pistol. The weapon came out of its holster unconsciously, but as I felt my finger rest in the curve of the trigger, I knew that some numbed and exhausted corner of my brain had prompted me to do this thing; indeed, as I weighed the matter with what coolness I could bring to bear, it did not seem particularly wicked. With the pistol in my hand and with the safety released, I believed that the rest would have been easy and even pleasant. What did I have in my favour? What prospect did I have of escaping the jungle? None whatever—none!

There was no shadow of hope for me, and I had long ago given up believing in miracles. For eight days I had scarcely had a mouthful to eat, excepting the broiled monkey at *tambo* No. 7, shot by the young Indian.

The fever had me completely in its grasp. I was left alone more than one hundred miles from human beings in absolute wilderness. I measured cynically the tenaciousness of life, measured the thread that yet held me among the number of the living, and I realised now what the fight between life and death meant to a man brought to bay. I had not the slightest doubt in my mind that this was the last of me. Surely, no man could have been brought lower or to greater extremity and live; no man ever faced a more hopeless proposition. Yet I could or would not yield, but put the pistol back where it belonged.

All night long I crawled on and on and ever on, through the underbrush, with no sense of direction whatever, and still I am sure that I did not crawl in a circle but that I covered a considerable distance. For hours I moved along at the absolute mercy of any beast of the forest that might meet me.

The damp chill of the approaching morning usual in these regions came to me with a cooling touch and restored once more to some extent my sanity. My clothes were almost stripped from my body, and smeared with mud, my hands and face were tom and my knees were a mass of bruises.

I have a vague recollection of hearing the barking of dogs, of changing my crawling direction to head for the sound, and then, suddenly, seeing in front of me a sight which had the same effect as a rescuing steamer on the shipwrecked.

To my confused vision it seemed that I saw many men and women and children, and a large, round house; I saw parrots fly across the open space in brilliant, flashing plumage and heard their shrill screaming. I cried aloud and fell forward when a little curly-haired dog jumped up and commenced licking my face, and then I knew no more.

When I came to I was lying in a comfortable hammock in a large, dark room. I heard the murmur of many voices and presently a man came over and looked at me. I did not understand where I was, but thought that I, finally, had gone mad. I fell asleep again. The next time I woke up I saw an old woman leaning over me and holding in her hand a gourd containing some chicken broth which I swallowed slowly, not feeling the cravings of hunger, in fact not knowing whether I was dead or alive. The old woman had a peculiar piece of wood through her lip and looked very unreal to me, and I soon fell asleep again.

On the fifth day, so I learned later, I began to feel my senses return, my fever commenced to abate, and I was able to grasp the fact that I had crawled into the *maloca*, or communal village, of the Mangeromas. I was as weak as a kitten, and, indeed, it has been a marvel to me ever since that I succeeded at all in coming out of the Shadow. The savages, by tender care, with strengthening drinks prepared in their own primitive method, wrought the miracle, and returned to life a man who was as near death as anyone could be, and not complete the transition. They fed me at regular intervals, thus checking my sickness, and when I could make out their meaning, I understood that I could stay with them as long as I desired.

Luckily I had kept my spectacles on my nose (they were the kind that fasten back of the ears) during the previous hardships, and I found these sticking in their position when I awoke. My khaki coat was on the ground under my hammock, and the first thing was to ascertain if the precious contents of its large pockets had been disturbed, but I found everything safe. The exposed plates were there in their closed boxes, the gold dust was also there and mocked me with its yellow glare, and my hypodermic outfit was intact and was used without delay, much to the astonishment of some of the men, standing around my hammock.

When my head was clear and strong enough to raise, I fumed and began my first visual exploration of my immediate surroundings. The big room I found to be a colossal house, forty feet high and one hundred and fifty feet in diameter, thatched with palm leaves and with sides formed of the stems of the *pachinba* tree. It was the communal residence of this entire tribe, consisting, as I learned later, of two hundred and fifty-eight souls. A single door and a circular opening in the roof were the only apertures of this enormous structure. The door was very low, not more than four feet, so that it was necessary to creep on one's knees to enter the place, and this opening was closed at night, that is to say, about six o'clock, by a sliding door which fitted so snugly that I never noticed any mosquitoes or *piums* in the dark, cool room.

The next day I could get out of my hammock, though I could not stand or walk without the aid of two women, who took me over to a man I later found to be the chief of the tribe. He was well fed, and by his elaborate dress was distinguished from the rest of the men. He had a very pleasant, good-natured smile, and almost constantly displayed a row of white, sharp-filed teeth. This smile gave me some confidence, but I very well knew that I was now living among cannibal Indians, whose reputation in this part of the Amazon is anything but flattering. I prepared for the new ordeal without any special fear—my feelings seemed by this time to have been pretty well exhausted and any appreciation of actual danger was considerably reduced as a result of the gamut of the terrors which I had run.

I addressed the Chief in the Portuguese language, and also in Spanish, but he only shook his head; all my efforts were useless. He let me know in a friendly manner that my hammock was to be my resting place and that I would not be molested. His tribe was one that occupied an almost unknown region and had no connection with white men or Brazilians or people near the river. I tried in the course of the inimical conversation to make him understand that, with six companions from a big Chief's *maloca* (meaning Coronel da Silva and the Floresta headquarters), I had penetrated into the woods near this mighty Chief's *maloca*,— here I pointed at the Chief—that the men had died from fever and I was left alone and that luckily, I had found my way to the free men of the forest (here I made a sweeping movement with my hands). He nodded and the audience was over. I was led back to my hammock to dream and eat, and dream again.

Although the Chief and his men presented an appearance wholly unknown to me, yet it did not seem to distract me at the first glance, but as my faculties slowly returned to their former activity, I looked at them and found them very strange figures, indeed. Every man had two feathers inserted in the cartilage of his nose; at some distance it appeared as if they wore moustaches. Besides this, the Chief had a sort of feather-dress reaching half way down to his knees; this was simply a quantity of *mutum* feathers tied together as a girdle by means of plant-fibres. The women wore no clothing whatever, their only ornamentation being the oval wooden piece in the lower lip and fancifully arranged designs on face, arms, and body. The colours which they preferred were scarlet and black, and they procured these dyes from two plants that grew in the forest near by. They would squeeze the pulp of the fruits and apply the rich-coloured juice with their fingers, forming one scarlet ring around each eye, outside of this a black and larger ring, and, finally, two scarlet bands reaching from the temples to the chin.

There were probably sixty-five families in this communal hut, all having their little households scattered throughout the place without any separating partitions whatever. The many poles which supported the roof formed the only way of distinguishing the individual households. The men strung their hammocks between the poles in such a way that they formed a triangle, and in the middle of this a fire was always going. Here the women were doing the cooking of game that the men brought in at all times of the day. The men slept in the hammocks, while the women were treated less cavalierly; they slept with their children on the ground under the hammocks around the little family triangle. As a rule they had woven mats made of grass-fibre and coloured with the juices of the *urucu* plant and the *genipapa*, but in many instances they had skins of jaguars, and, which was more frequent, the furs of the three-toed sloths. These were placed around the family fire, directly under the hammocks occupied by the men. In these hammocks the men did most of the repair work on their bows and arrows when necessary, here they fitted the arrow heads to the shafts; in fact, they spent all their time in them when not actually hunting in the forests.

The hospitality of my friends proved unbounded. The Chief appointed two young girls to care for me, and though they were not startling from any point of view, especially when remembering their labial ornaments and their early developed abdominal hypertrophies, they were as kind as anyone could have been, watching me when I tried to walk and supporting me when I became too weak. There was a certain broth they prepared, which was delicious, but there were others which were nauseating and which I had to force myself to eat. I soon learned that it was impolite to refuse any dish that was put in front of me, no matter how repugnant. One day the Chief ordered me to come over to his family triangle and have dinner with him. The meal consisted of some very tender fried fish which were really delicious; then followed three broiled parrots with fried bananas which were equally good; but then came a soup which I could not swallow. The first mouthful almost choked me,—the meat which was one of the ingredients tasted and smelled as if it had been kept for weeks, the herbs which were used were so bitter and gave out such a rank odor that my mouth puckered and the muscles of my throat refused to swallow. The Chief looked at me and frowned, and then I remembered the forest from which I had lately arrived and the starvation and the terrors; I closed my eyes and swallowed the dish, seeking what mental relief I could find in the so-called auto-suggestion.

But I had the greatest respect for the impulsive, unreasoning nature of these sons of the forest. Easily insulted, they are well-nigh implacable. This incident shows upon what a slender thread my life hung. The friends of one moment might become vindictive foes of the next.

Besides the head-Chief there were two sub-Chiefs, so that in case of sickness or death there would be always one regent. They were plainly distinguished by their dress, which consisted mainly of fancifully arranged feather belts of *arara*, *mutum*, and trumpeter plumes covering the shoulders and abdomen. These articles of dress were made by young women of the tribe: women who wanted to become favourites of the Chief and sub-Chiefs. They often worked for months on a feather dress and when finished presented it to the particular Chief whose favour they desired.

The chiefs had several wives, but the tribesmen were never allowed to take more than one. Whenever a particularly pretty girl desired to join the household of the Great Chief or of a sub-Chief, she set to work and for months and months she made necklaces of alligator teeth, peccary teeth, and finely carved ivory nuts and colored pieces of wood. She also would weave some elaborate hammock and fringe this with the bushy tails of the squirrels and the forest cats, and when these articles were done, she would present them to the Chief, who, in return for these favors, would bestow upon her the great honor of accepting her as a wife.

There seemed to be few maladies among these people; in fact, during the five weeks I spent with them, I never saw a case of fever nor of anything else. When a person died the body was carried far into the woods, where a fire was built, and it was cremated. The party would then leave in a hurry and never return to the same spot; they were afraid of the Spirit of the Dead. They told me that they could hear the Spirit far off in the forests at night when the moon was shining.

The men were good hunters and were experts in the use of bow and arrow and also the blow-gun, and never failed to bring home a fresh supply of game for the village. This supply was always divided equally, so that no one should receive more than he needed for the day. At first glance the men might appear lazy, but why should they hurry and worry when they have no landlord, and no grocer's bills to pay; in fact, the value of money is entirely unknown to them.

I was allowed to walk around as I pleased, everybody showing me a kindness for which I shall ever gratefully remember these "savages." I frequently spent my forenoons on a tree trunk outside the *maloca* with the Chief, who took a particular interest in my welfare. We would sit for hours and talk, he sometimes pointing at an object and giving its Indian name, which I would repeat until I got the right pronunciation. Thus, gradually instructed, and by watching the men and women as they came and went, day after day, I was able to understand some of their language and learned to answer questions fairly well. They never laughed at my mistakes, but repeated a word until I had it right.

The word of the Chief was law and no one dared appeal from the decisions of this man. In fact, there would have been nobody to appeal to, for the natives believed him vested with mysterious power which made him the ruler of men. I once had occasion to see him use the power which had been given him.

I had accompanied two young Indians, one of whom was the man we had met in the forest on our return trip not far from that fatal *tambo* No. 3. His name, at least as it sounded to me, was Reré. They carried bows and arrows and I my automatic pistol, although I had no great intention of using it. What little ammunition I had left I desired to keep for an emergency and, besides, I reasoned that I might, at some future time, be able to use the power and noise of the weapon to good advantage if I kept the Indians ignorant of them for the present.

We had scarcely gone a mile, when we discovered on the opposite side of a creek, about one hundred and fifty yards away, a wild hog rooting for food. We were on a slight elevation ourselves and under cover of the brush, while the hog was exposed to view on the next knoll. Almost simultaneously my companions fitted arrows to their bow-strings. Instead of shooting point blank, manipulating the bows with their hands and arms, they placed their great and second toes on the cords on the ground, and with their left arms gave the proper tension and inclination to the bows which were at least eight feet long. With a whirr the poisoned arrows shot forth and, while the cords still twanged, sailed gracefully through the air, describing a hyperbola, fell with a speed that made them almost invisible, and plunged into the animal on each side of his neck a little back from the base of the brain.

The hog dropped in his tracks, and I doubt if he could have lived even though the arrows had not been poisoned. Tying his feet together with plant-fibres we slung the body over a heavy pole and carried it to the *maloca*. All the way the two fellows disputed as to who was the owner of the hog, and from time to time they put the carcass on the ground to gesticulate and argue. I thought they would come to blows. When they appealed to me I declared that the arrows had sped so rapidly that my eyes could not follow them and therefore could not tell which arrow had found its mark first.

A few yards from the house my friends fell to arguing again, and a crowd collected about them, cheering first the one then the other. My suggestion that the game be divided was rejected as showing very poor judgment. Finally, the dispute grew to such proportions that the Chief sent a messenger to learn the cause of the trouble and report it to him.

The emissary retired and the crowd immediately began to disperse and the combatants quieted. The messenger soon returned saying that the Great Chief would judge the case and ordered the men to enter the *maloca*. With some difficulty the hog was dragged through the door opening and all the inhabitants crawled in after. The Chief was decked out in a new and splendid feather dress, his face had received a fresh coat of paint (in fact, the shells of the *urucu* plant with which he coloured his face and body scarlet were still lying under his hammock), and his nose was supplied with a new set of *mutum* feathers. He was sitting in his hammock which was made of fine, braided, multicoloured grass-fibres and was fringed with numerous squirrel tails. The whole picture was one which impressed me as being weirdly fantastic and extremely picturesque, the reddish, flickering light from the fires adding a mystic colour to the scene. On the opposite side of the fire from where the Chief was sitting lay the body of the hog, and at each end of the carcass stood the two hunters, straight as saplings, gazing stolidly ahead. In a semicircle, facing the Chief and surrounding the disputants, was the tribe, squatting on the ground. The Chief motioned to me to seat myself on the ground alongside of the hammock where he was sitting. The men told their story, now and then looking to me for an affirmative nod of the head. After having listened to the argument of the hunters for a considerable time without uttering a syllable, and regarding the crowd with a steady, unblinking expression, with a trace of a satirical smile around the corners of his mouth, which suited him. Admirably, the Chief finally spoke. He said, "The hog is mine.—Go!"

The matter was ended with this wise judgment, and there seemed to be no disposition to grumble or re-appeal to the great authority.

My life among the Mangeromas was, for the greater part, free from adventure, at least as compared with former experiences, and yet I was more than once within an inch of meeting death. In fact, I think that I looked more squarely in the eyes of death in that peaceful little community than ever I did out in the wilds of the jungle or in my most perilous adventures. The creek that ran near the *maloca* supplied the Indians with what water they needed for drinking purposes. Besides this the creek gave them an abundant supply of fish, a dish that made its appearance at every meal. Whatever washing was to be done—the natives took a bath at least twice a day—was done at some distance down the creek so as not to spoil the water for drinking and culinary purposes. Whenever I was thirsty I was in the habit of stooping down at the water's edge to scoop the fluid up in my curved hands. One morning I had been tramping through the jungle with two companions who were in search of game, and I was very tired and hot when we came to a little stream which I took to be the same that ran past the *maloca*. My friends were at a short distance from me, beating their way through the underbrush, when I stooped to quench my thirst. The cool water looked to me like the very Elixir of Life. At that moment, literally speaking, I was only two inches from death. Hearing a sharp cry behind me I turned slightly to feel a rough hand upon my shoulders and found myself flung backward on the ground.

"Poison," was the reply to my angry question. Then my friend explained, and as he talked my knees wobbled and I turned pale. It seems that the Mangeromas often poison the streams below the drinking places in order to get rid of their enemies. In the present case there had been a rumor that a party of Peruvian rubber workers might be coming up the creek, and this is always a signal of trouble among these Indians. Although you cannot induce a Brazilian to go into the Indian settlements or *malocas*, the Peruvians are more than willing to go there, because of the chance of abducting girls. To accomplish this, a few Peruvians sneak close to the *maloca* at night, force the door, which is always bolted to keep out the Evil Spirit, but which without difficulty can be cut open, and fire a volley of shots into the hut. The Indians sleep with the blow-guns and arrows suspended from the rafters, and before they can collect their sleepy senses and procure the weapons the Peruvians, in the general confusion, have carried off some of the girls. The Mangeromas, therefore, hate the Peruvians and will go to any extreme to compass their death. The poisoning of the rivers is effected by the root of a plant that is found throughout the Amazon valley; the plant belongs to the genus *Lonchocarpus* and bears a small cluster of bluish blossoms which produce a pod about two inches in length. It is only the yellow roots that are used for poisoning the water. This is done by crushing the roots and throwing the pulp into the stream, when all animal life will be killed or driven away.

It seems strange that during my stay among the Mangeromas, who were heathens and even cannibals, I saw no signs of idolatry. They believed implicitly in a good and an evil spirit. The good spirit was too good to do them any harm and consequently they did not bother with him; but the evil spirit was more active and could be heard in the dark nights, howling and wailing far off in the forest as he searched for lonely wanderers, whom he was said to devour.

Thinking to amuse some of my friends, I one day kindled a flame by means of my magnifying glass and a few dry twigs. A group of ten or twelve Indians had gathered squatting in a circle about me, to see the wonder that I was to exhibit, but at the sight of smoke followed by flame they were badly scared and ran for the house, where they called the Chief. He arrived on the scene with his usual smile.

He asked me to show him what I had done. I applied the focused rays of the sun to some more dry leaves and twigs and, finally, the flames broke out again. The Chief was delighted and begged me to make him a present of the magnifier. As I did not dare to refuse, I showed him how to use it and then presented it with as good grace as I could.

Some time after this, I learned that two Peruvians had been caught in a trap set for the purpose. The unfortunate men had spent a whole night in a pit, nine feet deep, and were discovered the next forenoon by a party of hunters, who immediately killed them with unpoisoned, big-game arrows. In contrast to the North American Indians they never torture captives, but kill them as quickly as possible. On such occasions a day of feasting always follows and an obscure religious rite is performed.

I had plenty of opportunity to investigate the different kinds of traps used by the Mangeromas for catching Peruvian *caboclos* or half-breeds. First of all in importance is the pit-trap, into which the aforesaid men had fallen. It is simple but ingenious in its arrangement. A hole about nine feet deep and eight feet wide is dug in the ground at a place where the *caboclos* are liable to come. A cover is laid across this and cleverly disguised with dead leaves and branches so as to exactly resemble the surrounding soil. This cover is constructed of branches placed parallel, and is slightly smaller than the diameter of the pit. It is balanced on a stick, tied across the middle in such a manner that the slightest weight on any part will cause it to turn over and precipitate the object into the pit whence egress is impossible. Besides this, the walls of the pit are inclined, the widest part being at the bottom, and they gradually slope inward till the level of the ground is reached. When the victim is discovered he is quickly killed, as in the case noted above.

The second trap, which I had an opportunity to investigate, is the so-called *araya* trap. It is merely a small piece of ground thickly set with the barbed bones of the sting-ray. These bones are slightly touched with wourahli poison and, concealed as they are under dead leaves, they inflict severe wounds on the bare feet of the *caboclos*, and death follows within a short period.

The third, and of all the most ingenious, trap is the blow-gun. One day the sub-Chief, a tall, gloomy-looking fellow, took me to one of these traps and explained everything, till I had obtained a thorough knowledge of the complicated apparatus. The blowgun of these Indians is supplied with a wide mouth-piece and requires but slight air pressure to shoot the arrow at a considerable speed. In the trap one is placed horizontally so as to point at a right angle to the path leading to the *maloca*. At the "breech" of the gun is a young sapling, severed five feet above the ground. To this is tied a broad and straight, bark-strip which, when the sapling is in its normal vertical position, completely covers the mouth-piece. The gun was not loaded on this occasion, as it had been accidentally discharged the day before. To set the trap, a long, thin, and pliable climber, which in these forests is so plentiful, is attached to the end of the severed sapling, when this is bent to its extreme position and is then led over branches, serving as pulleys, right across the path and directly in front of the mouth of the blow-gun and is tied to some small root covered with leaves. When the *caboclo* passes along this path at night to raid the Indian *maloca*, he must sever this thin bushrope or climber, thereby releasing suddenly the tension of the sapling. The bark-flap is drawn quickly up against the mouth-piece with a slap that forces sufficient air into the gun to eject the arrow. All this takes place in a fraction of a second; a slight flapping sound is heard and the arrow lodges in the skin of the unfortunate *caboclo*. He can never walk more than twenty yards, for the poison rapidly paralyses his limbs. Death follows in less than ten minutes.

The bodies of these captured *caboclos* are soon found by the "police warriors" of the tribe and carried to the *maloca*. On such occasions a day of feasting always follows and an obscure religious rite is performed.

It is true that the Mangeromas are cannibals, but at the same time their habits and morals are otherwise remarkably clean. Without their good care and excellent treatment, I have no doubt I would now be with my brave companions out in that dark, green jungle.

But to return to my story of the two Peruvians caught in the pit-trap: the warriors cut off the hands and feet of both corpses, pulled the big game arrows out of the bodies, and had an audience with the Chief. He seemed to be well satisfied, but spoke little, just nodding his head and smiling. Shortly after the village prepared for a grand feast. The fires were rebuilt, the pots and jars were cleaned, and a scene followed which to me was frightful. Had it not happened, I should always have believed this little world out in the wild forest an ideal, pure, and morally clean community. But now I could only hasten to my hammock and simulate sleep, for I well knew, from previous experience, that otherwise I would have to partake of the meal in preparation: a horrible meal of human flesh! It was enough for me to see them strip the flesh from the palms of the hands and the soles of the feet and fry these delicacies in the lard of tapir. I hoped to see no more.

An awful thought coursed through my brain when I beheld the men bend eagerly over the pans to see if the meat were done. How long would it be, I said to myself, before they would forget themselves and place my own extremities in the same pots and pans. Such a possibility was not pleasant to contemplate, but as I had found the word of these Indians to be always good, I believed I was safe. They were never false and they hated falsehood. True, they were cunning, but once their friend always their friend, through thick and thin. And the Chief had promised that I should not be eaten, either fried or stewed! Therefore I slept in peace.

I had long desired to see the hunters prepare the mysterious wourahli poison, which acts so quickly and painlessly, and which allows the game killed by it to be eaten without interfering with the nutritive qualities. Only three men in this village understood the proper mixing of the ingredients, although everybody knew the two plants from which the poisonous juices were obtained. One of these is a vine that grows close to the creeks. The stem is about two inches in diameter and covered with a rough greyish bark. It yields several round fruits, shaped like an apple, containing seeds imbedded in a very bitter pulp. The other is also a vine and bears small bluish flowers, but it is only the roots of this that are used. These are crushed and steeped in water for several days. The three men in our village who understood the concoction of this poison collected the plants themselves once a month. When they returned from their expedition they set to work at once scraping the first named vine into fine shavings and mixing these in an earthen jar with the crushed pulp of the roots of the second plant. The pot is then placed over a fire and kept simmering for several hours. At this stage the shavings are removed and thrown away as useless and several large black ants, the *Tucandeiras*, are added. This is the ant whose bite is not only painful but absolutely dangerous to man. The concoction is kept boiling slowly until the next morning, when it has assumed a thick consistency of a brown colour and very bitter to the taste. The poison is then tried on some arrows and if it comes up to the standard it is placed in a small earthen jar which is covered with a piece of animal skin and it is ready for use. The arrows, which are from ten to twelve inches long, are made from the stalks of a certain palm-leaf, the Jacy palm. They are absolutely straight and true; in fact, they resemble very much lady's hat-pin. When the gun is to be used, piece of cotton is wound around the end of an arrow and the other end or point inserted first in the barrel, the cotton acting as a piston by means of which the air forces the shaft through the tube.

The men always carry a small rubber-pouch containing a few drams of the poison; the pouch was worn strapped to the waist on the left side, when on their hunting excursions, and they were extremely careful in handling it and the arrows. The slightest scratch with the poison would cause a quick and sure death.

I was so far recuperated by this time that I thought of returning to civilisation, and I, accordingly, broached the subject to the Chief, who answered me very kindly, promising that he would send me by the next full-moon, with some of the wourahli men, down to the Branco River, and from there they would guide me within a safe distance of the rubber-estate, situated at the junction with the Itecoahy.

One day I was informed that a friendly call on a neighbouring tribe was being contemplated and that I could accompany the Chief and his men.

At last the time arrived and the expedition was organised. I was not absolutely sure how I would be treated by these up-stream Indians, and I am almost ashamed to confess that, in spite of all the faithful, unswerving friendship which the Mangeromas had shown me, I had it in my mind that these other Indians might harm me, so black was the name that people down at the settlements had given them.

Until this time, as related above, I had thought best not to exhibit the character of my automatic pistol, and I had never used it here, but before I started on this journey I decided to give them an example of its power, and possibly awe them. Inviting the Chief and all the tribe to witness my experiment, I explained to them that this little weapon would make a great noise and bore a hole through a thick tree. The Chief examined it gingerly after I had locked the trigger mechanism. He had heard of such arms, he said, but thought that they were much larger and heavier. This one, he thought, must be a baby and he was inclined to doubt its power.

Selecting an "assai" palm of about nine inches diameter, across the creek, I took steady aim and fired four bullets. Three of the bullets went through the same hole and the fourth pierced the trunk of the palm about two inches higher, The Chief and his men hurried across the creek and examined the holes which caused them to discuss the affair for more than an hour. The empty shells which had been ejected from the magazine were picked up by two young girls who fastened them in their ears with wire-like fibres, whereupon a dozen other women surrounded me, beseeching me to give them also cartridge-shells. I discharged more than a dozen bullets, to please these children of the forest, who were as completely the slaves of fashion as are their sisters of more civilised lands.

Early the next morning we started up the river. In one canoe the Chief and I sat on jaguar skins, while two men paddled. In another canoe were four men armed with bows and arrows and blow-guns, and a fifth who acted in the capacity of "Wireless Operator." The system of signalling which he employed was by far the most ingenious device I saw while in Brazil, and considering their resources and their low state of culture the affair was little short of marvellous.

Before the canoes were launched, a man fastened two upright forked sticks on each side of one, near the middle. About three and a half feet astern of these a cross-piece was laid on the bottom of the craft. To this was attached two shorter forked sticks. Between each pair of upright forked sticks was placed another cross-piece, thus forming two horizontal bars, parallel to each other, one only a few inches from the bottom of the boat and the other about a foot and a half above the gunwales. Next, four slabs of Caripari wood of varying thickness, about three feet long and eight inches wide, were suspended from these horizontal bars, so as to hang length-wise of the canoe and at an angle of forty-five degrees. Each pair of slabs was perforated by a longitudinal slit and they were joined firmly at their extremities by finely carved and richly painted end-pieces.

The operator strikes the slabs with a wooden mallet or hammer, the head of which is wrapped with an inch layer of caoutchouc and then with a cover of thick tapir-skin. Each section of the wooden slabs gives forth a different note when struck, a penetrating, xylophonic tone but devoid of the disagreeably metallic, disharmonic bysounds of that instrument. The slabs of wood were suspended by means of thin fibre-cords from the crosspieces, and in this manner all absorption by the adjacent material was done away with.

By means of many different combinations of the four notes obtained which, as far as I could ascertain, were DO—RE—MI—FA, the operator was able to send any message to a person who understood this code. The operator seized one mallet with each hand and gave the thickest section, the DO slat, a blow, followed by a blow with the left hand mallet on the RE slat; a blow on the MI slat and on the FA slat followed in quick succession. These four notes, given rapidly and repeated several times, represented the tuning up of the "wireless," calculated to catch the attention of the operator at the *maloca* up-creek. The sound was very powerful, but rather pleasant, and made the still forest resound with a musical echo. He repeated this tuning process several times, but received no answer and we proceeded for a mile. Then we stopped and signalled again. Very faintly came a reply from some invisible source. I learned afterwards that at this time we were at least five miles from the answering station. As soon as communication was thus established the first message was sent through the air, and it was a moment of extreme suspense for me when the powerful notes vibrated through the depth of the forest.

I shall never forget this message, not only because it was ethnographically interesting, but because so much of my happiness depended upon a favourable reply. I made the operator repeat it for my benefit when we later returned to our village, and I learned it by heart by whistling it. When printed it looks like this:

After each message the operator explained its meaning. The purport of this first message was so important to me that I awaited the translation with much the same feelings that a prisoner listens for the verdict of the jury when it files back into the courtroom.

Questions and answers now came in rapid succession. "A white man is coming with us; he seems to have a good heart, and to be of good character."

Whereupon the deciding answer was translated: "You are all welcome provided you place your arms in the bottom of the canoe."

Next message: "We ask you to place your arms in the *maloca*; we are friends."

After the last message we paddled briskly ahead, and at the end of one hour's work we made a turn of the creek and saw a large open space where probably five hundred Indians had assembled outside of two round *malocas*, constructed like ours. How much I now regretted leaving my precious camera out in the forest, but that was a thing of the past and the loss could not be repaired. The view that presented itself to my eyes was a splendid and rare one for a civilised man to see. The crowd standing on the banks had never seen a white man before; how would they greet me?

Little dogs barked, large scarlet *araras* screamed in the tree-tops, and the little children hid themselves behind their equally fearful mothers. The tribal Chief, a big fellow, decorated with squirrel tails and feathers of the *mutum* bird around his waist and with the tail feathers of the scarlet and blue *arara*-parrot adorning his handsome head, stood in front with his arms folded.

We landed and the operator dismantled his musical apparatus and laid it carefully in the bottom of the canoe. The two Chiefs embraced each other, at the same time uttering their welcome greeting "*He—He.*" I was greeted in the same cordial manner and we all entered the Chief's *maloca* in a long procession. Here in the village of the kindred tribe we stayed for two days, enjoying unlimited hospitality and kindness. Most of the time was spent eating, walking around the *malocas*, looking at dugouts, and at the farinha plants.

On the third day we went back to our *maloca* where I prepared for my return trip to civilisation. It was now the beginning of October.

I would, finally, have recorded many words of the Mangeroma language had not my pencil given out after I had been there a month. The pencil was all "ink-pencil," that is, a pencil with a solid "lead" of bluish colour, very soft, sometimes called "indelible pencil." This lead became brittle from the moisture of the air and broke into fragments so that I could do nothing with it, and my recording was at an end. Fortunately I had made memoranda covering the life and customs before this.

I was sitting outside the *maloca* writing my observations in the note-book which I always carried in my hunting-coat, when two young hunters hurried toward the Chief, who was reclining in the shade of a banana-tree near the other end of the large house. It was early afternoon, when most of the men of the Mangeromas were off hunting in the near-by forests, while the women and children attended to various duties around the village. Probably not more than eight or ten men remained about the *maloca*.

I had recovered from my sickness and was not entirely devoid of a desire for excitement—the best tonic of the explorer. The two young hunters with bows and arrows halted before the Chief. They were gesticulating wildly; and although I could not understand what they were talking about, I judged from the frown of the Chief that something serious was the matter.

He arose with unusual agility for a man of his size, and shouted something toward the opening of the *maloca*, whence the men were soon seen coming with leaps and bounds. Anticipating trouble, I also ran over to the Chief, and, in my defective Mangeroma lingo, inquired the cause of the excitement. He did not answer me, but, in a greater state of agitation than I had previously observed in him, he gave orders to his men. He called the "wireless" operator and commanded him to bring out his precious apparatus. This was soon fastened to the gunwales of the canoe where I had seen it used before, on my trip to the neighbouring tribe, and soon the same powerful, xylophonic sounds vibrated through the forest. It was his intention to summon the hunters that were still roaming around the vicinity, by this "C. Q. D." message. The message I could not interpret nor repeat, although it was not nearly as complex as the one I had learned before. After a while, the men came streaming into the *maloca* from all directions, with anxiety darkening their faces. I had now my first inkling of what was the cause of the commotion, and it did not take me long to understand that we were in danger from some Peruvian *caboclos.* The two young men who had brought the news to the Chief had spied a detachment of Peruvian half-breeds as the were camping in our old *tambo* No. 6, the one we had built on our sixth day out from Floresta. There were about a score of them, all ugly *caboclos,* or half-breed *caucheros,* hunting rubber and no doubt out also for prey in the shape of young Mangeroma girls, as was their custom. The traps set by the Indians, as described in a previous chapter, would be of no avail in this case, as the number of Peruvians was greater than in any previous experience.

The enemy had been observed more than ten miles off, in an easterly direction, when our two hunters were on the trail of a large herd of peccaries, or wild boars, they had sighted in the early morning. The Peruvians were believed to be heading for the *maloca* of the Mangeromas, as there were no other settlements in this region excepting the up-creek tribe, but this numbered at least five hundred souls, and would be no easy prey for them.

I now had a remarkable opportunity to watch the war preparations of these savage, cannibal people, my friends, the Mangeromas. Their army consisted of twelve able-bodied men, all fine muscular fellows, about five feet ten in height, and bearing an array of vicious-looking weapons such as few white men have seen. First of all were three club-men, armed with strong, slender clubs, of hard and extremely tough Caripari wood. The handle, which was very slim, was provided with a knob at the end to prevent the club from slipping out of the hand when in action. The heavy end was furnished with six bicuspid teeth of the black jaguar, embedded in the wood and projecting about two inches beyond the surface. The club had a total length of five feet and weighed about eight pounds. The second division of the wild-looking band consisted of three spear-men, each provided with the three-pronged spears, a horrible weapon which always proves fatal in the hands of these savages. It is a long straight shaft of Caripari wood, about one inch in thickness, divided into three parts at the end, each division being tipped with a barbed bone of the sting-ray. These bones, about three and a half inches long, were smeared with wourahli poison, and thus rendered absolutely fatal even when inflicting only a superficial wound. Each man carried two of these spears, the points being protected by grass sheaths. The third division was composed of three bow-and-arrow men, the youngest men in the tribe, boys of sixteen and seventeen. They were armed with bows of great length, from six to seven feet, and each bore, at his left side, a quiver, containing a dozen big-game arrows fully five feet long. These arrows, as far as I could ascertain, were not poisoned, but their shock-giving and rending powers were extraordinary. The arrow-heads were all made of the bones of the sting-ray, in themselves formidable weapons, because of the many jagged barbs that prevent extraction from a wound except by the use of great force, resulting in ugly laceration.

The fourth and last division consisted of three blow-gun men, the most effective and cunning of this deadly and imposing array. As so much depended upon the success of a first attack on the Peruvians, who not only outnumbered us, but also were armed with Winchesters, the blow-guns were in the hands of the older and more experienced men. All, except the club-men, wore, around the waist, girdles fringed with *mutum* plumes, and the captains added to their uniforms multi-coloured fringes of squirrel tails. Their faces all had the usual scarlet and black stripes. The Chief, and his principal aide, or sub-Chief, had on their gayest feathers, including head ornaments of arara plumes and egrets. The club-men were naked, except for their head-gear, which consisted simply of a band of *mutum* plumes. When the warriors stood together in their costumes, ready for battle, they presented an awe inspiring sight.

The Chief gave the order for the bow-and-arrow men to start in single file, the others to follow after, in close succession. The Chief and I fell in at the rear. In the meantime I had examined my Luger automatic pistol to make sure of the smooth action of the mechanism, and found besides that I had in all thirty-seven soft-nose bullets. This was my only weapon, but previous narrow escapes from death and many close contacts with danger had hardened me, so I was willing to depend entirely upon my pistol. The women and children of the *maloca* stood around, as we disappeared in the jungle, and, while they showed some interest in the proceeding, they displayed little or no emotion. A couple of sweethearts exchanged kisses as composedly as if they had been bluecoats parting with the ladies of their choice before going to the annual parade.

Soon we were in the dark, dense jungle that I was now so well acquainted with, and, strange to say, the green and tangled mass of vegetation contained more terrors for me than the bloody combat that was to follow.

For an hour we traveled in a straight line, pushing our way as noiselessly as possible through the thick mass of creepers and lianas. About three o'clock, one of the scouts sighted the Peruvians, and our Chief decided that an attack should be made as soon as possible, before darkness could set in. We stopped and sent out two bow-and-arrow men to reconnoitre. An anxious half hour passed before one of them resumed with the report that the Peruvians were now coming toward us and would probably reach our position in a few minutes. I could almost hear my heart thump; my knees grew weak, and for a moment I almost wished that I had stayed in the *maloca*.

The Chief immediately directed certain strategic movements which, in ingenuity and foresight, would have been worthy of a Napoleon.

We were between two low hills, covered with the usual dense vegetation, which made it impossible to see an advancing enemy at a distance of more than five yards. The three blow-gun men were now ordered to ascend the hills on each side of the valley and conceal themselves about half-way up the slopes, and toward the enemy. They were to insert the poisoned arrows in their guns and draw a bead on the Peruvians as they came on cutting their way through the underbrush. The bow-and-arrow men posted themselves farther on, about five yards behind the blow-gun men, with big-game arrows fitted to the bowstrings, ready to shoot when the first volley of the deadly and silent poisoned arrows had been fired. Farther back were the spear-men with spears unsheathed, and finally came the three brave and ferocious club-men. Of these last warriors, a tall athlete was visibly nervous, not from fear but from anticipation. The veins of his forehead stood out, pulsating with every throb of his heart. He clutched the heavy club and continually gritted his white, sharp-filed teeth in concentrated rage. It was wisely calculated that the Peruvians would unconsciously wedge themselves into this trap, and by the time they could realize their danger their return would be cut off by our bow-and-arrow men in their rear.

After a pause that seemed an eternity to most of us no doubt, for the savage heart beats as the white man's in time of danger and action, we heard the talking and shouting of the enemy as they advanced, following the natural and easiest route between the hills and cutting their way through the brush. I stood near the Chief and the young club-man Arara, who, on account of his bravery and great ability in handling his club, had been detailed to remain near us.

Before I could see any of the approaching foe, I heard great shouts of anger and pain from them. It was easy for me to understand their cries as they spoke Spanish and their cursings sounded loud through the forest.

The blow-gun men, perceiving the Peruvians at the foot of the hill only some twenty feet away, had prudently waited until at least half a dozen were visible, before they fired a volley of poisoned arrows. The three arrows fired in this first volley all hit their mark. Hardly had they gone forth, when other arrows were dexterously inserted in the tubes. The work of the blow-gun men was soon restricted to the picking out of any stray enemy, their long, delicate, and cumbersome blow-guns preventing them from taking an active part in the mêlée. Now the conflict was at its height and it was a most remarkable one, on account of its swiftness and fierceness. The bow-and-arrow men charging with their sting ray arrows poisoned with the wourahli took the place of the cautiously retreating blow-gun men. At the same instant the spear-men rushed down, dashing through the underbrush at the foot of the hill, like breakers on a stormy night.

The rear-guard of the Peruvians now came into action, having had a chance to view the situation. Several of them filed to the right and managed to fire their large-caliber bullets into the backs of our charging bow-and-arrow men, but, in their turn, they were picked off by the blow-gun men, who kept firing their poisoned darts from a safe distance. The fearful yells of our men, mingled with the cursing of the Peruvians, and the sharp reports of their heavy rifles, so plainly heard, proved that the center of battle was not many yards from the spot where I was standing.

The club-men now broke into action; they could not be kept back any longer. The tension had already been too painful for these brave fellows, and with fierce war-cries of "YOB—HEE—HEE" they launched themselves into the fight, swinging their strong clubs above their heads and crushing skulls from left to right. By this time the Peruvians had lost many men, but the slaughter went on. The huge black clubs of the Mangeromas fell again and again, with sickening thuds, piercing the heads and brains of the enemy with the pointed jaguar teeth.

Suddenly two Peruvians came into view not more than twelve feet from where the Chief, Arara the big club-man, and I were standing. One of these was a Spaniard, evidently the captain of this band of marauders (or, to use their correct name, *caucheros*). His face was of a sickly, yellowish hue, and a big, black mustache hid the lower part of his cruel and narrow chin. He took a quick aim as he saw us in his path, but before he could pull the trigger, Arara, with a mighty side-swing of his club literally tore the Spaniard's head off. Now, at last, the bonds of restraint were broken for this handsome devil Arara, and yelling himself hoarse, and with his strong but cruel face contracted to a fiendish grin, he charged the enemy; I saw him crush the life out of three.

The Chief took no active part in the fight whatever, but added to the excitement by bellowing with all his might an encouraging "AA—OO—AH." No doubt, this had a highly beneficial effect upon the tribesmen, for they never for an instant ceased their furious fighting until the last Peruvian was killed. During the final moments of the battle, several bullets whirred by me at close range, but during the whole affair I had had neither opportunity nor necessity for using my pistol. Now, however, a *caboclo*, with a large, bloody machete in his hand, sprang from behind a tree and made straight for me. I dodged behind another tree and saw how the branches were swept aside as he rushed toward me.

Then I fired point-blank, sending three bullets into his head. He fell on his face at my feet. As I bent over him, I saw that he had a blow-gun arrow in his left thigh; he was therefore a doomed man before he attacked me. This was my first and only victim, during this brief but horrible slaughter. As I was already thoroughly sick from the noise of cracking rifles and the thumping of clubs smashing their way into the brains of the Peruvians, I rushed toward the center of the valley where the first attack on the advance guard of the enemy had taken place, but even more revolting was the sight that revealed itself. Here and there bushes were shaking as some *caboclo* crawled along on all fours in his death agony. Those who were struck by the blow-gun arrows seemed simply to fall asleep without much pain or struggle, but the victims of the club-men and the bow-and-arrow men had a terrible death. They could not die by the merciful wourahli poison, like those shot by the blow-gun, but expired from hemorrhages caused by the injuries of the ruder weapons. One poor fellow was groaning most pitifully. He had received a well-directed big-game arrow in the upper part of the abdomen, the arrow having been shot with such terrible force that about a foot of the shaft projected from the man's back. The arrow-head had been broken off by striking a vertebra.

The battle was over. Soon the *urubus*, or vultures, were hanging over the tree-tops waiting for their share of the spoils. The men assembled in front of the Chief for roll-call. Four of our men were killed outright by rifle bullets, and it was typical of these brave men that none were killed by machete stabs. The entire marauding expedition of twenty Peruvians was completely wiped out, not a single one escaping the deadly aim of the Mangeromas. Thus was avoided the danger of being attacked in the near future by a greater force of Peruvians, called to this place from the distant frontier by some returning survivor.

It is true that the Mangeromas lay in ambush for their enemy and killed them, for the greater part, with poisoned arrows and spears, but the odds were against the Indians, not only because the *caboclos* were attacking them in larger numbers, but because they came with modern, repeating fire-arms against the hand weapons of the Mangeromas. These marauders, too, came with murder and girl-robbery in their black hearts, while the Mangeromas were defending their homes and families. But it is true that after the battle, so bravely fought, the Indians cut off the hands and feet of their enemies, dead or dying, and carried them home.

The fight lasted only some twenty minutes, but it was after sunset when we reached the *maloca*. The women and children received us with great demonstrations of joy. Soon the pots and pans were boiling inside the great house. I have previously observed how the Mangeromas would partake of parts of the human body as a sort of religious rite, whenever they had been successful with their man-traps; now they feasted upon the hands and feet of the slain, these parts having been distributed among the different families.

I crept into my hammock and lit my pipe, watching the great mass of naked humanity. All the men had

> "Directly above me, suspended from the roof by slender strips of bamboo fibre, hung a circle of dried human heads, each one equally distant from its neighbor. White, wooden eyes had been placed in the eye-sockets of these heads—white eyes unnaturally large and distended. The expression was a bewildered, quizzical one,—they were all staring at something which was hidden in the dark shadows of the inner roof—something inside those mysterious, barred rooms."
>
> —zoologist WILLIAM BEEBE
> among the Dyaks of Borneo

laid aside their feather dresses and squirrel tails, and were moving around among the many fires on the floor of the hut. Some were sitting in groups discussing the battle, while women bent over the pots to examine the ghastly contents. Here, a woman was engaged in stripping the flesh from the palm of a hand and the sole of a foot, which operation finished, she threw both into a large earthen pot to boil; there, another woman was applying an herb-poultice to her husband's wounds.

Over it all hung a thick, odoriferous smoke, gradually finding its way out through the central opening in the roof.

This was a feast, indeed, such as few white men, I believe, have witnessed.

That night and the next day, and the following four days, great quantities of *chicha* were drunk and much meat was consumed to celebrate the great victory, the greatest in the annals of the Mangeromas of Rio Branco.

Earthen vessels and jars were used in the cooking of food. The red clay (Tabatinga clay) found abundantly in these regions formed a superior material for these utensils. They were always decorated symbolically with juices of the scarlet *urucu* and the black *genipapa*. Even when not burned into the clay, these were permanent colours.

Men and women wore their hair long and untrimmed as far as I could observe. The older and more experienced of the tribesmen would have quite elaborate head-gear, consisting of a band of *mutum* plumes, interspersed with parrot-tail feathers, while the younger hunters wore nothing but a band of the *mutum* plumes. The body was uncovered, save by a narrow strip of bark encircling the waist. A broad piece, woven of several bark-strips into a sort of mat, protected the lower anterior part of the abdomen. The women wore no clothing whatever.

Their colour was remarkably light. Probably nothing can designate this better than the statement that if a Mangeroma were placed alongside of an Italian, no difference would be noticeable. Their cheek-bones were not as high as is usual with tribes found on the Amazon; they seemed to come from a different race. Their eyes were set straight without any tendency to the Mongolian slanting that characterises the Peruvian *caboclos* and the tribes of the northern affluents. The women had unusually large feet, while those of the men were small and well-shaped. The general appearance of a young Mangeroma was that of a well-proportioned athlete, standing about five feet ten in his bare feet. No moccasins, nor any other protection for the feet, were worn.

The supply of wourahli poison had run low and three wourahli men were to go out in the forest to collect poison plants, a journey which would require several days to complete. This occasion was set as the time of my departure.

It was a rainy morning when I wrapped my few belongings in a leaf, tied some grass fibers around them, and inserted them in the large pocket of my khaki-coat. The box with the gold dust was there, also the boxes with the exposed photographic plates. Most of the gold had filtered out of the box, but a neat quantity still remained. One of my servants—a handsome girl—who excepting for the labial ornaments, could have been transformed into an individual of quite a civilized appearance by opportunity, gave me a beautiful black necklace as a souvenir. It was composed of several hundred pieces, all carved out of ebony nuts. It had cost her three weeks of constant work. I embraced and was embraced by almost everybody in the *maloca*, after which ceremony we went in procession to the canoe that was to take me down to the Branco River. The Chief bade me a fond farewell, that forever shall be implanted in my heart. I had lived here weeks among these cannibal Indians, had enjoyed their kindness and generosity without charge; I could give them nothing in return and they asked nothing. I could have stayed here for the rest of my natural life if I had so desired, but now I was to say good-bye forever. How wonderful was this farewell! It was my opportunity for acknowledging that the savage heart is by no means devoid of the feelings and sentiments that characterize more elevated, so-called civilized individuals.

For the last time I heard the little dog bark, the same that had licked my face when I fainted in front of the *maloca* upon my first arrival; and the large *arara* screamed in the tree-tops as I turned once more toward the world of the white man.

The journey was without incident. The wourahli men set me off near the mouth of the Branco River, at a distance which I covered in less than five hours by following the banks. I was greeted by Coronel Maya of the *Compagnie Transatlantique de Caoutchouc*, who sent me by canoe down the old Itecoahy, until we reached the Floresta headquarters.

Here I gave Coronel da Silva an account of the death of Chief Marques, and the brave Jerome, which made a deep impression upon this noble man.

The three men, Magellaes, Anisette, and Freitas, had returned in safety after they separated from us.

A Little Bit About John Richard Stephens

John has had many different occupations ranging from driving an armored truck and working as a professional photographer to being a psychiatric counselor at a couple hospitals and a security officer for the U. S. Navy. He was an intelligence officer and squadron commander in the U. S. Air Force before he moved on to writing full time in 1990. Since then, he's written more than three dozen articles, poems, and short stories for newspapers and magazines that range widely from a short story for the literary journal *Nexus* to an article about anti-American propaganda on postage stamps for *Penthouse*. He is a member of the Authors Guild and the Horror Writers Association.

He is the author/editor of the following books:

A Skeleton at the Helm
Weird History 101
Wyatt Earp Speaks!
Wyatt Earp Tells of the Gunfight Near the O.K. Corral (booklet)
Captured by Pirates
Into the Mummy's Tomb
Vampires, Wine and Roses
The King of the Cats and Other Feline Fairy Tales
Mysterious Cat Stories (co-edited with Kim Smith)
The Dog Lover's Literary Companion
The Enchanted Cat

John's books have been selections of the Preferred Choice Book Club, the Quality Paperback Book Club, and the Book of the Month Club. His work has been published as far away as India and Singapore and has been translated into Japanese and Finnish. He can be contacted at pirates@ferncanyonpress.com.

Acknowledgements

"Raiding Mummies' Tombs": Amelia Edwards, *A Thousand Mile up the Nile*, London: George Routledge & Sons, 1891; Theodore Davis, *The Tomb of Iouiya and Touiyou*, London: Constable and Co., 1907; Giovanni Battista Belzoni, *Narrative of Operations and Recent Discoveries in Egypt and Nubia*, London: John Murray, 1820.

"Opening King Tutankhamen's Tomb": Howard Carter and A. C. Mace, *The Tomb of Tut·Ankh·Amen Discovered by the Late Earl of Carnarvon and Howard Carter*, vol. I, London: Cassell & Co., 1923.

"The Man Who Would Be King": Rudyard Kipling, *The Phantom Rickshaw and Other Eerie Tales*, London: Samson, Low, Marston, Searle & Rivington, 1888.

"Ravaged by a Lion": Rev. Dr. David Livingstone, *Missionary Travels and Researches in South Africa…*, London: John Murray, 1857.

"Deadly Expedition Through Unknown Africa": Sir Henry M. Stanley, *Through the Dark Continent*, vol. I, New York: Harper & Bros., 1878.

"Battle of the Witchdoctors": H. Rider Haggard, *Allan's Wife*, London: Spencer Blackett, 1889.

"Exploring the Labyrinth": John Lloyd Stephens, *Incidents of Travel in Incidents of Travel in Yucatán*, vol. I, New York: Harper & Brothers, 1843.

"Repositories of the Dead": John Lloyd Stephens, *Incidents of Travel in Egypt, Arabia Petræa, and the Holy Land*, 1837.

"Caves of the Thousand Buddhas": Sir M. Aurel Stein, *Ruins of Desert Cathay*, vol. II, Macmillan & Co., 1912.

"The Strange Ride of Morrowbie Jukes": Rudyard Kipling, *The Phantom Rickshaw and Other Eerie Tales*, London: Samson, Low, Marston, Searle & Rivington, 1888.

"Cliffhanging Archeology": Sir Henry Creswicke Rawlinson, *Notes on Some Paper Casts of Cuneiform Inscriptions upon the Sculptured Rock at Behistun*, London: Society of Antiquaries of London, 1852.

"Excavation of an Assyrian Palace": Sir Austen Henry Layard, *Nineveh and Its Remains: with an Account of a Visit to the Chaldæan Christians of Kurdistan, and the Yezidis, or Devil-Worshippers; and an Inquiry into the Manners and Arts of the Ancient Assyrians*, vols. II, New York: George G. Putnam, 1849.

"A Night's Ride with Arab Bandits": Charles Wellington Furlong, "A Night's Ride with Arab Bandits", *Harper's Magazine*, vol. CXII, no. 670, March 1906.

"Island of Crabs": Frank Bullen, *Idylls of the Sea*, New York: D. Appleton & Co., 1899.

"Wrestling an Alligator": Mr. Warburton, "Battle with an Alligator", *Appleton's Journal*, August 31, 1872.

"Spiderama": W. H. Hudson, *The Naturalist in La Plata*, London: Chapman and Hall, 1892; Algot Lange, *In the Amazon Jungle*, New York: G. P. Putnam's Sons, 1912.

"An Expedition with Headhunters": F. W. Up de Graff, *Head Hunters of the Amazon*, New York: Duffield & Co., 1923.

"Ancient Ruins, Sacred Stones": John Lloyd Stephens, *Incidents of Travel in Central America, Chiapas, and Yucatan*, vol. I, New York: Harper & Brothers, 1841.

"Piranha": Theodore Roosevelt, *Through the Brazilian Wilderness*, New York: Charles Scribner's Sons, 1914.

"Trapped in Mexican Quicksand": Captain Mayne Reid, *The Scalp Hunters: or, Romantic Adventures in Northern Mexico*, Philadelphia: Lippincott, Grambo, 1851.

"Rescued by Cannibals": Algot Lange, *In the Amazon Jungle*, New York: G. P. Putnam's Sons, 1912.

PHOTO CREDITS

Quotation References

RAIDING MUMMIES' TOMBS

Amelia B. Edwards
"Dead men are not useless…", Arthur Weigall, *The Glory of the Pharaohs*, New York: G.P. Putnam's Sons, 1923.

"I was looking intently…", John Lloyd Stephens (under the name of George Stephens), *Incidents of Travel in Egypt, Arabia Petræa, and the Holy Land*, New York: n.p., 1837.

Theodore Davis
"We broke through…", Amunpanefer as quoted in Christine El Mahdy, *Mummies, Myth and Magic*, New York: Thames & Hudson, 1989.

Giovanni Belzoni
"It is difficult to give…", M. Mathey as quoted in Christine El Mahdy, *Mummies, Myth and Magic*, New York: Thames & Hudson, 1989.

"At Tanis the mice were…", Amelia B. Edwards, *Pharoahs, Fellahs and Explorers*, New York: Harper & Brothers, 1891.

"[…] secure your head to your bones…", Pyramid Texts as quoted in Christine El Mahdy, *Mummies, Myth and Magic*, New York: Thames & Hudson, 1989.

OPENING KING TUTANKHAMEN'S TOMB

Howard Carter with A. C. Mace
"The whole mountainside…", John Lloyd Stephens (under the name of George Stephens), *Incidents of Travel in Egypt, Arabia Petræa, and the Holy Land*, New York: n.p., 1837.

"Mohammed Ahmed Abd-er-Rassul's report…", Sir Gaston Maspero, "Rapport sur la trouvaille de Deir-el-Bahri", *Institut Egyptien Bulletin*, Ser. 2, No. 2, 1881, translated by W. R. Trask and quoted in Leo Deuel, ed., *The Treasures of Time*, New York: World Publishing Co., 1961.

THE MAN WHO WOULD BE KING

Rudyard Kipling
"Young women are very…", Sir George Scott Robertson, *The Kafirs of the Hindu Kush*, London: Lawrence & Bullen, 1896.

"I found five countries oppressed…", Albert Edwardes quoted in Maud Diver, *Honoria Lawrence*, London: John Murray, 1936.

RAVAGED BY A LION

Rev. Dr. David Livingstone
"About five o'clock I was off…", Mary Kingsley, *Travels in West Africa, Congo Français, Corisco and Cameroons*, London: Macmillan, 1897.

"Percival had a narrow escape…", Theodore Roosevelt, *African Game Trails*, New York: Charles Scribner's Sons, 1910.

"While still warming up…", Carl Akeley, *In Brightest Africa*, Garden City, New York: Doubleday & Page, 1923.

A DEADLY EXPEDITION THROUGH UNKNOWN AFRICA

Sir Henry M. Stanley
"As I advanced slowly…", Henry Morton Stanley, *How I Found Livingstone: Travels, Adventures and Discoveries in Central Africa including four months residence with Dr. Livingstone*, London: S. Low, Marston, Low, and Searle, 1872.

"The American flag…", David Livingstone, *The Last Journals of David Livingston in Central Africa*, New York: Harper & Brothers, 1875.

"We were becoming exhausted…", Henry Morton Stanley, *Through the Dark Continent*, New York: Harper & Brothers, 1878.

"Sechele had by right…", David Livingstone, *Missionary Travels and Researches in South Africa…*, London: John Murray, 1857.

"I needed but to hear…", Henry Morton Stanley, *In Darkest Africa*, New York: Charles Scribner's Sons, 1890.

"Unlawful intercourse…", Paul du Chaillu, *Explorations and Adventures in Equatorial Africa*, London: John Murray, 1861.

"Jabu, our cook…", Henry Morton Stanley, *In Darkest Africa*, New York: Charles Scribner's Sons, 1890.

"It seemed to me so absurd…", Henry Morton Stanley, *Through the Dark Continent*, New York: Harper & Brothers, 1878.

"The news of the white man's arrest…", Richard Lemon Lander, *Records of Captain Clapperton's Last Expedition to Africa, with the Subsequent Adventures of the Author*, London: Henry Colburn & Richard Bentley, 1829.

EXPLORING THE LABYRINTH

John Lloyd Stephens
"I was much entertained…", Gilbert White, The Natural History and Antiquities of Selborne, London: B. White and Son, 1789.

REPOSITORIES OF THE DEAD

John Lloyd Stephens
"[Going down a corridor…]", Anonymous, "The Catacombs of Kief", *The Penny Magazine*, no. 215, August 8, 1835.

CAVES OF A THOUSAND BUDDHAS

Sir M. Aurel Stein
"When I visited Angkor Vat…", Edmund Chandler, "Angkor: A Marvel Hidden in the Jungle" in Sir J. A. Hammerton, *Wonders of the Past*, New York: G. P. Putnam's Sons, 1923.

CLIFFHANGING ARCHEOLOGY

Sir Henry Rawlinson
"A most admirable servant…", William Beebe, *Edge of the Jungle*, New York: Henry Holt & Co., 1921.

EXCAVATION OF AN ASSYRIAN PALACE

Sir Austen Henry Layard
"Henry Layard, a headstrong youth…", *The New Yorker*, as quoted in Sir Austen Henry Layard (originally Henry Austen Layard), *Nineveh and Its Remains*, H. W. F. Saggs, ed., New York: Frederick A. Praeger, 1969.

"The Arabs marvelled…", Sir Austen Henry Layard (originally Henry Austen Layard), *Nineveh and Its Remains*, New York: George P. Putnam, 1849.

"The stone attracted my attention…", E. G. Squier, *Travels in Central America, particularly in Nicaragua*, New York: Appleton & Co., 1853.

"[…] on examining the interior…", Sir Austen Henry Layard (originally Henry Austen Layard), *Nineveh and Its Remains*, New York: George P. Putnam, 1849.

"For the belief still exists…", Albert von Le Coq, *Buried Treasures in Chinese Turkestan*, London: George Allen & Unwin, 1928.

A NIGHT'S RIDE WITH ARAB BANDITS

Charles Wellington Furlong
"I well remember one day…", Charles Wellington Furlong, "Days and Nights with a Caravan", *Harper's Magazine*, July 1906.

"More than forty men…", Evariste Regis Huc, *Travels in Tartary, Tibet and China 1844–1846*, William Hazlitt, trans., London: Office of the National Illustrated Library, 1851.

"You will find an occasional Arab…", Charles Wellington Furlong, "Days and Nights with a Caravan", *Harper's Magazine*, July 1906.

"For days we travelled…", Charles Wellington Furlong, "Days and Nights with a Caravan", *Harper's Magazine*, July 1906.

AN EXPEDITION WITH HEADHUNTERS

F. W. Up de Graff
"I remember those few days…", F. W. Up de Graff, *Head Hunters of the Amazon*, New York: Duffield & Co., 1923.

"We were now in the land…", Theodore Roosevelt, *Through the Brazilian Wilderness*, New York: Charles Scribner's Sons, 1914.

ANCIENT RUINS, SACRED STONES

John Lloyd Stephens
"It is impossible to describe…", John Lloyd Stephens, *Incidents of Travel in Central America, Chiapas, and Yucatan*, New York: Harper & Brothers, 1841.

"The top of the Sacrificatorio…", John Lloyd Stephens, *Incidents of Travel in Central America, Chiapas, and Yucatan*, New York: Harper & Brothers, 1841.

"It was enough to make a man…", Albert von Le Coq, *Buried Treasures in Chinese Turkestan*, London: George Allen & Unwin, 1928.

PIRANHA

Theodore Roosevelt
"One day we came to a place…", F. W. Up de Graff, *Head Hunters of the Amazon*, New York: Duffield & Co., 1923.

"[…]I learned that certain Indian tribes…", Algot Lange, *In the Amazon Jungle*, New York: G. P. Putnam's Sons, 1912.

"In the historical documents…", Couto de Magalhães, as quoted in Dr. George S. Myers, *The Piranha Book*, Neptune City, New Jersey: T. F. H. Publications, 1972.

"Perhaps the most dangerous…", Cecil Gosling, *Travel and Adventure in Many Lands*, New York: E. P. Dutton & Co., 1926.

RESCUED BY CANNIBALS

Algot Lange
"In order to pick up matter…", Charles Waterton, *Wanderings in South America the North-West of the United States and the Antilles in the years 1812, 1816, 1820 and 1824…*, London: J. Mawman, 1825.

"From time to time a tapir…", F. W. Up de Graff, *Head Hunters of the Amazon*, New York: Duffield & Co., 1923.

"The poison of venomous serpents…", Theodore Roosevelt, *Through the Brazilian Wilderness*, New York: Charles Scribner's Sons, 1914.

"Directly above me…", William Beebe, *Pheasant Jungles*, New York: G. P. Putnam's Sons, 1927.